a building goes up

a building goes up

the making of a
skyscraper

Mary
Gooderham

HarperCollins*PublishersLtd*

http://www.harpercollins.com/canada

HarperCollins books may be purchased for educational, business, or sales promotional
use. For information please write: Special Markets Department, HarperCollins Canada,
55 Avenue Road, Suite 2900, Toronto, Ontario M5R 3L2.

First edition

Canadian Cataloguing in Publication Data

Gooderham, Mary, 1962–
A building goes up : the making of a skyscraper

ISBN 0-00-255764-9 (bound)
ISBN 0-00-638557-5 (pbk.)

1. Simcoe Place (Toronto, Ont.). 2. Skyscrapers — Ontario — Toronto — Design
and construction. I. Title.

TH4311.G66 1998   690'.523   C98-930567-8

98 99 00 01 02 03 04 HC 10 9 8 7 6 5 4 3 2 1

Printed and bound in the United States

To my parents, Nancey and Bill Gooderham

FOREWORD

The scene is spell-binding: a hill of spirited ants carry grains of sand to communal mounds, their impulse to build larger, more elaborate quarters as if directed by some higher authority. Looking down on a busy construction site evokes the same sense of wonder: workers tote materials and tools, talk on radios and operate mammoth machines, their seemingly random labours creating something lasting day by day. Spectators stand at peepholes and marvel at the tangle of machinery and men, technology and nature, breakneck pace and seasonal rhythms that make it possible. In a sense, the office towers, shopping malls and houses that rise in our cities are not much different from the tiny ant hills that sprout in the cracks in our sidewalks. Few of us know how a building came to be. Who decided where and how it would be built? Who made it and what is it made of? What makes it work?

For more than two years I pursued those questions while writing about the construction of a skyscraper week by week as a science writer for my newspaper, the *Globe and Mail*. Like the megalithic tombs left by the Druids and Egyptians, buildings today retain their mysteries. My assignment was to deconstruct a growing one into its component parts, examining how it was conceived and executed, by whom and how. The weekly column, called Work in Progress, was a series of secrets unfolded, moments of illumination and, right from the start, daunting challenges. The first was to find work that was actually in progress. Construction projects were in short supply in Toronto at the time, I learned, after combing a long list of real estate developers who were in financial straits. My search finally came to an end at the building of the new thirty-storey headquarters of the Workers' Compensation Board, called Simcoe Place. The next problem was that the project's developers and contractors—under pressure to scuttle the expensive and, some say, wasteful project—were a little shy. Convincing them that the dirt I would describe would come only from the ground was delicate and they did not want me to disclose sensitive information in my column. It is gratifying to reveal the whole story of the project that took place from 1993–1995, now, from beginning to end.

My first call to make an appointment with the project manager for the contracting company proved the most difficult. Noticing that the first of the site's giant tower cranes was about to be erected, I requested an interview with a crane operator or, "Say, why not a trip up the crane itself?" It didn't seem like a good idea now, he said. A second call ended abruptly. "Too busy, sorry." Further attempts seemed to move us further away from the subject of cranes. Taking a trip up one was clearly out of the question. We talked about whether I would focus on technical or human-interest issues. My work cried out for the human element that the engineer in him saw as unnecessary. The reasons for the cool reception were stated, bluntly, on the fourth call: "The more you know, the more you'll get wrong." It was a dubious logic I had not heard in more than a decade of reporting.

Greeted with such *froideur* on site, denied access to people or intelligence about the building's progress, my voyage of discovery would be short. I had little familiarity with construction and few materials or sources of information beyond the developer, the building's major tenant, city officials, contractors and construction workers. I called again, this time meeting my subject face-to-face in his office, a trailer panelled with ersatz wood and lit by bare fluorescent bulbs, its floor coated with a crust of clay tracked in by a steady stream of workboots. Sitting on scaffolding, the whole thing shuddered alarmingly as dump trucks rumbled by and backhoes scraped bedrock from the hole twenty metres below. "It sways like the bridge of a ship," the manager said, in a tone that suggested he considered himself the captain.

I leaned forward with a determined pen and recorded the

metaphor for future use in my notebook. When the subject moved to cranes, he offered a lengthy explanation of how the giant machines hoist and swing their loads. Soon, more contractors and engineers entered the office and joined the seminar. A succession of sketches were scribbled on graph paper and pink telephone message slips. Architectural diagrams were unrolled and vital figures were pulled from crammed file drawers. Hours later, surveying the grimaces of concentration on the faces ranged around the desk, acknowledging my bulging notebook and sheaf of papers covered with drawings, lines, boxes, circles and arrows, I sensed a modest victory. I had won them over.

The next day I clambered over the side of the growing hole and down a rough-hewn wood ladder. Dressed in safety boots, jeans and a bright white hard hat, I drew surprised stares from the workers. Through the course of my tenure on the site they seemed at once suspicious of me and eager to take a break and have a chat. They came to talk about their jobs, their home life, the hard months of unemployment before Simcoe Place and facing them when they left, their family histories and aspirations for their children—usually far away from construction. They opened their lunch boxes, revealing the mountains of sandwiches and old-country delicacies inside and proudly sharing the home-made wine that they brought to the site Christmas party.

Recording the progress of the building and milestones along the way—the end of the excavation, the benefits of mirrored glass curtain wall and the power of prefabricated formwork to construct the main tower—I learned about Simcoe Place's design, architecture and construction. The background music of our conversations was the hiss of welding torches, the whine of drills and the rumble of concrete trucks. My reporting took me into the pit, under the scaffolding, up to the high beams. It took me to the architects' offices, the manufacturers' factories, the contractors' meetings and the planners at City Hall. And after months of requests, it would finally take me to the top of the crane, marking a turning point for both the building and me. I had arrived.

ONE

OVERTURE

Like musicians tuning for a concert performance, the construction workers scattered about in the gaping hole deep in the ground have prepared for this moment for a long time. A chorus of dump trucks rumbles across the exposed earth, the bass of their diesel engines deepening on the steep climb to the street above. High-pitched saws whine through planks of plywood. A rhythmic thud-thud-thud reverberates from a drilling rig making holes in the stubborn clay and rock for piles that will hold up the walls of the pit, the ground trembling with each blow it strikes. Finally the soloist, a giant crane mounted on a truck trailer comes to life, the operator revving its hydraulic gears as he deftly extends, raises and lowers its boom and hook in a series of warm-up exercises.

Abel deCarvalho, a diminutive man in a bright orange safety vest, sprints across the construction site like a waterbug, his arms pumping and chest heaving. He stops to direct a concrete truck backing into position in front of the crane. When the truck has stopped, he strains to reach up to the driver to take a slip of paper showing that the concrete in its spinning reservoir was mixed at a nearby plant an hour earlier, a quality-control measure designed to ensure that the material is at its peak. Most things are a stretch for the tiny man known around the site simply as Carvalho. Even in his requisite hard hat and steel-soled boots, he is dwarfed by the other workers. The wide smile that illuminates his lined and darkly tanned face reinforces his boyishness. But Carvalho is one of the most important men here. It's his job to make sure that objects are properly hitched and then hoisted by the crane to the right place. He is a swamper, a title that would seem to come from the conditions of this day, the ground still sodden from the spring thaw and heavy rains. Actually, the earliest uses of the word, in the nineteenth century, referred to workers who cleared roads for lumberers, assisted drivers of horse-teams and trucks or mopped up in saloons and kitchens. The construction-site swamper, without whom the crane operator would be lost, continues this tradition of helping. Despite having acquired only a grade four education in his native Portugal, Carvalho speaks four languages: Portuguese, Italian, an intricate sign language needed to communicate with the crane operator, and enough English to keep up with the instructions and banter that crackle across the two-way radio clipped to his belt.

Now he waits, dancing from one foot to the other and blowing on his hands to keep warm in the crisp May dawn, as the concrete truck disgorges its slurry of cement, stone and water down a chute and into a large steel bucket. When it is full, Carvalho reaches up to a loop in a cable attached to its rim and slides the crane's dangling hook through. He lifts his hand to get the crane operator's attention. A consummate conductor of construction, he twirls his fingers gently above his head, the signal to hoist the bucket high. With a few more motions of his hand and commands shouted into the radio in thickly accented English—"Dowen . . . dowen. . . . Shtopp."—the bucket swings like a two-ton pendulum over the site. It finally hangs at a precise point just above a long trench that has been dug deep in the rock and criss-crossed with bars of steel. There, a construction worker heaves on a spring-loaded bar to open the base of the bucket and send its contents whooshing downward.

The concrete will form the foundation below the first wall of a high-rise tower to be called Simcoe Place. Another 125,000 buckets will be added in the next year to make thirty storeys of offices, three floors to house mechanical and electrical equipment, a shopping and restaurant concourse and three levels of underground parking. The concrete will be reinforced by hundreds of tons of steel. Outside, 450,000 kilograms of aluminum panels and eight thousand windows will enclose the building and give it its identity. The project will take Herculean organization and a small army of workers who come from around the world. In all, it will take more than two years and cost $100 million.

The site is a three-acre rectangular gravel parking lot running along Front Street in downtown Toronto, at the edge of the city's financial core. Sidewalks and roads line its southern and eastern sides. The block-long mirrored glass wall of the Canadian Broadcasting Corporation's new Broadcast Centre looms directly to the west. Adjoining the site to the north is another parking lot, land owned by the same developer, Cadillac Fairview Corp., and slated for future development. Simcoe Place will grow out of the eastern two-thirds of the construction site itself. At the other end there will be an underground parking lot topped at ground level by a small park, an apostrophe of green between the new tower and the Broadcast Centre. To the north a tunnel will connect the building to the city's maze of below-ground shopping malls and passageways.

While monumental, the tower's construction is only the final part of a much longer process that has been going on for the last four years and continues to take place behind the scenes. Before the first hole is dug, a project developer must acquire land, secure financing and get zoning permission and city approvals. Architects and engineers design the building according to a vast range of artistic, technical and practical considerations, prepare extensive drawings and instructions to make it a reality and monitor its progress and quality. Tenants who will eventually occupy the building are sought, and their wishes for the space accommodated. They then work on their own designs and responsibilities. The job of building the project is awarded to a contractor, who in turn tenders the work to subcontractors, suppliers and finally workers practised in myriad specialized trades.

The work on site can be divided into three stages: preparation, construction of the structure itself—reduced in industry terminology to the *base building*—and finishing work. It began six months ago, with testing the soil and rock beneath the ground even while cars were parked here. Ninety days ago the lot was cleared and protective hoarding erected around its perimeter. Excavators and shorers moved in to create an ever-bigger hole.

Meanwhile, the contractor, Eastern Construction Co., has organized and tendered contracts for the future work. The actual construction of the building, mostly made of reinforced concrete, is expected to occupy the lion's share of time and money, with the concrete work alone taking a year and accounting for $14 million of the total $100-million contract price. Once some of the building has been erected, cladding will be fixed to the outside piece by piece. Inside there will be electrical and mechanical systems to install, from banks of elevators, fire-fighting hoses and sprinklers to window shades and office lighting. Finishing work begins with the main contractor, who is responsible for everything from erecting interior walls and landscaping the grounds to washing the building's windows. It ends with the tenants, who will be handed over floors to add their own wiring, carpeting, partitions and finally furniture for the thousands of workers who will move in.

The arrival of the first concrete is a milestone. Many of the men stop to watch the trucks roll down the pile of rubble left during the course of the excavation to form a ramp between the street and the bottom of the pit. Some of them descend rough wooden ladders to where the trucks stop. There they watch a crew coaxing the new concrete between the reinforcing steel bars using shovels and thick vibrating rods to help it settle.

In earlier times, elaborate ceremonies—even sacrifices—would have accompanied the laying of such a foundation. To ensure that the building would be strong and blessed by the gods or spirits, ancient cultures were known to bury objects, animals and even humans under the first stones they placed. Modern builders are a largely conservative lot, but they are not beyond the occasional superstition. Brian Gardner, the head of the project as construction manager for Eastern Construction, approaches the river of concrete flowing from the bucket. He stops, pulls a quarter from his pocket, considers the coin and then tosses it in, watching it sink into the grey muck before he turns away. He makes a point of dropping some "silver" into the first and last loads of concrete in every project he works on, a ritual he first saw a boss perform when he was an apprentice engineer working his way up from the ranks of bricklayers in England in the 1950s.

"It's for luck, son," the man explained. Gardner, now 52, has carried on the tradition ever since. He laughs that he has fifty cents invested in each building he's built.

This project could use some luck. These are difficult times in the construction industry. After a decade of explosive growth in North America, building in the city and indeed most of the continent has all but stopped. Prospective tenants are cutting back or moving to quarters in the suburbs that are cheaper and closer to where workers actually live. This cost-cutting and decentralization is obvious in the floors of empty office buildings adjacent to the construction site. Many private-sector building projects have been cancelled or postponed, and governments have responded with little in the way of public works to generate construction jobs. Unemployment in the building trades has hit 50 per cent or more, and some contractors have laid off most of their staff or are working at cost just to stay alive, with the hope of better times ahead. Most of the workers involved in this project consider themselves fortunate, but even these jobs are not secure. There is talk that the government agency committed to taking two-thirds of the building, the Workers' Compensation Board of Ontario, could pull out of the deal. The opposition parties in the provincial legislature are asking why the organization needs to build elaborate headquarters when there is so much vacant office space around and the board's unfunded liability—the difference between what it takes in and what it owes injured workers—hovers above $10 billion. On the construction site it is business as usual, but everyone wears worried looks, from the engineers to the labourers. They listen to the news for updates on the building's fate as much as critical reports of the next day's weather.

Beyond the wooden hoarding that surrounds the top of the hole, a knot of people are watching on this warm spring morning. They have no real sense of the occasion below, the preoccupations of the workers or even what the building is. Still, they are transfixed. They peer through the familiar square holes hewn in the plywood, the larger of the openings covered by veils of chain-link fence to stop the more curious or brazen from jumping in. The human traffic is constant through the day. Some linger *en route* to cafés, theatres, shops or the convention hall across the street. Others appear regularly, emerging from nearby offices to monitor the work up close during morning constitutionals or lunch breaks.

Tall buildings have fascinated people for generations. Around the world and through time, they have stood out as landmarks of civilization. The earliest skyscrapers—massive pyramids, fortified castles, towering pagodas and soaring cathedrals—provided protection against enemies and inspired religious devotion. These structures defied gravity, science and even human ability. Today's skyscrapers accomplish a very different function, accommodating the greatest number of people in the least amount of space to work or live. But they are still a miracle of architectural skill and engineering ingenuity.

At root, the people watching have little understanding of the process that produces the office buildings, hotels, apartment buildings and shopping complexes that make up the urban landscape beyond the peepholes. The construction workers call them sidewalk superintendents, for their loyal observance and pent-up desire to monitor the progress of the work. They say they could build bleachers here to give their audience a better view, even charge admission and spend all day answering questions about what is happening and what is to come.

Casual observers would see only frenzied activity in every part of the site, but on closer inspection what looks unorchestrated is in fact very deliberate. While the concrete foundation is being made in the southeast corner of the lot, the digging has barely begun at the opposite end. In the middle, crews are still erecting temporary underground perimeter-shoring walls out of wood to ensure the sheer sides of the hole do not cave in while the building is going up. The work is much further ahead to the east because the thirty-storey tower there will take much longer to build. The rest of the underground garage and the park can follow at a more leisurely pace.

Modern construction means choreographing endless activities and establishing priorities. The mammoth backhoes, for instance, that scrape the soil and rock and load it into a succession of waiting dump trucks appear to be working independently around the site. But while some merely make the pit deeper, others are creating holes for the building's foundations, similar to those being filled with concrete today. Meanwhile, at ground level high above, a team of carpenters cuts spicy-smelling plywood into forms or moulds that will be used to make the exterior concrete walls underground. Next to them, another crew assembles lengths of thick grey rubber to run down each joint in the still-to-be-built walls to keep groundwater from eventually seeping in.

Three months into the job, about forty men work here. At the peak of construction, there will be ten times that many from dozens of different trades. Some won't start for months; they need most of the structure to be finished before they can install doors, test fire sprinklers or plant grass in the park's freshly turned earth. Meanwhile, off-site, engineers and consultants pore over drawings, contracts and balance sheets to plan and oversee the entire process. Factories and foundries as far away as Wisconsin, Vancouver and Japan are beginning to make each light fixture, air duct and pipe that will become part of the building. It's a grand wheel of many spokes.

A frequent visitor to the site, Gary Dunlop, the vice-president of project management for developer Cadillac Fairview, spends most of his time in the kinds of posh office buildings that surround it. He works out the fine points of a building's design and oversees its progress. Before the first backhoe arrived, he had already spent two years in negotiations with Workers' Compensation, revising the building's plans to match the agency's needs as an occupant. This is known in the construction business as a design-build process. The agency hopes Simcoe Place will make it more productive as well as more accessible to the tens of thousands of injured workers it serves. The design must also suit the extensive computer technology that has become *de rigueur* in modern offices. After all, the board justified its decision to build a new headquarters by arguing that none of the available office space in the city was big enough or met these requirements.

The original plan for the building was revised by reducing the size of the lobby and squeezing another storey and an extra bank of elevators into the large podium at the base. The extra level was needed to house all of the case workers, doctors and counsellors who work for the board and meet with injured workers day-to-day. Throughout the building there will be false "access" floors to hide and organize the usual tangle of wires and cables that accompany high-tech equipment. As the plans were changed to satisfy the agency, there was work for each of the four main consultants who designed the original building—the architects and the structural, mechanical and electrical engineers. Month after month the drawings were reviewed, until they finally formed the basis of legal agreements that could be sent out to a handful of general contractors vying to construct the building, among them Eastern, the successful bidder.

Watching the building go up is satisfying for Dunlop, but his involvement is not over. He and a team from Cadillac must also administer the contract, making sure the progress of the work jibes with the plans and the millions of dollars of bills that are already beginning to pour in. This final role brings him frequently to the construction site, where he stands out in his shiny white hard hat and dark suit, his required safety footwear disguised as business shoes. Mud splatters the backs of his pant legs and there is a smear of paint on the collar of his open topcoat, but he doesn't mind. This is the part of the project he likes, watching the dirty, physical work as he strides through the site. "This is not an automated process," he says grandly. "This is something you're not going to computerize, even though you can computerize some aspects of the process and the design. When it comes right down to it, building things is hands on."

He practises the philosophy in his own work as much as possible, coming to look in on the project and meeting with the builders when there is time. There is a lot to learn from the tone and tenor of the on-site progress meetings held between the job's major consultants, subcontractors and suppliers. "You don't get the feeling of the job by talking about it in offices or reading memos," he says. But his visits can bring as much conflict as clarity. Today he has come to talk with Gardner about the extra costs and delays from the discovery of an ancient brick sewer running under the middle of the site from north to south. The backhoe shovels encountered the artifact when they dug down about ten feet. None of the soil and rock samples taken around the site or the maps of the city's underground going back to 1850 had shown the sewer, but there it was, gushing murky water from spring rains.

Dealing with the resulting mess has cost Eastern time and money. The sewer's flow had to be captured and redirected to a nearby storm drain. Although the point of an excavation is to take earth away from a site, here the contractor had to import dozens of loads of crushed brick from a nearby demolition project to pour on the damp ground to allow trucks and excavators to drive safely across it. Instead of moving from east to west as planned, the excavators are working in several small sections. With the part where the new building will stand not entirely cleared, the start of construction has been delayed. Gardner and the staff at Eastern suggest the sewer and other underground surprises—like some stubborn concrete and brick remains of railway buildings that once stood here—have already set the job back six to eight weeks. Meetings between the two men, long-time friends who for two decades have met across the table at projects such as this one, are amiable but terse. Dunlop agrees in principle that the contractor has a right to some extra time and money, but he won't tell Gardner how much of each Cadillac will allow right now. "We've only just dug a hole and it may be fourteen months before they pour the roof on the building, so there's plenty of time to make some of the time up," he says.

Gardner does not share Dunlop's confidence. Construction schedules have to be flexible and are constantly being revised to reflect changing conditions, both good and bad. The real moment of truth is the final contract date, two years away, by which time the builder has agreed to complete all but 1 per cent of the contract or face a penalty. (An early completion date usually means a sizeable bonus.) Each overlapping job that must be performed by the deadline is plotted on an intricate timetable in the Eastern trailer. The contractor builds in a certain amount of flexibility, or float, but any extraordinary delays—because of weather, work conditions or discrepancies with the contract documents, as is the case here—are the responsibility of the developer.

The two sides will haggle over just how much time is involved and eventually come to an understanding of how long the contract period should be extended, but developers never agree to a claim too early in the game, fearing a builder will have no incentive to try to finish on time. Contractors counter that such efficiency should result in a reward. The situation inevitably leads to friction between the two sides. Delays, especially this early in the job, are also bad for morale on the site. The problem with the sewer set back the work on the concrete structure and will push more of it into the winter, when building is costlier, riskier and especially unpleasant. The contractor's most hopeful schedule when the job began in February suggested that most of the concrete work might be finished by the end of the year. But these first foundations should have been started in March, not now in May.

Constructing a building was once a seasonal enterprise. Not only were builders averse to working outside in the cold, their materials, tools and techniques were not up to it. Concrete, for instance, will spoil if it freezes while it sets. Today, however, thrifty developers want to get their buildings up and occupied. Builders want to move through work as quickly as possible. And cold-weather technologies allow construction in all but the most freezing temperatures. In the case of concrete, during the winter the area underneath where the new material will be laid is enclosed in a tent of lightweight tarps and warmed with gas heaters. Even the concrete itself comes pre-heated from the plant where it is mixed to help it cure without freezing. But there are still substantial costs and risks, and the prospect of having to fire up temperamental heaters for a few extra months this coming winter provokes anxiety on the Simcoe Place site, even on this mild spring day.

The conditions are perfect for working with concrete. The sun has finally risen above the buildings that surround the hole to warm the workers fifty feet down. Foreman Corrado Patullo keeps one eye on the men still coaxing the concrete into more long foundation trenches and another on a second crew, called cement finishers, who have come to tend to the batch that was made earlier. Corrado is one of five southern Italian brothers who own Avenue Structures, the company hired to construct the building's concrete skeleton. Avenue will also provide

and operate the site's three main tower cranes, which are especially critical to the concrete work. This gives the company by far the biggest
contract on the site. It will also have the largest pool of workers, about
125 men, a third of the peak workforce.

Most of the managers are Patullos because of a division of labour
among the brothers that ensures they all have jobs and reduces the
need for outside help. The oldest, Carmine, known as the Big Boss
for his command of the company as well as his quick temper, sets the
price of the projects, with input from his brothers according to each
one's expertise. Emilio, a shy, methodical electrical engineer whose
uniform is a baggy coverall, looks after all of the heavy equipment
Avenue owns, including nursing about a dozen assorted tower cranes
kept in pieces in the company's huge storage yard north of Toronto.
Tony, the youngest and most gregarious because of his exposure at a
younger age to English, is responsible for paperwork, contracts, meetings and keeping the peace among the fractious siblings. Middle
brothers Victor, known for his brooding disposition, and Corrado, the
family member with the sunniest nature, work in the field, overseeing sites like this one. For a supervisor, Corrado is particularly active,
pitching in when hands are short to become part of the concrete crew
or to fit together fly-forms, the reusable wood and aluminum moulds
that he designs to create the identical concrete floors of the main
tower. He has had a hands-on role since his early days as a carpenter
building houses three decades ago, but his involvement will put him
in danger on this job. Several of the Patullo brothers' children do
manual labour on the projects during the summer, and Corrado's son,
Jimmy, and Tony's son, David, are studying at university to be civil
engineers. They hope to join the family business.

Most of the Avenue workers on the site have worked for the
company for thirty years or more. Although much of Corrado's time
is currently spent in meetings—today he'll discuss the week's concrete
shipments and the timing of the installation of the cranes—the rest
is spent on the site, checking on the men. Dressed in a worn blue
winter jacket and baggy work pants, he fits in well with the men. He
has a curious management technique "that gets me away from the
phone," but it seems to work. He greets each man in Italian, and they

either return the salutation or raise any problems. Most of Avenue's employees, like Carvalho, are Portuguese, but they have learned to speak Italian fluently to work in construction, their conversation peppered with English terms like *timesheet* and *telephone*.

Corrado watches as Carvalho moves breathlessly past, then shakes his head in awe at the swamper's speed and alacrity. "He covers more ground than anyone else here," Corrado says. Carvalho does the work of at least two men. He does not complain, except when there is no crane to guide. Before this one arrived on site mounted on a truck, he was seconded to the ranks of Avenue labourers who assemble and take apart formwork and clean up garbage. Carvalho is happy to get back to his role as swamper; he knows he'll especially be in demand when there are three tower cranes working overtime here.

His job is one of the most exacting in construction. An unexpected movement of a few inches by the crane's loaded hook can send a concrete bucket or bundle of steel lurching into a truck, the new building, construction workers or the swamper himself. Alertness, energy and agility are essential. The pace allows Carvalho only a couple of cigarettes from the package of Rothmans he keeps tucked under the top of his red hard hat. Most of his lunch waits until the end of the day, when he retires to the trailer the Avenue workers use as a locker room. There, from a vinyl flight bag he got for free on a trip to Portugal, Carvalho produces a sandwich wrapped in waxed paper made with a crusty roll and thin slices of presunto ham, which he makes himself by salting and drying a leg of pork. There are two apricots carefully cushioned in a paper towel and a large orange, all packed by his wife.

His meal finished, he tucks his hard hat into a cubby-hole and dons the sweater and jacket he wore to work some twelve hours ago. There is a nip in the air as he leaves the trailer, threading his way along the edge of the hole where he can peer down at the now-idle crane and curing concrete far below. He lets himself out of a gate in the wooden hoarding and walks towards the subway station, up a street teaming with business people heading for home. The route takes him past the glass-faced symphony concert hall next door, which will soon open its doors for the evening's performance.

TWO

THE GHOSTS OF SIMCOE PLACE

They are everywhere, empty building sites scattered over the face of the city like scars and blemishes. Most people hardly notice them on their route to work, across from the gym or next door to their doctor's office, with well-weathered signs promising grand schemes for redevelopment sometime in the future. Maybe a site has a derelict building on it slated for demolition, even the subject of a battle by conservationists trying to preserve at least the barest historical façade to be incorporated into a new design. Or perhaps it was long ago reduced to a hardscrabble lot, the owner reaping some income from the cars that park there while the land lies fallow, awaiting rezoning or sale. In the summer, the cornflowers and golden rod that flourish in the parched gravel are a reminder of its origins as a wild patch of earth and a contrast to the close-cropped lawns and granite paving stones that surround it. In the winter, the ice and snow left to collect on its forgotten sidewalks prove treacherous for adventurous pedestrians. This urban wilderness belies the grand edifice that might once have graced the site. And passers-by have long lost interest in what may come, accepting the scar as part of a contemporary urban visage.

In the heart of a city, any site that can be built on *has* been built on—usually many times. Construction materials deteriorate, designs fall out of fashion, economics make larger, more lucrative structures desirable. Architects prefer not to think of their work as disposable, but sometimes a building lasts only a matter of decades before it is torn down, prompting few protests because a relatively recent structure seems to have little historical significance. Cities are constantly changing, although, barring disasters and warfare, a complete revolution can take several lifetimes, making it impossible for most people to follow or influence. The public authorities, community groups, financiers, architects, contractors and construction workers who are involved in each development come nearest to having a say in what goes into a city. They follow the footsteps of history in the succession of plans they encounter in the archives and the foundations they find underground. With their ideas, money, designs, machines and hands, they add their own.

Just west of the modern monoliths of Toronto's financial district, within sight of shimmering Lake Ontario and in the shadow of the landmark CN Tower, lies one such plot of land slated for redevelopment. Known only as 200 Front Street West, it reveals little of its past or its future. It is in the centre of what has become the city's Entertainment District, so named for its theatres, concert halls, clubs, restaurants, shops and other diversions. Each street sign proudly proclaims the designation, and glossy brochures promote hotels, bars and eateries. There is little evidence that at the turn of the century this was a dominion of industry, railway tracks and water-towers, the air heavy with the smoke of factory boilers and fly-ash from shunting locomotives. The lot and those around it before that boasted magnificent homes, stately public buildings and formal gardens, lawns dotted with poplar trees and traversed by strolling gentry. Its transformation can be traced through the changes in the economy, society and culture of the city.

Since its beginnings as a Native gathering place in the wilderness, Toronto has drawn significance from its location along important traffic routes. The name comes from the Huron language, and is interpreted as "place of meeting." It was an agreeable encampment at the base of a broad trail that Natives and later fur traders travelled to cut several days from a journey through the Great Lakes. In the early to mid-eighteenth century, Toronto served sporadically as a French fort and trading post. When the British took over in the late eighteenth century and divided their colonial holdings into Upper and Lower Canada, they recognized the value of Toronto's natural harbour, inland passage and defensible location. However, there was little compelling about its geographical setting: no mountains, seacoast or river forks, just an outspread, gentle-sloping shore plain suitable for habitation. Its physical setting—between two major rivers and intersected by many smaller ones—also had its drawbacks; the lakeside margin was low and flat and prone to mosquito-ridden marshes. Nonetheless, the British decided to build.

John Graves Simcoe, a distinguished British army commander, was the first to impose order on this soggy wilderness. He became Upper Canada's first lieutenant-governor, and his regiment, the Queen's Rangers, laid out the town in precise military fashion, a grid of ten square blocks at the far eastern edge of the harbour. Simcoe renamed the town York, for the king's brother and Britain's commander-in-chief, the duke of York. Although the governor and his energetic wife, Elizabeth, spent most of their three years of service in a makeshift canvas house surrounded by reeds outside the town's log garrison, Simcoe proposed a grand plan for a settlement, with an urbanity and dignity that would mirror some of the finest capitals of Europe. He dictated what each future home should look like, outlining for instance how many floors it should have and where it would sit on its lot. Instant city planning. His supporters considered him a brilliant visionary, although his critics, who maintained he was "a little wild in his project," accused him of being a fanatic for order.

Lieutenant-Governor Simcoe first established Upper Canada's capital in the town of Newark, today's Niagara-on-the-Lake. But mindful of that more southerly village's vulnerability to invasion from the nascent United States, he looked for other candidates. Both Kingston and London were considered, but Simcoe settled for York, with its "natural arsenal," protected harbour, dockyard and large stands of pine for shipbuilding. A pair of single-storey brick buildings constructed in 1796 at the water's edge served as a Parliament, as well as the frontier town's courthouse and church. Functional but unembellished, the buildings served their purpose until they were ransacked and burned to the ground by American forces, who took the capital for a short time during the War of 1812. A similar Parliament rebuilt on the site was destroyed when an overheated chimney flue caught fire in 1824.

Muddy York, as it was called for the poor drainage that left its streets a succession of sink-holes set between clods of dense clay, grew with the arrival of merchants, craftsmen and workers. It was quickly transformed into a busy market and banking centre. Peter Russell, the colony's administrator between the departure of Simcoe in 1796 and the installation of a new governor in 1799, extended the original settlement far to the west. He doubled the size of the old Town of York grid, creating an area that came to be known as New Town. To recognize the contribution of the colony's first governor, Russell designated two streets ending at the water as John and Graves (later renamed Simcoe). The six-acre plot between them was made into a public square, called Simcoe Place, a name that would prove delightfully convenient for developers trying to market a skyscraper on the land two hundred years later. On a 1798 map, the name is written in pencil. Before he was replaced, Peter Russell also took the opportunity to establish Peter Street and Russell Square, and gave the name Russell's Creek to a rivulet that meandered recklessly through the eastern side of Simcoe Place. It is believed by archeologists to be the site of a seasonal hunting and fishing camp for Mississauga Indians. It might once have seemed idyllic, but the stream would eventually come to frustrate the builders of the modern tower.

Meanwhile, the government was without a suitable home. Each time the Parliament building was rendered uninhabitable, the members moved about the town as if in exile, setting up quarters in private residences, the new courthouse, the general hospital and even public taverns. In the late 1820s, they decided to build new quarters fittingly on Simcoe Place. The final design was a sprawling Georgian structure of red brick with stone trim facing Lake Ontario. But there was little tax base in the nascent colony, and the money that could be raised by duties and fines from its few inhabitants was limited. Plans for the building were continually revised, even during its construction. A large stone pediment designed to give dignity to the front entrance was scrapped, although the four stone pillars that were to hold it up had already been cut at a quarry west of the town. Nevertheless the completed building was still impressive for its time. Inside, the two chambers that housed the province's elected representatives and appointed senators were lofty rooms decorated with arches, Corinthian columns and extravagant chandeliers. On occasion, the province's lieutenant-governor hosted gala balls in the building and threw open the two chambers for dancing.

The setting was urban, symbolizing the increasing wealth of the province and the stability of its institutions, the successful taming of the wilderness that Simcoe had so desired. Indeed, York prospered even beyond his grandiose plans. When the construction of the Parliament on Simcoe Place began in 1829, the town had just 2,250 inhabitants; by 1834, with four times that many residents, it declared itself a city and, in a gesture of independence from the Crown, reclaimed the old name Toronto. Well-to-do merchants, bankers and politicians built adjacent mansions and schools, churches and public buildings to equal those of New York and Boston, and lived on adjoining avenues called King, Queen, Duke and Duchess.

The best address of all was Front Street, so named because it ran along the shore of Lake Ontario. It was home to such aristocrats as the colony's receiver general and its chief justice. The Reverend John Strachan, who was to become the first Anglican archbishop of Toronto, lived next to Simcoe Place in a home eventually known as the Palace, which was one of the most important buildings in the city. Built of brick, it was the sort of small Georgian mansion popular in Britain at the time, a design brought over by architects and skilled craftsmen trickling into Canada, the first group of immigrants to influence building in the city. Villas, cottages and townhouses sprang up, taking advantage of generous lots with views of breezy Toronto Bay.

The city then had an intimate connection with the lake that is missing today, vanquished by the growth of industry and railways along an extended shoreline in the nineteenth century and the more recent construction of an elevated expressway and rows of high-rise condominiums. A group of wealthy landowners resisted pressure from shipbuilders, lumber yards and storehouses to locate on the waterfront by vesting in perpetuity a strip of waterside land, called The Esplanade, as a public promenade and carriageway. But the lake and its shoreline had become too crucial to Toronto's economy. The water, excellent roads and railways, and the city's location on major traffic routes though Ontario and with the prosperous northeastern American states gave the city a prominence second only to Montreal. Soon burgeoning distilleries, mills, factories and slaughterhouses crowded along the shore. The port bristled with activity, and its harbour was dotted with sailing vessels. The streets around Simcoe Place teemed with delivery carts.

Toronto was still compact, a pattern dictated before the arrival of the horse-drawn omnibus and electric street railway by the distance that a person could comfortably walk. There was little segregation of residential development. Some of the best homes in the city were found along Front Street, hard by banks, hotels and factories. One curious mixture particularly noted at the time was at the intersection of King and Simcoe streets, adjacent to Simcoe Place. On the southwest corner stood "Legislation" (the Parliament buildings), on the northwest was "Education" (Upper Canada College), to the northeast was "Damnation" (a pub called the British Hotel) and on the southeast was "Salvation" (St. Andrew's Presbyterian Church, a turreted Gothic cathedral and formidable bastion of Toronto's Scottish Presbyterian movement, the only one of the four buildings remaining).

The Parliament buildings at Simcoe Place were handsome but poorly built and not considered a technical success. The roofs leaked and, despite the fact that the land was firmed up with gravel and underlaced with sewers, the basement was damp, scuttling plans to locate government offices there. A public archeological dig conducted in 1984 before the first construction began on the site unearthed frog skeletons amid its foundations, evidence of the wet conditions of this poorly drained backwater. According to the archeologist's report, the original bed of Russell's Creek had been filled in to accommodate the east wing of the building, and the stream itself was eventually enclosed with a brick drain, which would be found by builders more than a century later.

Simcoe Place was to be a sporadic site for a Parliament. In 1841, just seventeen years after the building opened, the provinces of Upper and Lower Canada were joined, and a new United Parliament was formed. It resided in a succession of cities, including Kingston, Montreal and Quebec City, coming twice to Simcoe Place in Toronto in its peripatetic existence. Still, the building had a remarkably long life. When not required for the government, it was turned into a medical college for the University of Toronto and then an army barracks, and finally one wing served as a lunatic asylum while the province's first public mental hospital was designed and built. When Confederation created a new Dominion of Canada in 1867 and Toronto was chosen as the political capital of Ontario, its most populous province, the creaky old Parliament buildings were again refurbished as a seat of government, but in the end, the arrangement was unsuitable. Although still stately, the buildings had suffered equally from inattention and from their years hosting soldiers, students and mental patients. Moreover, they were too small for the new province's burgeoning assembly and its bureaucracy, proved costly to heat and were considered a fire-trap.

Besides, the lawmakers of important Ontario demanded better accommodation. As early as the middle of the century, in the hope that the federal capital would settle permanently in Toronto, there had been plans to build a new legislature in Queen's Park, an island of green expropriated from the University of Toronto. Work finally began on a new legislature there in the late 1880s, and the government finally relocated in 1893, vacating Simcoe Place. To help pay for the new building, the old one was sold to the Grand Trunk Railway. It stood unused until 1903, when, almost without comment, it was demolished and the land designated as the future site for a new railway station.

It was no surprise. That nineteenth-century miracle of progress, the steam locomotive, which allowed for efficient year-round transportation through the area's difficult terrain and extreme weather conditions, now dominated the city. The railway linked Toronto's factories, foundries, fuel companies, grain elevators and lumber yards to sources of raw materials as well as hungry markets. As the fragmented rail companies that served points east and west amalgamated, lines were run right through the centre of the city. There they built yards for marshalling and servicing the trains and shipping and receiving goods. Starting in the 1850s, more and more tracks crisscrossed the working waterfront, cutting off the city from the lake and dramatically altering the outline of the shore. The entire length of

The Esplanade was sacrificed as a right of way for the Grand Trunk, and landfill added to accommodate more tracks.

By 1910, railways and private companies controlled three-quarters of the waterfront lands. The railways attracted more and more manufacturers and warehouses to the area around Simcoe Place, bringing noise, congestion and poisonous fumes. Wealthy residents fled to new suburban enclaves, and their fine homes were replaced by, or even turned into, hostelries to serve the railway. After Bishop Strachan's death in 1867, his stately Palace became the Palace Boarding House, outlasting most of the other Front Street villas until it too was demolished in 1896 to make way for a brick warehouse. Upper Canada College relocated to the leafy northern suburb of Deer Park, and the land it stood on was commercially redeveloped, despite a campaign by the editor of the daily *Toronto Telegram* to turn it into a playground for underprivileged children.

All hope for Simcoe Place wasn't lost. The first building to be constructed on the former college grounds was the Royal Alexandra Theatre, a small *beaux-arts* performance hall designed by Toronto architect John M. Lyle in 1907 to welcome travelling theatrical productions from New York and London, England. Steel magnate Cawthra Mulock, who at twenty-one was Canada's youngest millionaire, built the theatre on the college's former playing-field in an effort to put Toronto on the cultural map. It was named for the wife of the reigning British monarch, Edward VII, and there was no expense spared in its French design and opulent Edwardian furnishings. It boasted hand-carved woodwork, imported marble and silk wallpaper.

During this period, construction methods were radically transformed. The Royal Alexandra was one of the first theatres of its size to be made with a frame of steel, a tribute to young Mulock's position in the industry. The technique meant a building's weight could be supported by an internal skeleton of steel rather than heavy exterior brick and stone. Walls could be lightweight, even decorative, rather than having to bear the weight of the building. More significantly for a theatre, balconies could be bolted and welded directly to the frame, obviating the need for interior columns that blocked views in similar halls. The Royal Alexandra was initially surrounded by parkland, although as a "road house" it benefited from its proximity to the ever-encroaching railways. The touring companies that played there travelled from city to city by train. A string of railcars filled with sets, props and actors could shunt up to a siding near the theatre and be unloaded by handcarts.

The railways brought much more to the area around Simcoe Place. Victorian factories sprouted everywhere. These were not today's industrial parks on the edges of town, with their glaring nondescript homogeneity but ornate classical revival castles commissioned by manufacturers who sought an image of solidity and prosperity. Façades were decorated in terra cotta, carved stone and ornamental precast concrete, with company names proudly emblazoned across the front. One of the largest to occupy the old Upper Canada College lands was the Canadian General Electric Company, which opened offices, a showroom and a warehouse there. It shared the space with cartage and storage companies, clothing manufacturers, packagers, mills, printers and book-binders. The buildings were constructed by a steady stream of immigrant labourers arriving from Britain and Ireland, who for the first time moved into crowded housing separated from the "propertied classes."

In the early 1900s, one last eruption of the railway in the city made the transition complete and incidentally set the fate of Simcoe Place for the next half-century. The last grand residential buildings in the area, the John Gordon House, an Italianate mansion on the western edge of the New Town to the west, and Government House, the sumptuous mansard-roofed residence of the provincial lieutenant-governors to the north, met their end. They were each torn down in 1912 and the land sold to the Canadian Pacific Railway for a right of way and railyard to handle the massive flow of goods in and out of the area. Meanwhile, the plans to turn the old Parliament build-ing land into a new railway station were dropped when a massive fire, a well-proven leveller of cities since the time of Nero, cleared a more desirable spot slightly to the southeast. Instead, the Grand Trunk put a railyard and sheds on Simcoe Place to match those of Canadian Pacific to the north.

The railways continued their expansion around the lot until they found themselves with too many miles of track serving declining freight and passengers. As early as the First World War, a number of rail companies collapsed, and the Grand Trunk and its subsidiaries were soon nationalized by the Canadian government. By the Second World War, rail freight was losing ground to the transport truck and air cargo. So through the 1950s, the area began to change again. Manufacturers drifted away to cheaper and less congested space outside of the city, or fell prey to competition from imported goods.

Attention had long since shifted to Toronto's financial centre in a new part of the city, between the New and Old Towns. The revenues from the successful commerce, transportation routes and factories built trust, loan, insurance, legal and brokerage firms. By the middle of the nineteenth century a new building type, referred to as the "office chamber," had replaced the tiny offices that traditionally sat atop the area's houses and shops. By the early 1900s, structural-steel construction and the invention of the electric elevator had allowed for taller and taller buildings, vastly increasing the value of the area's real estate. Toronto city council was initially opposed to "skyscrapers" because of concerns about sanitation, safety, traffic and aesthetics, but finally assented to the fifteen-storey Traders Bank in 1905 and eventually decided not to limit height. As business expanded and land values increased, office buildings were continually replaced by larger, more versatile ones that afforded larger floor areas and, of course, higher rents. By the 1960s and 1970s, Toronto began to outpower Montreal. Sleek International-style skyscrapers crowded into the financial district, making Toronto indistinguishable from other modern North American cities. With little more room for expansion, they began to creep westward.

By the 1960s, the area around Simcoe Place was a wasteland of desolate warehouses and little-used railway yards. The Royal Alexandra had fallen into disrepair and was slated for sale or demolition. But then in 1963 it was bought by discount-store mogul Edwin (Honest Ed) Mirvish for $250,000, a third of what it had cost to build, and he agreed as a condition of purchase to try to make a go of the theatre for five years before tearing it down. He renovated the building, started an aggressive subscription program for travelling shows and converted nearby dry-goods warehouses into restaurants for theatre patrons. The formula worked.

Meanwhile, planners were desperate for a way to rejuvenate the entire area and reintroduce the city to the lake, but the extensive train yards and tracks stood in the way of redevelopment of the whole southern portion of Toronto. The railways were told to move outside the city. The suggestion fell on deaf ears until the companies realized the rising value of the land. They countered with a commitment not only to move to the suburbs but also to put the tracks that remained downtown into tunnels, freeing almost 190 acres for apartments and office buildings and replacing the grand Union Station with a stripped-down "transportation terminal."

The idea was scuttled by a left-wing city council in 1972. The council was opposed to the destruction of the station and concerned that the railways, among other developers, were getting a sweetheart deal. Reform-minded councillor John Sewell, who was later to become mayor, called it in his book, *Up Against City Hall,* "the greatest swindle that we can expect in Toronto in our lifetime." The vast development was abandoned, save for the construction of its centrepiece, the CN Tower, a spire built for communications signals that succeeded as a tourist attraction. The company also removed the tracks and sheds on Simcoe Place and readied the land for redevelopment, turning it in the meantime into a vast parking lot, first for CN employees, and later for visitors to the tower and adjoining Metro Toronto Convention Centre.

Over the next decade, the area slowly filled with entertainment emporiums and public projects, built by legions of immigrants who had flooded into the country following the Second World War. By the late 1960s, fewer and fewer of the new arrivals were British, coming instead from southern Europe, willing to work hard and equipped with innovative building techniques learned in the reconstruction of Europe, especially the use of reinforced concrete. On the Canadian Pacific lot between Simcoe Place and the Royal Alexandra they built Roy Thomson Hall in 1982, a home for the Toronto Symphony Orchestra resembling an inverted cupcake of criss-crossed mirrored glass. SkyDome, a stadium with a seven-acre retractable roof that allows sixty thousand fans to view baseball and football either in or out of doors, appeared in 1989, kitty-corner to Simcoe Place. The area once again became home to government offices with the construction of Metro Hall in 1992, the seat of the Metropolitan Toronto council, built on a lot that included a large public square just north of Simcoe Place.

The Canadian Broadcasting Corporation had bought the entire six-acre Simcoe Place lot in 1978 for a future headquarters, since its central Toronto operations were scattered through dozens of buildings around the city. It held the land vacant until 1987, when it entered into a controversial deal with Cadillac Fairview to build its new home as well as an office building, hotel and stores on the site. The CBC would rent, and eventually buy, its own building from Cadillac, while the other buildings would be the property of the developer, which would lease the land from the corporation. More attention was directed at the project when Phillip Johnson, an American post-modern architect who had studied under Ludwig Mies van der Rohe, was chosen to design the corporation's Broadcast Centre, which ended up resembling a colourful stack of plastic children's blocks.

Grand plans were made for the adjacent lands in the heady 1980s. There was to be a large hotel and condominium, and not just one but two thirty-five-storey Simcoe Place office towers developed by Cadillac, connected at ground level by a four-storey building that was to include an eighteen-hundred-seat live theatre run by impresario Garth Drabinsky. Then economic reality and recession intervened. A sharp decline in the demand for hotel rooms and office space scuttled the development. The developer that was to build the residential building went under, and the office project was shelved until the Workers' Compensation Board came looking for a new Toronto headquarters. The project was resurrected as a single thirty-storey tower, more than two-thirds of which would be leased to the agency, while the rest of the development remained on hold.

Today there is no sign of the bubbling stream or poplar trees at Simcoe Place. There is considerably more "damnation" around the corner of King and Simcoe streets than there was in the last century, with a proliferation of dance clubs and ersatz British pubs. There are still a number of warehouses and industrial lofts, but their Victorian scale and exposed brick are favoured by tony restaurants. The brick warehouse on the site of Bishop Strachan's former Palace has been turned into Remo's, a plush restaurant where comely waitresses serve Italian food, a favourite lunch place for Simcoe Place contractors, subcontractors and consultants discussing business. Sandwich boards advertising seared peppered halibut and Thai lemon grass chicken beckon from sidewalks. The pavement itself, the city has announced, will soon be studded with Hollywood-style stars, the first of which has been granted to Ed Mirvish, who still owns nearby landmark blocks. The fate of the railway lands to the south has continually absorbed city council, which several times has approved and then rejected plans to develop them. The latest agreement involves a mixture of homes, offices and other commercial development. Until it begins, the occupants of the new building at Simcoe Place will look down upon the huge space, yet another anonymous empty lot awaiting redevelopment.

THREE

LAYING THE GROUNDWORK

The handiwork of Mike Clarke and his carpenters is the most visible component of many construction sites in the city. But observers should not look for doors expertly hung by these wood-crafters or the fine detailing in a building's lobby. Their signature specialty comes long before almost anything else happens on the site. It is the wooden wall with its mesh-covered peepholes that afford passers-by a view of the construction project. Clarke owns the small firm of Clarke and Adamson Construction, which was hired to erect the plywood barrier that will surround the Simcoe Place site for more than two years. By the time the project is finished, his contribution will be long gone.

Three generations of Clarkes have played a supporting role in Toronto's building boom. Beginning in 1955, Mike's grandfather and father made the wooden frames that were used to shape the sidewalks of the city's growing suburbs. Today, the third Clarke concentrates on larger, but equally provisional, work. He builds hoarding. This word—associated with a miser's treatment of gold—may seem out of place on a construction site, but not if you consider how builders feel about their equipment. Hoarding of the type used at Simcoe Place was first erected in the nineteenth century to keep thieves from carrying off builders' tools and materials. Little thought was given to the passers-by who might be struck by falling objects or wander onto the hazardous site. But people put the unsightly barriers to good use. The walls became a public bulletin board for posting notices and advertisements.

Today the hoarding—often pluralized as hoardings—is a symbol of work in progress everywhere, transformed from a poster-filled wall guarding tools to an often sterile but critical fixture for protecting the public from danger. The construction of the hoarding at Simcoe Place on a blustery February day marks the practical and symbolic start of work. It makes the preparation of the site possible, from the intricate surveys to the erection of the contractors' trailer offices and the excavation and shoring up of the ground where the new building will go. It all seems to appear at once in a blur of activity that contrasts sharply with a week earlier, when this was a parking lot filled with the cars of people visiting trade shows and annual shareholder meetings at the convention centre across the street. The hoarding turns the site into a separate world, removed from the hustle of humanity and the demands of the business day around it.

Cities set strict standards for hoarding design. Roofs, for instance, must be able to deflect falling hammers, steel bolts or stray chunks of concrete. Nothing could protect bystanders from falling concrete buckets, so pedestrian and motor traffic is stopped when anything heavy is hoisted above the street by the crane. Even so, people are leery about walking near hoarding, and with good reason—debris has been known to shatter the plywood, especially on demolition sites. In 1987, a woman walking along a Toronto sidewalk was killed when a piece of concrete fell off a building that was being torn down and crashed through such a barrier.

The hoarding at Simcoe Place was designed by engineer Grant Milligan and his staff at Quinn Dressel Associates, the structural consultants to the project. They took the standard provided by the city's Department of Public Works and reinforced it, substituting fir posts fifteen centimetres square for the usual nine-centimetre ones and replacing simple nails with steel brackets and bolts for extra reinforcement. They also strengthened the roof over the sidewalk to give the structure a longer life, topping it with waterproofing rubber to preserve the wood and shelter pedestrians underneath. To help market the unrented stores and office space in the building, Cadillac Fairview will paint the hoarding grey to project a conservative, buttoned-down image and top it off with a billboard showing the building's completion date and the phone number of its leasing office.

It takes Clarke and six carpenters from his company two months to build. Hoarding, though temporary, doesn't come cheap: this one will cost $200,000. Modern builders are resigned to its price, but going against tradition, they are determined to keep it free of notices advertising political rallies, sexual services and rock concerts. "Posters look ratty and perhaps reflect on the project being built," explains Cadillac's Gary Dunlop, who prefers the look of Simcoe Place's stern Post No Bills notices stencilled in white.

Not that the warning carries any legal weight. A year ago, the Supreme Court of Canada ruled that municipal regulations prohibiting posters in such public places are unconstitutional. Clarke doesn't feel strongly one way or the other. His artistic pride is not hurt by seeing his work plastered with advertising, dented by delivery trucks and dismantled at the end of a project. "You're not building a piano," he shrugs. The hoarding at Simcoe Place will remain until it is time to landscape to the edge of the project and it is no longer needed. Eastern will look for someone to dismantle the hoarding; in exchange, it will invite them to take the posts, plywood and other material, which are still suitable for building barns, fences—and, of course, more hoarding. Clarke is not tempted to take the job; Milligan's design and his carpenters have done such good work that it's not going to be easy to take it apart.

One of Clarke's final duties is to cut the holes in the plywood that let pedestrians peer into the site. The holes are not as random as they seem. Indeed, those voyeurs who stand and look may discover a well-kept secret: a nail driven into the sidewalk directly below. The holes are actually placed, not to give passers-by the best views of the construction project, but to give the surveyors clear sightlines across it. Each hole and its nail are often situated opposite another identical set on the other side of the site, so that two surveyors can take measurements, placing their equipment directly on top of the nails for accuracy.

The sidewalk nails are just a few of the survey markers that ensure the building goes up where it should. The educated eye can spot others in the area around a construction site: on roads, the walls of neighbouring buildings, even rooftops blocks away. To understand the meaning of these markings, it's necessary to know that surveying is not limited to the ground. To keep a high-rise tower straight, within a margin of scant millimetres, the measuring has to continue right up to the top.

The work of sizing up the project started a year ago. A company called Rabideau Czerwinski Ontario Land Surveyors was hired by Cadillac to map the property lines. At four critical points along the boundary, a sturdy marker—referred to in the vernacular as a standard iron bar, or SIB—was driven deep into the ground with a sledgehammer. Then the job was handed over to Eastern. Even before winning the contract, the contractor began working out a finer and finer grid pattern on a map, called the setting-out plan. The main reference point was the property line to the south, running along Front Street, which is relatively straight. (Despite the best intentions of urban planners such as Peter Russell two centuries ago, city streets are notoriously haphazard. Simcoe Street, running up the side of the lot, is not at all perpendicular to Front Street.)

Having established a good straight starting line, the surveyors' next job was to mark off points around the site at intervals of 60 to 120 feet. Then lines were drawn across the site between these opposing points. Called the control-grid lines, these become constant reference points for the building and are drawn on every plan for the project. The lines will also be marked on each new level that is built, to guide the placement of features such as columns and walls. Daily measuring and marking may seem tedious, but it is critical; an oversight of just three millimetres on each floor would eventually throw the building off by ten centimetres. While not as noticeable as the lean in the Tower of Pisa, the discrepancy could mean that features added to the building do not line up.

The modern surveyor's trademark is a spray can of neon orange paint, which is marked For Commercial and Industrial Use Only, making it irresistible to graffiti artists. The paint is used to mark the SIBs, nails and various crosses etched in the ground and fences that together make up the points on the control grid. The most important tool in the surveyor's kit is a tripod topped with either a transit or a theodolite, instruments that measure angles, establish true lines and act as telescopes to bring tiny targets even a couple of kilometres away into view. Distances are determined with a long, steel tape-measure, called a chain, mounted on a wheel. To be precise, the survey crew takes into account factors such as the effect of the weather on the steel. The measurements are guaranteed at only twenty degrees, and must be subtly adjusted when the temperature is hotter or colder. Finally, the surveyor carries a brass plumb-bob, that old-fashioned vertical-line chalk marker familiar to amateur hangers of wallpaper, in a leather holster on his belt to mark straight lines on floors and walls.

Once the control grid has been set in a series of markings on the ground, the engineers begin eyeing the buildings surrounding the site. These will serve as aerial targets when the building rises out of the hole. This job is not for the faint of heart, even though it may conjure up summer images of orange-vested construction workers leaning over metal tripods on roadsides. For D'Arcy Gorman, Dean Sabean and Eugene Bristow, three young field engineers employed by Eastern, hanging from tall buildings is all in a day's work. Laced with safety harnesses, they have already crawled out onto the roofs of the Broadcast Centre to the west, Roy Thomson Hall to the north, the Victorian brick warehouse on the site of the former Bishop's Palace to the east and the Crowne Plaza hotel to the southeast to affix bull's-eye decals, which they paint by hand, to their walls. They will soon scramble onto the Metro Toronto Convention Centre's atrium roof on the south side of the site to put up a similar set of targets. Simcoe Place will one day tower over its neighbours, so the surveyors will have to look farther afield for reference points. Their work ends after the project is complete, when they will have to climb out on the buildings to remove the decals.

The engineers, thirty-somethings with prickly short haircuts and wearing permanently soiled jeans, are the project's workhorses. They coordinate and oversee all of the activity in the field, dealing with the foremen for each of the subcontractors and organizing the work each day. They take the theoretical information from the project drawings and translate it into practical work on the site, such as the survey markings.

The work is set out in an elaborate division of labour critical to the site's sophisticated chain of command. Everything that happens and everyone who comes here must be managed, from the workers who keep areas clear of clutter and direct city traffic to the army of suppliers, developers, designers, consultants and government and union officials who have a hand in the building's creation. Building Simcoe Place is like a military campaign.

The contractors have begun to operate in a field office, one of a series of trailers raised on scaffolding at the edge of the site that serve as boardrooms, offices and lockers for the workers. Known as mobile modular buildings but commonly referred to as construction shacks, they can be found in places ranging from building sites to refineries, mines and shipyards. Far from being homes away from home, they are simply wooden boxes with steel frames and rudimentary decoration, made to be both portable and lightweight but also sturdy and reusable. They are equipped with electricity, plumbing and liberal telephone lines for the contractors and subcontractors. Five of the trailers at Simcoe Place are the property of Eastern. The largest one, the main project office, was custom-made for the company's last big job, the building of the Broadcast Centre next door. It's actually three separate trailers linked side by side to make one large space. It provides four private rooms for senior managers, as well as open offices. There are storage areas and two bathrooms equipped with not only a toilet and sink but also a large shower. The latter is not hooked up, but serves as a repository for the baseball equipment that the group uses for occasional games against teams from some of the subcontractors and consultants, played after work at a diamond on the Toronto Islands.

Of Eastern's other four trailers, one is provided to the architectural and structural consultants, another is a meeting room and two more have become the office and lunch room for structural subcontractor Avenue Structures. The companies responsible for the project's mechanical work, exterior curtain wall and reinforcing steel have installed their own trailers as well. It isn't easy to fit all of these trailers on a site that must be entirely developed. The architects' plans originally called for them all to be sandwiched into a space that does not have to be excavated at the east end of the lot. However, Eastern decided to reserve that area for a loading dock for materials coming to the site and instead elevated the trailers on steel scaffolding in Cadillac Fairview's parking lot next door. This allows forty cars to park below, while offering an enviable view of the project to those up in the trailers. Recalling the bartering that has existed between crafts-people for centuries, Avenue was given free use of the two Eastern trailers in exchange for providing the tall steel scaffolding on which they are perched. With a deck and railings made of thick planks of wood, the office evokes the bridge of a ship. Swaying in strong winds or with the passing of trucks, it feels like a sailing vessel.

On some days at this early stage in the project, the number of workers on the site is dwarfed by the managers up above, who are busy preparing plans, schedules and budgets for the job ahead. One person—project manager Brian Gardner—can be called the ship's captain, the man directly responsible for everything that happens, while a legion of officers and deck-hands carry out his commands. Gardner meets with members of his contracting company, the project's architects and engineering consultants, the developer and the tenants to talk about the work in progress and any major prob-lems. Like the head of any corporation, he deals with the biggest headaches. "The higher up you go, the further you get away from the day-to-day stuff and the closer you get to the long-range and compound problems, ones that people below you haven't been able to deal with."

He is up to the job. Gardner, an avuncular man in his early fifties with a salt-and-pepper beard and soft English accent, has spent his life working in construction. He started out on sites in his native Britain, where his father and both grandfathers worked as carpenters. As a young boy he fetched tea and sandwiches for the men, by thirteen he was working summers as a labourer and then he became a bricklayer, all the while taking trade-school courses in building mechanics and apprenticing to become a construction manager. In the 1960s, he laid bricks on projects to redevelop areas of London still devastated by the Second World War two decades earlier. At night he studied and on weekends and after work he took up competitive rowing for a club at the London Polytechnic. Between the construction site and the rowing matches, he learned a lesson in human relations and class structure. His rowing crew of eight working-class men performed like a well-oiled machine, becoming the fifth-fastest team in England in 1966, beating one of the squads from Oxford University and placing in prestigious matches around the country. But there was never any doubt that, off the river, they did not mix with their blue-blooded competitors. On the site, managers with professional degrees and backgrounds tend to have little appreciation for the "hourly paid" men, he says, giving the impression that the work they do is less worthy or valuable. "I had a better understanding early in my life of how to get people motivated in the field, having worked with them and been one of them."

Gardner is also unique in the ranks of construction management because he lacks a professional degree, which is *de rigueur* on modern projects. Most people in his position, and those much more junior in Gardner's office, sport the familiar stainless-steel pinkie ring given to Canadian engineers as a symbol of their profession and a reminder of their duty to society. The crew of three people whom Gardner directly oversees—the construction manager, the project coordinator and the safety and security manager—all travelled more typical routes to the top, coming from engineering programs at universities to rise to middle-management roles at Eastern.

The construction manager, Renato Tacconelli, known to his colleagues as Tac, is Gardner's first mate, responsible for ensuring that all of the work done on the site jibes with the specifications in the building plans and is completed on time. Tall, serious, and handsome, there is something boyish about Tac. Constant meetings and the drawing up of schedules are the mainstay of a business where trades and their tasks remain stubbornly independent. Tac oversees the three field engineers, who act as intermediaries with the workers on the site, passing on commands and information. Each of them is responsible for a specific part of the building. When it comes to the subcontractors who do the actual work, there is one final level of management, the foreman of each crew, who discusses and coordinates each day's activities with the field engineers.

Back on the bridge, the two other senior managers, the project coordinator and the safety and security manager, are taking care of other aspects of the job. Project coordinator Robert Leonardelli, a stalky, slightly hunched man with dark curly hair and wire-rimmed glasses who looks the part of the bean-counter, could be compared with the ship's purser. He watches over the paperwork and money, keeping track of shop drawings, product samples and progress reports, ordering materials and paying the bills. He is helped by expediters who, as their title suggests, organize it all, in particular arranging for the delivery of drawings, samples and materials. Rosy Pereira, the only woman in the trailer, joined Eastern five years ago, just two weeks after emigrating from Tanzania. She works as a project secretary but will later double as an expediter.

The safety and security manager, Maurice Dupuis, a balding man whose brow seems permanently knitted and who has the punctiliousness needed to interpret reams of safety regulations, checks on conditions on the site. He meets with health and safety coordinators appointed by each of the major unions. This job is not typically a full-time one, but this project is large, safety has taken on a more important role across the industry and, after all, Simcoe Place is being built for the Workers' Compensation Board. Construction can be a dangerous, unpredictable undertaking. The agency responsible for safeguarding workplace health and safety would not want to be responsible for injuries or deaths on its own site.

Half a century ago, general contractors—as the title suggests— were generalists, and included labourers, carpenters, bricklayers, plumbers and electricians on their staffs. Gradually, though, those trades became specialized and split off. Today, Eastern employs a handful of carpenters and labourers to do maintenance around the site. The rest of the trades are represented by their own union locals, which appoint shop stewards and health and safety representatives among the workers and periodically send business agents to see that everything is running smoothly.

Coming onto an underground construction site in full swing is arresting. Like a wound, a deep gash exposes the bedrock, gravel and soil beneath the land's normal costume of concrete, steel and glass. Changing colours and consistencies of each layer of earth are exposed by restless backhoes and bulldozers. The site offers up lessons of history and soil dynamics, and yields the occasional fossil or mineral-studded boulder casually deposited here a few millennia ago.

For the builders, the layers of earth present a dual challenge: how to dig a hole to accommodate a building while ensuring that neighbouring ones do not fall in. The task is divided between excavators and shorers, two of the first subcontractors to arrive on the scene. Part geologists, part diviners and part moles, they figure out what's down there and how best to get it out in order to leave a neat, safe hole that can be filled up again. They are helped by soil consultants, who tested the ground when the building was just a figment of the architect's imagination. Much like the earlier surveyors, soil consultants are hired by a developer so the designers, engineers and contractors bidding on the job know exactly what they are dealing with. Is it granite, sand, soil, crumbly rock or fill? What is the water content? How far down is bedrock? The answers can affect the project's foundation, timing and costs. The builders already have a good idea of what to expect, based on the geology of the area and the conditions in neighbouring lots recently built on. The more precise information comes from drilling rigs, which take random test borings of the ground around the perimeter and throughout the site. The samples of the soil and rock are sent to a laboratory for testing, generating a neat profile of the site's geology.

The results are interpreted by the shoring and excavating contractors, both to determine the method of their work and to calculate the final cost and time needed. The price for digging out, trucking away and disposing of the material can vary from $20 to $50 per cubic metre, depending on whether it is loose soil or solid rock. The difference in price can be substantial, with more than 250,000 cubic metres of material to come out on this site.

Typical of downtown Toronto, the tests at Simcoe Place reveal three layers of ground. The top three metres are landfill from previous generations, no doubt brought in to shore up notorious Muddy York. Another five metres brought up by the drill are loose rock and soil original to the area. This includes material left by successive glaciers that scoured the earth's surface through the ice age. When the last of them retreated one hundred thousand years ago, they deposited gravel and boulders, some as big as cars. There is a dense layer of clay from the silt once at the bottom of a large lake created by the melting glacier. There is also soil left by decaying vegetation that grew after the lake retreated. Finally, the bottom eight or ten metres of the sample are sedimentary shale bedrock. This was laid down 445 million years ago, when another body of water, a warm and shallow salt-water ocean rich with sea creatures, covered much of North America. At that point, the continent was considerably south of where it is now, even below the equator. The shale and limestone in the bedrock were once the clay and lime mud at the bottom of this ocean. As each generation of this sediment settled, it compressed the one below it to form layers and layers of rock. The ocean dried up as the continent heaved and drifted northward to its current position.

This rock first appears at a depth of about ten metres below the surface of the ground, according to the core samples taken at the start of the project. Under part of the lot, it will later be shown to start two metres higher, a headache for excavators, the general contractor and those who pay the bills for the work because it is much more costly to dig and remove stubborn rock than to deal with gravel, clay and soil.

The shape of things below ground is especially of interest to the project's shoring contractor, who ensures the construction can proceed without the earth and the roads, sidewalks and buildings around the site falling in. If there were ample surrounding land—as in the construction of a small house in the country or even a suburban shopping mall—an "open-cut" or "slope-excavation" process could be used. A pit much bigger than is needed for the structure would be dug and its upper levels angled back so they would not cave in. However, like many contemporary urban structures, Simcoe Place is being built right to the edge of the lot line in the heart of a city, so shoring is critical.

The job is accomplished with the use of soldier piles, which guard the site not against urban marauders but against collapsing earth.

More than 150 of these steel beams are placed at three-metre intervals around the perimeter of the site. They are sunk as deep as eighteen metres into the underlying bedrock, held in place with concrete
"toes" and anchored with steel cables in the rock surrounding the site.
Wooden planks are slowly placed between them as the soil and rock
are removed from the site, forming a neat wall around the sheer face
of the hole and holding back the soil.

"With shoring you're holding up the street above, where people
are walking and driving," says Dawn Tattle, vice-president of Anchor
Shoring and Caissons, a company started by her father in 1968 that
has shored up sites for twenty-six hundred construction projects in
the city in the last twenty-five years. "Each job is unique. You can't
look in a book and say, 'This is the shoring that I'm going to do
here.'" It can be done even if a building is to stand in nothing but a
pit of soft sand, she says, although it is much easier to anchor the
temporary walls when there are layers of hard-packed soil and shale
rock in which to set the piles.

Armed with the soil consultants' report, Anchor decided how best
to do the work and gave Toronto's municipal departments twenty-two
copies of its plans to ensure that its underpinnings for the temporary
walls did not interfere with services such as water pipes and electrical
cables that surround the site. In cities oblivious to noise, the soldier
piles—long, structural-steel beams that in cross-section are shaped like
the letter H—can be bashed in with a pile-driver, but Toronto is more
sensitive. Here, holes must be dug, each almost a metre in diameter,
and the soldier piles dropped in. They are secured in the rock below
with concrete and held in place in the hole with earthen fill.

Tattle says the success of the shoring often sets the tone for the
whole project; snags hold up each of the follow-on specialties. "We're
the leaders; we've never been at the end." If all goes well, the excavation can get under way quickly, carried out by a battalion of backhoes,
bulldozers and dump trucks that dig out and truck the soil and rock
away from the construction site. The subcontractor responsible for the
job here, Rumble Contracting, expects to remove two hundred to
three hundred truck-loads of material a day for at least four months.
And the way the hole is carved out will help make the structure stable.

When each truck is full, it goes its separate way, depending on what it's carrying. A worker from Rumble stationed at the gate examines and sorts each load into three classes. The best material is labelled lakefill, meaning it's pure enough to be dumped in the water from which much of it originally came. Usually this goes to extend the Leslie Street Spit, a headland reaching five kilometres into Lake Ontario built entirely from the sand, clay and rock excavated from building sites across the city. Started by the Toronto Harbour Commission in 1959 to protect the bustling Port of Toronto, the spit has become a walking and cycling trail and tranquil bird sanctuary (when dump trucks are not rumbling along it). But on this project, the fill is being used to build the ramps for a new cloverleaf interchange on a highway north of the city, which will serve a giant amusement park. As well as being a large-scale recycling project, the arrangement helps recover costs. Rumble is paid for the fill by the grateful highway contractor; ordinarily the company would have to pay to dump each load on the Spit.

Excavators prefer to deal with soft organic matter, which is far easier to dig, remove and dispose of, but the top layers of earth on a site that has been previously built on in the middle of a busy city present their own challenges. At Simcoe Place, massive chunks of concrete and masonry from former building foundations litter the site. Some two hundred tonnes of soil are contaminated with hydrocarbons from a fuelling station that probably operated when Simcoe Place was a railway freight yard. This is tagged by Rumble to be taken to a special landfill for contaminated waste. A third batch of soil is less polluted, this time with heavy metals likely contained in the exhaust from the former train traffic. It is acceptable for use as fill at an industrial park. Finally, the giant granite boulders left behind by the glaciers are blasted with dynamite into pieces small enough for the dump trucks to carry away.

Dynamite was once used to excavate all of the rock on construction sites like this one. When the city's first massive skyscraper, the Toronto-Dominion Centre, went up nearly twenty-six years ago, the shale bedrock had to be blasted loose, a time-consuming, expensive and dangerous endeavour, but modern technology has changed the picture dramatically. Today, the same shale is known as rippable rock, because the hydraulic backhoe can do the job of removing it. Several of the ninety-tonne machines, known in the business as track excavators, work together, the lead one fitted with a high-carbon steel "ripper tooth." This sharp, hooked implement tears at the bedrock like Godzilla digging into a hut full of innocents. The other backhoes follow along with toothed buckets, scooping up the loosened rock and debris and loading it into a procession of waiting dump trucks.

As the excavators reach the perimeter of the site, they encounter the steel soldier piles and expose the edge of each, leaving bare one long side of the H. Wooden planks, each about three metres long, are fitted one by one between the vertical side bars, effectively holding back the earth on the other side and forming a wall of boards, or "lagging." As the hole is dug deeper, more and more boards are added. When the wall is about three metres deep, it must be anchored at each beam with a supporting cable, called a tie-back. A rock drill is used to make a hole for the cable, first through the steel beam and then on a forty-five-degree angle deep into the rock beyond. A steel cable is threaded into this narrow channel and anchored in the rock with high-strength concrete. Each cable is then tightened using a hydraulic jack to withstand the 150,000 pounds of pressure that will come from the other side. The shoring must resist not only the horizontal load from the weight of the soil, which increases with depth, but also the surcharge load, the weight of anything heavy, such as the concrete trucks that will constantly make their way around the outside of the site.

The shoring stops at rock that is considered sound. The concrete will be poured directly against the rock below this point to form the walls of the building's lowest two levels. When the construction rises to the wooden lagging, both the inner and outer parts of the walls will be formed of concrete a half-metre thick and the shoring will no longer be needed. The space between the concrete wall and the lagging and piles will be filled with soil and all of the shoring abandoned. Once the building is up, the highly strung tie-backs will also be loosened, at the insistence of municipal officials. If this is not done a work crew digging up a sewer or laying an electrical cable on the other side of a building wall might accidentally trip across and trigger a tie-back to release its tens of thousands of pounds of pressure.

Eventually the wooden shoring walls are forgotten. They turn out to be as temporary as the hoarding the project started with, critical to the process but never seen again once the skyscraper is built. For Dawn Tattle, that isn't a problem. "Maybe people don't see the wood at the end of the day, but our work is recognized as a very specialized area, and there aren't very many people who know what we know and can do what we do," she says. "Isn't everyone unappreciated?"

FORM AND FUNCTION

The huge panels of steel being unloaded from flatbed trucks are pitted with holes and caked with rust, looking like abstract sculpture left to weather in front of an art gallery. But to Corrado Patullo, these panels—called flying-wall forms—are old friends. The concrete-forming contractor runs a lined hand over the familiar bumps and dents on each of them, and surveys the parts of the city skyline around him that these panels have helped create: bank towers, insurance offices, landmark shopping centres, the glass Metro Toronto Convention Centre across the street and the mammoth new Broadcast Centre next door to the site.

Concrete-forming—erecting moulds to make a building's concrete walls, floors and columns—is a constant recycling effort. The forms "fly" from place to place around the site, removed once the concrete they are holding up has cured and then erected again for the next job. These hoary old steel panels were first bought by Avenue Structures in 1974 to make Toronto's giant downtown Eaton Centre mall. Since then, they have been used hundreds of times, and have even made two trips to construction projects in Calgary. Soon they will be used to create all of Simcoe Place's core walls, which surround the central features such as the elevators and service rooms in the middle of each floor and help to support the building.

With the arrival of the panels, the site looks less like an open-pit mine and more like a building project. The digging out and shoring will continue for months, but now the builders can begin the main tower. Some of the steel will be set up in preparation for a massive shipment of concrete that will create the building's giant core.

Corrado isn't taking any chances, checking to make sure each panel is accounted for and ready for the long job ahead.

"Wherever I go, they come along," he says in a low voice, his burly hands fluttering as he talks and shaggy, grey-tinged eyebrows rising and falling under a white hard hat marked with concrete and soot. His name is stamped in block letters on a blue plastic strip stuck over the visor in front. "I spend more time here with them than I do at home." For the fifty-nine year old Corrado, the construction site is much like home. He and his brothers—Tony, Carmine, Emilio and Victor—not only work together, they all live in houses on the same quiet cul-de-sac in the east-end suburb of Etobicoke. Their sister, Theresa, also lives there, and their eighty-five-year-old mother Concetta lives on a street directly behind, in a house approached by the side of Emilio's garage. When asked about their proximity, the brothers protest that it wasn't intentional, just an accident of timing. The series of lots came available in the early 1970s, just as their families and their business began to prosper.

In the three decades since, the Patullos have not only built a lot of Toronto's major buildings, they have seen and contributed to a vast transformation in the concrete-forming industry. In the early days, concrete was limited to small projects; steel had long been the medium of choice for builders in North America because it was quick and efficient. The technique even became part of popular culture. On theatre screens, Laurel and Hardy teetered on steel girders and the lampooning Three Stooges threw hot rivets at each other. Working with concrete, on the other hand, meant erecting and dismantling complex temporary forms, adding significantly to the cost, trouble and time it took to build.

But after the Second World War, an influx of workers from southern Europe who were practised in handling and finishing concrete, combined with a sharp rise in the price of steel and the introduction of lighter aluminum forms, began to tip the balance. If only the process of setting up the forms could be accelerated, concrete could compete with steel. The breakthrough was the flying-form, pioneered by the Patullos and others. Contractors learned to construct one form elevated on steel trusses—for instance, to make one small section of one floor of a building—and then reuse it in the same position on each of the levels above. Once the concrete was set, the steel trusses below the still-intact form were lowered and it was slid out and hoisted by the crane to be set up on the floor it had just created, where the process was repeated.

By the late 1960s, the Patullos were using the technique to make apartment buildings, hospitals and shopping malls. They refined the method by incorporating stronger beams into their flying-forms, enabling them to make taller and taller structures, including office towers that could be built for the price of steel ones. Tony Patullo proudly says he has transformed major projects in Toronto from structural steel into reinforced concrete by making a convincing case that they could be done more cheaply. Even Simcoe Place was originally supposed to be made out of steel. Avenue's success has made it one of the largest concrete-forming companies in Canada.

The family is believed to have originated in Scotland, with the name Pittiloch. The Scottish lineage is evident in some of the family today. Grandfather Patullo had green eyes, as does Theresa, who, along with her brother Emilio, has a slender build, unlike her more heavyset siblings. The other Patullos have dark colouring typical of southern Italians and look more like their mother, who is called Ma, or Nona, for grandmother.

Little is known about how the family ended up in Boiano, a tiny village tucked in a deep valley at the foot of the Apennine Mountains in the south-central Molise region of Italy. The area is known for its smooth boccocini and mozzarella cheeses. But as in much of southern Italy, there was little work beyond the barest subsistence agriculture. Semi-feudal land tenure, political neglect, the sale of ecclesiastical estates and the laws of succession that fragmented already tiny landholdings left many southern Italians destitute. As Franca Iacovetta says in her book, *Such Hardworking People: Italian Immigrants in Postwar Toronto*, emigration was "a popular response to the economic problems in Italy at the beginning of the century."

The Patullo's father, Alessandro, saw all of his older siblings move to new lives in New Jersey in 1924. But according to custom, the youngest son must stay to look after the parents. He married in 1930 and started his own family, carrying on his father's sawmill and making planks for roofs and furniture in a small shop on the ground floor of the simple family home. All around, his *paesani* (fellow villagers) suffered from falling farm incomes, overcrowded towns and poor nutrition. Corrado and his brothers learned early on to work with their hands, and contributed to the family finances by spending time in the sawmill each day after school, at Concetta's insistence. "My mother, she was the law enforcer," Corrado says. From the age of six, their job was to turn scraps of softwood into rectangular crates to hold three-kilogram balls of cheese from the local dairy. An old family photograph, which Tony's wife, Linda, refers to as "the destitutes," shows the five boys sitting on the front steps of the shop with dirty but smiling faces, wearing stretched undershirts and baggy overalls covered in a generous layer of dirt.

The Second World War took a terrible toll on Molise, as it did on the rest of southern Italy, but the Patullos were lucky. Alessandro secured the job of supplying wooden planks to the liberating British Fifth Army to build and repair the roadbeds of the area's temporary Bailey Bridges. The structures, designed by British engineer Sir Donald Coleman Bailey and used widely in the Italian campaign, were prefabricated, easy-to-assemble spans capable of supporting heavy loads across the widest rivers. But from the time of the Allied bombing in 1943, which narrowly missed the family home, Alessandro began suffering from a nervous condition. In 1945, at the age of thirty-nine—with his youngest son, Tony, just three weeks old—he suddenly died.

The family was thrown into turmoil. A competing sawmill had opened in town and the market for wood products was declining. Even the classic cheese boxes were being abandoned in favour of post-war Styrofoam and plastic. Jobs were scarce, and recovery policies were concentrated, as usual, in the north. More than 80 per cent of the people of Molise were still farming the already overworked land. The Patullos, like many of their better-off artisan and shopkeeper neighbours, were eager to escape the misery of poverty, overcrowding, unsanitary conditions, malnutrition and illiteracy. The older brothers, financed with the money their father had earned from the Bailey Bridges, began to leave.

The first was Emilio, who went with his mother's sister and brother-in-law in 1949 to Argentina, where he studied electrical engineering. A year later, Carmine travelled to Toronto with two more uncles, taking advantage of Canada's decision to admit southern Europeans willing to do critical but unappealing work in farming, industry and the building trades. They rented rooms in a house owned by a Russian Orthodox Jewish family in an area of the city around College Street populated by migrants from eastern Europe. With the heavy southern Italian migration, the neighbourhood was fast turning into a Little Italy, and by 1961 the Italians had replaced the Jews as Toronto's largest non-British ethnic group.

Toronto was a dream for Italian immigrants, Iacovetta says. Manufacturing plants rose and expanded, head offices moved into what was quickly becoming Canada's financial centre, and expressways, suburbs and subways proliferated. Carmine took a short-lived job in a hotel laundry, worked in an automobile plant dismantling war vehicles for their parts and then made extra money on weekends by joining friends from Boiano building houses. He finally settled in the construction business, forming a company with his landlady's son, who taught him English and acted as administrator while Carmine toiled on the job sites, his crew made up of *paesani* willing to do long, sometimes dangerous and back-breaking jobs that Canadians shunned. These were no strangers to hard work, Iacovetta says. Seasonal construction offered jobs to immigrants from farms with few industrial skills, little formal education and almost no knowledge of the language. Italians played a critical role in the city's building boom, making up the majority of its construction workforce and as much as 85 per cent of trades such as bricklaying.

Successive Patullos joined in the construction work as they arrived in Canada. Corrado came in March 1955, at the age of twenty-one, just three months short of earning a degree in Italy as an elementary-school teacher. He knew little more about construction than "how to pound in a few nails," but like many immigrants was dismayed at the prospect of having to learn English in order to assume a professional career in Canada. By 1959, all of the Patullo brothers, their mother and sister had moved to Toronto. Their company, first called

Associated Forming, then Etna Structures and finally Avenue Structures, thrived in the postwar baby boom. Growing families were so desperate for accommodation that they moved into houses long before the brothers had finished their work.

When it came time for the Patullos to build their own homes in the late 1960s, they didn't have to look far. Land was being sold on a new street that backed on to a creek near their west-end office. Tony and Carmine, who had been renting apartments, bought adjoining lots, and Corrado decided to move there as well because he could get a larger, treed lot. While their homes were under construction (the family company was busy, and the brothers contracted out most of the work), the rest of the Patullos followed suit, and in 1984 they also found their mother a house on the adjoining street. Each brother pays her a dawn visit before heading off to the construction site or office. They stay for a slice of chestnut or honey cake and a small cup of the strong espresso that is continually surging in a traditional two-level stainless-steel pot on the stove. Most nights they return for a glass of what they call punch, a concoction of pure alcohol, water and sugar that has little to do with fruit save for a small strip of orange or lemon peel floating in it. "If we don't go, she remembers," says Corrado. Although the Patullos live in separate homes, they have maintained their traditional nuclear family, which Franca Iacovetta calls "the fundamental social institution" of southern Italy.

Corrado says family ties have made the company strong, and the brothers hope to pass the company down to those of their fifteen children who want to carry on. They are also close to many of the workers on the site, some of whom they have employed since the company started, even when work was thin. Today, half a dozen of the men doing physical jobs at Simcoe Place come from Boiano. "They're good men," Corrado says. "I'm glad they're here."

Deep in the excavated construction site, the concrete core of the building begins to take shape on the backs and shoulders of these labourers, carpenters, ironworkers and cement-finishers. Concrete-forming, especially the method called loose forming used in the building's underground or substructure, is one of the most demanding jobs imaginable. The time- and labour-saving fly-form technique can be used only to make floors that are carbon copies of each other and built above ground, since each form has to be brought to the edge of the building and lifted up by the crane. This will be possible later, when the work climbs above ground level and the floors of the building are duplicated. In the substructure, however, with its one-of-a-kind shapes and hard-to-reach position, most of the forming is done the old-fashioned way. Each feature is made by erecting and later dismantling an intricate mould made of steel scaffolding, wood, aluminum beams and sheets of plywood.

It is pure drudgery. First the form is erected in a pattern dictated by the building's plans. The flat part of the plywood or aluminum that will sit next to the concrete is coated with a dark paste called form oil so the concrete does not stick to the form. Even so, the pattern of the wood grain and seams in the plywood are often left imprinted on the surface of the finished product, like butter stamped by a mould. Next, reinforcing steel bars—abbreviated in the business to rebar—are laid out and tied together with wire in a basket-weave pattern within the space where the concrete will go. The amount and configuration of the rebar is specified in the plans, and is calculated so that it will give the structure tensile strength, meaning it will provide flexibility under tension.

The concrete, which gives the building solidity or compressive strength, is dumped in the form directly from a concrete truck, is carried to where it is needed in buckets hoisted by the crane or flows through a massive hydraulic pump mounted on a truck brought to the site. The concrete pump was seen as revolutionary when it was introduced to the construction industry twenty years ago, but it is expensive and cumbersome to use, and is now mostly brought in for large operations, if cranes are overtaxed or when the concrete is needed in an out-of-the-way place that the crane cannot reach.

There is a saying among those who work with concrete that grey is not a colour but a condition. In most modern buildings and throughout our cities, the colour dominates from pillar to post. The ancient Romans are responsible for this monochromatic urban landscape. Builders for millennia had used mud, adobe and mortar to hold together structures of rock or wood. The Romans in 40 B.C.

added a new element, a volcanic sand they called *pozzolana*, which was first found at Pozzuoli, a port near Naples. By accident, builders making wharves and piers around the port found that a mixture of this magical sand, limestone and rubble hardened into a solid mass of artificial stone when water was added. As word of the discovery got around and greater supplies of *pozzolana* were found, the use of concrete spread to the splendid roads, theatres, baths and aqueducts that for centuries have influenced Western architecture.

Historian Daniel Boorstin, in his book *The Creators*, complains that the importance of concrete was overlooked at the time of its discovery because observers were blinded by the marble glories of ancient Greece. Vitruvius, a Roman military engineer in the first century B.C. who recorded the Roman orders of architecture, included concrete in his treatise only as a material for making polished floors. It does not get much more respect today. "In modern times [it] has borne the stigma of the commonplace. Concrete is the everyday substance of our sidewalks, driveways and roads, of dams, bridges and office buildings," Boorstin writes. "How could it have been the raw material of a revolution in architecture and the shaper of new beauties?"

This humble mixture still contains broken stone, sand, water and some kind of cement. The most common is Portland cement, a mixture of ground limestone and clay baked in an oven, so named by its British inventor, Joseph Aspdin, because it reminded him of the colour of the limestone in Portland, England. The water combines chemically with the cement to form a paste that binds together the sand and gravel. Any extra water is expelled, and the mixture turns into a solid mass of artificial stone. It has many of the characteristics of the real thing—it's strong, weather-resistant and fireproof—with the added advantage that it can be moulded while wet into any shape or size. Concrete sets rather than needing to dry, like mud or adobe. In construction, this means it will harden in confined spaces, such as behind steel wall panels or in footings in the ground where air barely reaches. It is also popular because its components are easy to come by almost anywhere in the world. The drab colour comes from the cement, which rises to the surface with the finer sand as it sets and gives freshly formed concrete its smooth appearance.

While scientists have had little interest in producing concrete in anything but cheerless grey, they have transformed it in other ways into a product the Romans would have coveted. Ancient chemists experimented with different proportions of lime and *pozzolana*, and discovered how to handle the fluid concrete so successive layers of it fused into a single mass. But it took almost another two millennia for the most significant improvements to be made. In 1868, a French gardener crafting delicate basins for his water gardens laid steel rods through the middle of wet concrete. The technique vastly expanded the finished product's strength and thus the uses to which it could be put. Concrete now makes up walls, smokestacks, water tanks and even the toboggans and canoes crafted by young civil-engineering students in class projects.

Recent experimentation has made concrete even better and more versatile. Improvements in its mix mean that less and less of it goes further and further. Simcoe Place is among the first buildings in North America to use a concrete that is several times stronger than the norm. Its strength is measured in the megapascal (MPa), a unit derived by taking the vertical load of a concrete column and dividing by its area. The standard concrete used in most construction, such as house foundations and the bulk of Simcoe Place, is 30 MPa, but today's structural engineers, who design the skeletons of buildings to support typical loads as well as any extra weight or unusual conditions, can take advantage of concrete with strengths of 85 MPa and more. This means the features holding up a building can be made much smaller and use less steel, offering the same support without costing as much or taking up as much space.

This high-performance concrete contains less stone, instead using more cement and new varieties of cement that weren't available a decade ago, but it must be handled carefully. It needs more water to bond properly, so two extra substances are added: a water-reducing agent, to soak up some of the extra water, and a "super-plasticizer," to give the stiffer concrete a jelly-like consistency for easier handling. Special controls are also needed on-site to make sure the right material goes to the right spot—so that, for instance, one of the slimmed-down columns meant to be constructed of high-performance concrete does not end up being made of the standard, weaker mix. To keep track of the concrete, each load and the area it is destined for are marked with ribbons that correspond to colours on the plans. Grant Milligan, the main structural consultant for the Simcoe Place project, says the harder-setting concrete is also faster-setting, and it must be used much more quickly so it doesn't begin to set in the truck. The improved concrete has reduced the size of the building's supporting columns, which would otherwise have been uncomfortably large. The result is a real-estate agent's dream: there will be more leasable space in the tower offices, in the shops on the building's concourse and ground floor and in the underground garage.

Concrete in all strengths and shapes is quickly dominating the day-to-day development of Simcoe Place. The building will be a veritable fortress of 135,000 tonnes of concrete. More than 1,800 tonnes will be placed in the core at the base in a single day. Note the verb: place. To an aficionado of the art of building, concrete is never poured. And *cement* is not a synonym for *concrete*. Builders are not usually sensitive to the myriad misconceptions about their art, but they fume when they hear people talk about cement trucks and cement shoes, because cement is, of course, just one ingredient of concrete. "It's like looking at a cake and calling it flour," Milligan laments.

Placing the concrete is a messy but often delicate job for Leo De Jesus, a foreman at the site. The crew of labourers and concrete finishers he works with actually has to stand in the concrete, so the right clothing and equipment are critical. De Jesus wears long rubber safety boots in a size smaller than his feet, so they don't get trapped and pulled off by the deep concrete as he walks. He tucks his baggy blue work pants into the tops of his boots after first tying them with a shoelace—making them look like Cossack trousers—to prevent stones from falling in. The squat blue hard hat covering his weather-beaten face and shiny bald head is strapped under his chin like a pith helmet so it doesn't fall off as he bends to work with the concrete. It is topped with well-worn safety glasses that will keep concrete from splashing into his eyes. A wrench, hammer and switchblade knife hanging from a holster slung around his waist help to straighten misplaced reinforcing steel before the concrete arrives. The whistle on a shoelace around his neck is used to summon the concrete bucket or alert his fellow workers on the noisy site.

Most concrete comes in the bucket, which has a spring-loaded trap door at the bottom that opens and shuts when a handle is pulled down or pushed up. Once each load of concrete flows out into a form, it is immediately treated with a long rod that vibrates with the spinning of a spring inside to continue mixing the basic ingredients together, force out any pockets of air, help the concrete flow around the woven reinforcing steel and bring the finer cement, referred to by the men as fat or juice, to the outer surfaces. It's a bit like a Moulinex blender. Shovels and a long board called a scree are used to level off the top of the concrete, and a second board attached with a long pole called a bull-float is pulled over the surface to smooth it and again bring the cement to the top.

Some six to twelve hours after the concrete is placed—when De Jesus can walk on it with the heels of his work boots sinking in just half a centimetre or so—the concrete is ready for finishing by a second crew. They polish its damp surface with the whirring blades of a power-trowel, a large hand-operated device that looks like an upside-down helicopter. This operation must be performed before the concrete gets too hard, so it sometimes goes on under floodlights long into the night. When the concrete is three-quarters set—usually after about three or four days, depending on the weather—the form-work can be dismantled, removed and lugged piece by piece to the next place it is needed.

Each part of the work takes its toll. Pulling the hatch on the bucket strains De Jesus's back, the vibrators turn his arms to jelly and just walking around in the sticky, dense concrete hour after hour requires legs with the strength of tree trunks. But at sixty-four years old, after thirty years on the job, twenty-five of them working for Avenue, De Jesus has no plans to retire. His $38-an-hour wages, including benefits, help pay the bills. Small investors have been just as hard hit by the recession; De Jesus, for one, took a huge loss on the house he bought as an investment just before the real-estate market crashed. "I have to work. . . . I'm still in good shape and I like to work," he says, pulling up his light blue T-shirt and patting a rock-hard stomach as evidence. "It never killed nobody to work. . . . For me, I have no problems, thanks God." The job is also satisfying, especially when De Jesus surveys the smoothly finished slabs and columns of concrete. "When I see something wrong, some little stones on the surface, I feel sick in my stomach, because I'm proud when I place concrete, when it is nice and beautiful."

The whole process of concrete-forming is made easier by the presence of the tower crane. The first of three such cranes has begun operating, lifting loads of concrete, bundles of reinforcing steel and aluminum beams at the east end of the site. Something that weighs seventy tonnes and is forty metres tall can hardly be considered agile, but a tower crane manoeuvring a bucket heaving with concrete is a mixture of brawn and ballet. Cranes are not just a constant source of fascination for sidewalk superintendents; they are a symbol of construction and a handy barometer of the economy. People involved in development count the tower cranes on the skyline to gauge business. The tower cranes cost from $500,000 to more than $1 million apiece. They can be rented like any other piece of construction machinery, although often, as in the case of Simcoe Place, they are owned by the subcontractor responsible for the building's main structure.

There are two types of tower cranes, identified by the appearance of the boom, the part that does the hoisting. The first crane erected at Simcoe Place, and the one most common on construction sites, is called a fixed-boom or hammerhead crane because it has an arm that extends straight out and remains horizontal when its cable lifts objects, resembling the flat top of a capital T. At the far western end of the site, the builders will soon erect another type, called a luffing-boom crane, that can work in confined spaces. The luffing-boom crane looks a bit more like the graceful-necked bird that this huge machine is named for, with a fifty-metre-long boom that rises and falls to avoid obstructions, in this case the mirrored glass offices of the Broadcast Centre next door.

As the word *boom* suggests, the names for the parts of the land-locked crane borrow heavily from maritime terminology. The tower, which is the crane's vertical support, is also referred to as its mast, while the boom can be called the jib. The shorter counterweight section on the back of the crane opposite the boom is the counter-jib. This is the part no one notices as they admire the crane's fetching and hoisting, but it is where six or more slabs of concrete—each weighing two and a half tonnes—provide balance, stopping it from tipping over in a wind or when it picks up heavy objects. The counterweight section also houses the crane's all-important motors and its spool of hoisting cable. Above it all sits the crane's linchpin, the A-section, named for its shape. Two pendants—massive cables—extend down from the very top of the tower to form each side of the A, holding up the crane's boom on one side and its counterweight section on the other. Between the A and the tower is a table that turns the crane, a function referred to by another nautical term, *slewing*. Finally comes the cable for hoisting. It begins in the motor on the counterweight section, passes up to the top of the A, then goes straight down the tower and out along the boom. At its end is a trolley holding the large block and hook, which are painted bright tangerine orange so they can easily be seen by the operator and the construction workers.

The crane is brought to the site in pieces that sit on several flatbed trucks. It is bolted together like a giant Erector set by a crew that specializes in assembling and servicing the giant devices. The tower is pieced together first and then the boom and counterweight are added, one section at a time to maintain the delicate balance. The crane's size, radius and, most important, its position on-site depend on how big a building is to be, the speed with which it must be built and the location of the pick-up points where most materials will be brought to be hoisted. Four cranes were required to construct the massive Broadcast Centre, which occupies an area roughly the size of a city block.

In determining the exact position of the cranes within the site, the contractor is mindful that it will be some time before the spaces where they stand can be finished. Cranes must therefore be put where they cause the least amount of disruption to the building's mechanical and electrical fixtures and any important structural features, such as the beams that hold up floors. This means extensive consultation with the mechanical, electrical and structural engineers and the architects.

The crane operator sits or stands in an exalted position, a small cab hanging near the central turntable or along the crane's boom. He is the star of any construction site, and his is a job that requires some unusual qualities. Wedged in a tiny box suspended from the boom of a swaying tower crane a hundred or more metres in the air, an operator obviously has to be comfortable with heights and small spaces. It also helps to be a bit of a loner in such a solitary job, and to have the sort of bladder that can withstand few bathroom breaks. The operator is also under constant pressure, from making sure the crane is used efficiently to performing intricate, precise movements with objects weighing several tonnes at the end of a narrow cable as a steady stream of orders comes from those far below.

The position and characteristics of the operator's cab vary with the make of crane, but the dominant feature of each is a window to survey the scene around and below. Demands come thick and fast, either by radio or, on clear days, by hand signal. With his partner's raised finger or flick of the wrist, the operator knows to move the load up and down, to turn, to take it slowly or to stop altogether. This early in the project, the lone crane operator spends most of his time hoisting formwork components and concrete. The hand-signalling summons him to pick up from trucks at street level buckets and bundles that will then be lowered into the excavated hole. This relatively simple operation will become more complicated when two more cranes and many more trades join in, and the operator's vision becomes obscured by the growing building. Soon there will be daily or even hourly meetings and elaborate schedules to work out who uses the machines and when.

There are limits to a crane's abilities. Its hoisting capacity—plotted on a chart unique to each style and model of crane, and dependent on the boom's length—is posted in Avenue's trailer office. The first crane erected at Simcoe Place can carry as much as eight tonnes of material if the hook travels only twenty-one metres out along the boom and the hoist cable is doubled for extra strength. To carry a lighter and more typical load, such as a four-tonne bucket of concrete, the hook can reach out as far as forty metres. If the hook is extended along the boom's full forty-eight metres, it can carry only three tonnes. There are many safety features built into the crane, including one that automatically shuts it down if it is overloaded. A crane may be massive, but it can bend or fall over if it picks up too much.

All machines used in construction are vulnerable to technical failures and human error, and accidents involving cranes have been few but catastrophic. High-rise construction sites are, of course, full of workers and are usually surrounded by a dense population, so anything falling from high up can inflict a lot of damage. In San Francisco in 1989, a crane toppled from a sixteen-storey building under construction, raining concrete and steel on the city's financial district and killing five people, including the operator. The accident was believed to be caused by the loosening of the bolts that held together the tower. In 1983, a giant crane used to construct Calgary's Petro Canada Building crumpled when a freak gust of wind caught the three-thousand-kilogram slab of marble that it was lifting. The crane spun around and buckled, throwing the operator to his death fifty-three storeys below.

He may have one of the riskiest jobs on the site, but the crane operator takes it all in stride, confident of the many safety measures built into the device. He would face another restriction if the crane did not rise simultaneous with the growing building's progress: eventually there would not be enough clearance below the hook to move large loads. So the crane, initially anchored in the ground by a concrete foundation, will eventually leave its mooring and rise up along with the building it creates. This way, the crane gets most of its support from the new building instead of its original concrete foundation. It is anchored there until the next time the operation has to be carried out.

This step will be ordered by Corrado Patullo after discussions with Eastern to determine the best timing. The operation is usually carried out in the middle of the night, when the operator is sleeping and the crane is not needed, or on days when there is nothing to hoist. The break will be appreciated, allowing for cleaning up the site and catching up with paperwork. But Corrado and his concrete crews will be anxious for the work to resume on the building's main structure.

FIVE

DESIGNS ON THE SKYLINE

B uilding is a long and difficult process. The construction of Simcoe Place will take more than two years. It took longer than that to plan the development and secure a tenant. There are thousands of people in dozens of professions, trades and manufacturing companies involved in its design and creation. But architect Bill Neish holds a secret about the beginning of this project: it was thought up by a couple of people in about a week. Along with Carlos Ott, the designer of the Bastille Opera in Paris, Neish huddled over a pad of white graph paper and sketched out the design that has since been rendered on drawings, formed into plastic models, embossed on glossy marketing brochures—and is now taking shape in concrete and steel on the construction site, where the lowest level of the main tower is almost complete.

"It's pretty scary. In fact, it's very scary," says Neish, a soft-spoken, slight man of sixty with thinning grey hair who is the N in the NORR Partnership Ltd. The other parts of the design firm's acronym are Owen, Roland and Roy, though the active partnership has grown to nine people. On a winter day several years ago, NORR and three of its competitors were invited by Cadillac Fairview to submit proposals for Simcoe Place. Based on Neish's preliminary work with Ott, who is a design consultant to NORR on this and other projects, the company was awarded the contract to create the building less than a month later.

The winning design did not spring entirely out of the two men's fevered imaginations. Each of the four firms of architects in the competition had been given Cadillac's requirements for the project.

It was to include two million square feet of office space spread over two large towers, as well as an 1,800-seat live theatre at ground level linking the two buildings, a small park, two floors of shopping and a substantial underground parking garage. In creating a project on paper, the architects had to keep in mind how it would fit into the neighbourhood, the constraints that zoning imposed on anything built on the site and the city's urban-planning guidelines. The final ingredient of a winning plan would come from the designers' knowledge of what a successful office building should possess, right down to a liberal supply of corner offices and efficient toilet locations.

Allowing architects only four weeks to decide so many details might seem unreasonable, but such abbreviated competitions have become common in the real-estate business. The conventional wisdom among cash-strapped developers is that architects and engineers who are given more time will end up spending more money. Neish and Ott and their firm worked with a timetable that allowed only one week to evolve a basic concept, another to flesh out that concept and two weeks to render it in models and drawings to present to Cadillac. Faced with such deadlines, architects have to work fast. Their goal is to get inside their clients' heads to see what will suit all requirements; then they must turn those heads by going a little further.

Neish took his cue from Cadillac's ownership in the nearby TD Centre. Thinking the developer might want to draw an association between the two complexes, Neish and Ott designed an updated version of the 1964 design. There, buildings initially designed by Ludwig Mies van der Rohe are angled around a large site to give people on each side of every building a generous view. The two thirty-five-storey towers that Neish and Ott designed at Simcoe Place were similarly set apart, but they added a new feature to further improve the vista: a series of angled cuts to create sixteen corner offices on every floor.

The layout of the twenty-six-year-old TD Centre also had to be improved to satisfy the city's current urban-planning goals. No longer are office buildings surrounded by open plazas—the equivalent of windswept plains—as they were back in the 1970s. These days, a structure extends out to the sidewalk, and in fact becomes part of the street, through an unimposing, low-rise building called a podium at its base. Office floors are set back on a narrower tower above. The city especially insists that new buildings offer shops, parks and inviting public spaces at ground level for people to move through.

What began as two rectangles drawn by the two designers on graph paper was delivered to Cadillac Fairview as two plastic models and forty-two full-colour drawings showing every aspect of the proposed project. After NORR was awarded the contract, Neish and the firm's design team got down to details with Cadillac Fairview, creating architectural flourishes and working out every material that would be used in the development.

Neish's direct involvement with Simcoe Place ended after a year, when he moved on to other projects. Now, as the building begins to rise, he has taken on the role of anxious parent. "You start driving by that site and you realize the moment of truth is approaching—whether you got it right and the building's going to be accepted and successful, or you missed. Design is not a precise science by any means, and we're just hoping that it's going to work out. If there's disappointment, it goes right to the heart."

In earlier times, the designer would have continued to be deeply involved at this point. Indeed, in Ancient Greece, the word *architekton* meant master carpenter, and the architect was not set apart or paid more than the engineers, contractors and skilled workmen. By the time of the Romans, the architect had been elevated to master builder, engineer, planner and interior designer. Such a person, Vitruvius declared in the orders of architecture, required a knowledge of science, with natural ability and quick learning. To undertake this "great profession," he must "be educated, skillful with the pencil, instructed in geometry, know much history, have followed the philosophers with attention, understand music, have some knowledge of medicine, know the opinions of the jurists and be acquainted with astronomy and the theory of the heavens."

An intricate division of labour within today's architectural firms, throughout the development industry and on the construction site has spread such expertise and lofty expectations around. An architect is merely a building's prime consultant. For a start, an architect's grand vision is passed along to architectural drafters, as well as engineers, to work out the fine points of its structural, mechanical and electrical systems.

"Generally speaking, we're able to find a way to make it possible," says Grant Milligan of Quinn Dressel, a civil engineer and the leading structural consultant at Simcoe Place. "Someone has to decide how to physically make the building stand up." That means taking the architect's outline and deciding on the size, shape and composition of features such as the building's columns and its core, which, like the trunk of a tree, must especially withstand the horizontal forces the structure will encounter. The three separate consulting engineers also help determine a building's total cost. They design the most efficient way for the structure and systems not only to fulfil the architect's vision but also to meet the developer's needs and, hopefully, budget. The skeleton alone accounts for about 20 per cent of the final price. If Milligan can do justice to the architect's plans but use less concrete or steel, it will ultimately cost less.

Architects make their reputations on their flair and flamboyance, not necessarily on whether they design economical buildings. They can also find artistic expression in more daring designs and spectacular shapes that are not practical to implement. It's said that if engineers and contractors designed buildings, they would come in two varieties: rectangular and square. Milligan disagrees. If that were so, he says, "You'd end up with a downtown full of buildings that all look the same and are rather dull and no one wants to rent." Besides, he likes the challenge of designing features such as Simcoe Place's corner offices, which are not supported by columns (why spoil the view?) but are cantilevered out from the main part of the floor on each level.

At only thirty-seven, and with a cherubic face and shock of light brown hair that make him look ten years younger, Milligan has designed some of the most significant buildings in the city and beyond. He started at Quinn Dressel just after graduating from university in civil engineering in 1979 and has always had an interest in building. His grandfather was a violinist with the Toronto Symphony Orchestra who encouraged his son, an apprentice construction carpenter, to work on building stage sets for theatres. Milligan's father's first job in the 1950s was at the Royal Alexandra Theatre, which was then surrounded by derelict factories and disused railway tracks. Milligan remembers his father predicting that the area would be a good place to invest. He moved on to a series of other theatres, where Milligan later worked during the summers building scenery. He also considered stage building as a career, but was frustrated with its temporary nature. "I wanted to do something that was visible. It mattered to me that people could see the results of what I was doing." In the last fifteen years, he has worked on buildings in Toronto, Calgary, Paris and Shanghai. In that time, he has seen the development industry expand and contract. Simcoe Place is the last substantial project in Canada on Quinn Dressel's drafting tables, with the rest overseas.

Bill Neish may have ceded work on Simcoe Place to Milligan and his fellow consultants, but NORR Associates has continued to be very much involved in the project. The work has moved on to another facet of the architect's operation. As well as the up-front job of deciding on the building's concept, the firm has two other roles: turning the design into detailed drawings and supervising its construction. Neish's original design work took about a year, and overseeing the project requires about two years. The step in the middle, the preparation of the contract drawings, lasted an additional eight months but accounts for the bulk of NORR's effort and more than half of its fee.

Visit any one of the hundreds of subcontractors, suppliers and engineering consultants involved in Simcoe Place and this drafting work is very much in evidence, an immense sheaf of drawings weighing down entire desks in offices and long tables on shop floors. The collection is 1.5 metres long, 1 metre wide and 220 pages thick, often dog-eared at the corners, held together in places with tape, edges studded with little yellow Post-It notes. At one time these would have been the building's blueprints, but architects and engineers long ago stopped reproducing their diagrams on distinctive light-sensitive paper that turned Prussian blue. Designs now roll out of computer printers and photocopiers and are called black-line prints. These form what are known as the building's contract documents, because together with a set of written directions, or specifications, they make up the contract between the developer and the general contractor.

The result is an architectural recipe for the office tower. The man in charge of assembling it, the Julia Child of Simcoe Place, is Henton Hung. An architect at NORR and the project's manager, Hung took over where the designers left off. His team figures out how to turn the loftiest architectural vision into "working drawings." His involvement began with the phase of this project called design development, where the first hard details and dimensions of the building finally began to be worked out. At this early stage, Milligan's team of structural engineers and drafters, as well as the project's mechanical and electrical consultants, also started working on drawings for their own separate contributions. Altogether, developer Cadillac Fairview will pay the four parties $5 million for their work, 60 per cent of which will go to the architect.

NORR's first formal task was to prepare drawings for the two towers, the theatre and other features that would be needed to get approval for the project from municipal planners and politicians. The city council looked over the plans in a process called development review that lasted several months, finally giving them the go-ahead.

Then economic reality intervened. The abrupt decline in demand for office space made such a huge development out of the question, especially as none of the office space had even been rented. Simcoe Place was put on hold for a year, until the Workers' Compensation Board came looking for a new headquarters. Twenty-one floors of one of the two towers appeared to fit their requirements as long as significant changes were made. So Hung went back to the drawing board. A second, scaled-back development-review proposal was quickly drawn up and again approved by the city. By now, the entire project and its timing had changed considerably. Instead of two thirty-five-storey towers, a single thirty-storey building would be built first, with a forty-storey tower to come later, assuming the economy picked up and tenants could be found in advance. The theatre was scrapped altogether. It was to have been part of the development that bridged the two towers, which for now would remain unbuilt.

Four months before the deal with the WCB was signed, Hung's working drawings began to take shape. Like most professionals in the information age, Hung has traded his drafting table and pencils for a computer workstation. Plans that were roughed out in the earlier design-development stages were "hard-lined"—or finalized—using software that lets the architect draw, label features and easily make changes. Each member of Hung's staff specializes in certain tasks, such as designing the emergency stairs in the building's core or the inner workings of the ceiling.

The process is divided into two stages. To have a clear sense of what the final working drawings should include, the architects first map out the various aspects of the project on manageable letter-sized pieces of paper, called storyboards. The project's busy underground concourse, for instance, was portrayed on one page for those who wanted a quick overview. But for contractors who need detail, the workings of the concourse were split into two or more sections in subsequent drafts.

The drawings, combined with thousands of pages of written details called specifications, are now guiding the contractors through every construction technique and material. They have also been copied by the hundred and are sent to municipal officials, contractors who bid for jobs and companies that will make building components. The plans will also be an important resource for the third team of NORR architects and technicians to work on Simcoe Place, those who will review the construction and the bills that flow in.

For a sizeable renovation, $22,000 seemed reasonable. After all, several floors at the top and bottom of the building had to be altered, the entrances changed and the roof completely rebuilt. However, considering that the structure in question is two metres tall and made entirely of plastic, the perspective on price changes. In fact, perspective is the whole point of the model of Simcoe Place, which stands in an opulent office on the fifty-first floor of a TD bank tower overlooking the construction site.

This is no doll house but an impressive scale model of Simcoe Place, complete with twinkling lights and surrounded by leafy poplar trees designed to sell the project to prospective investors and tenants. It took model-makers, machinists and artists several months to make at a cost of $87,000 plus the $22,000 in changes. Next to it is a model of just the marble-floored lobby, which cost another $42,000. Finally, there is a foam representation of the building set amidst the city, which cost $41,000. The money spent on the three models could have built a good-sized house, but sophisticated scale representations such as these are the price of competing in the high-stakes commercial-development game. They have been photographed for use in glossy brochures and shown off by Cadillac Fairview in its sky-high presentation centre to scores of potential tenants over the last three years.

The models are the work of Ted Bassken and his staff at Architectural Dimensions, which is housed in one of those nondescript units in an industrial park north of the city. The interior, though, unfolds like a Santa's workshop of miniature houses, Tom Thumb furniture and lilliputian condominium suites. Like many young boys, Bassken constructed balsa-wood models of cars and airplanes as a child in the 1950s. He never dreamed he would end up making a living from his hobby using the latest in computers and electronics. In fact, there isn't a single piece of balsa wood anywhere in the process or in the workshop, "because computers hate dust and wood makes lots of dust." Instead, sheets of Plexiglas and styrene, two types of plastic that come in various thicknesses and are easy to cut and shape, are the commercial model-maker's medium of choice.

Like a full-sized construction project, each model starts with the building's architectural drawings. These are loaded into a computer, which breaks down the three-dimensional structure into hundreds or even thousands of two-dimensional pieces. These are numbered, cut by machine from the plastic, then assembled by hand to recreate the building. Intricate finishing touches by Bassken's crew give the model its authenticity. Lights are fitted inside and out. Plastic cars and pedestrians fill streets and sidewalks. Trees made of wire encircle the building and dot the park. Finally, automotive paint is applied to the styrene to mimic a myriad of finishes, including granite, chrome, wood, plaster or brick. Authenticity is paramount. A chart displaying samples of marble from each region of Italy is consulted to recreate the appropriate rich, veined rock.

Achieving perfection on a structure this small is not easy. More detailed models, such as the one portraying Simcoe Place's lobby or the various mock-ups of furnished condominium suites, are made at a scale of three-quarters of an inch to one finished foot, but larger models, including those of entire buildings, are reduced further, to the point where one-quarter of an inch represents a foot.

Model-makers know designs are never final, so they must be flexible. When Simcoe Place was reduced to thirty storeys and other amendments were made to the building, Bassken performed the costly renovations. The budget for pre-marketing buildings, from making models to constructing presentation centres decorated with a building's finishes, has soared in the past two decades. But developers can save a lot of trouble by selling space while buildings are still on the drawing-board. "What you are trying to do is create the ambience and the reality of something that does not yet exist," Bassken says. "You're showing the prospective tenant what they're going to get."

As well as helping developers secure financing and occupants, the models have practical purposes, such as showing whether proposed furniture or fixtures fit in a space and displaying the architect's finished materials and colours. Three-dimensional models are preferred to artists' sketches for this because people feel as though they can walk around them. Bassken says they are also evocative for prospective tenants who are childhood model enthusiasts like him. "There is a natural fascination with seeing miniature things," he says.

The model and presentation centre are not the only ways to drum up business for the finished Simcoe Place. The developer has also hired graphic designers to promote the project. The hand of Michael Malloy, of Taylor and Browning Design Associates, is apparent all around the construction site. His designs are stamped on all of the architectural drawings and correspondence, embossed on glossy brochures and stencilled in white paint on the hoarding surrounding the site's perimeter. He and the artists at his firm began working on

Simcoe Place's marketing and communication plan when the two architects at NORR first drew up their winning concept of the building. Malloy started creating a logo, known in the business as a graphic identity, featuring a stylized version of Simcoe Place's profile. He is also responsible for the building's grey-and-black promotional colour schemes, brochures (also known as leasing tools) and the directional signs that will be posted in and around the building when it is finished.

Taylor and Browning occupies the ground floor of an office building that sits directly on top of the subway line at the edge of Rosedale, one of the first neighbourhoods in Toronto to be developed when wealthy homeowners fled the increasingly busy waterfront around Simcoe Place. Tables and bookshelves shake as each train passes underneath; the evening rush hour is a continuous tremor. Still, it would appear that all of the vibration has been good for creativity, judging from the labels on products ranging from beer and ice-cream pies to computers and vitamins that got their start in these rooms.

But the decline of commercial real estate is also noticeable here. When the company started eleven years ago, developers represented 70 per cent of Taylor and Browning's clients; now they account for just 5 per cent. But to Malloy, the principle of designing an identity, whether it's a label for beer or a brochure for a high-rise office tower, is the same. "Every product has a visual problem," he says. "We're visual problem-solvers."

The first task when Cadillac Fairview hired the company to help sell Simcoe Place was to create a suitable logo, a lengthy process that required Malloy to come up with thirty-five or forty variations on a theme before a final choice was made by the developer. Most of the logo options showed different views of the architect's stepped profile of Simcoe Place, with a solid, corporate look, Malloy said, to "emanate the overall feeling of the building." The chosen design also had to be easily reproducible in a variety of sizes and applications.

Graphic design is a combination of psychology and sales, and the target of a campaign must be kept in mind as an identity is developed. Most of the promotional material for Simcoe Place was given a granite-and-marble look to appeal to lawyers, accountants, banks and corporate head offices looking for space. Meanwhile, a rose-coloured folder for the building's shopping and eating areas was put together with retail tenants in mind. It includes bright photographs of nearby shops and theatres and an artist's drawing of the planned underground food court. Most of the glossy artwork shows the building as if it is already standing in the middle of the city. "There's no guesswork," says Malloy.

Simcoe Place's graphic identity will live on long after the actual building is standing, turning up on stationery, T-shirts, security-guard uniforms and computer-kiosk screens in the public areas of the building's concourse. Almost every modern development on the city skyline displays some sort of symbol, reflecting either its name or its major tenant. Often this is done in brilliant, eye-catching lights high up on the roof. So far, there are plans only to etch the logo of Simcoe Place's profile, designed by Neish and Ott, miniaturized by Bassken and stylized by Malloy, discreetly into the glass of the building's lobby doors.

SIX

THE PROJECT TAKES SHAPE

Jeff Abrams has an enviable view from his office on the twenty-sixth floor of Metro Hall. He can gaze upon the serene archipelago of the Toronto Islands kissed by the hot summer sun, the looming bulk of SkyDome and, far below, his children's day-care centre reflected in the mirrored windows of the Broadcast Centre next door. But most important, the spectacled lawyer for Metropolitan Toronto, who calls himself a professional observer, watches the Simcoe Place site across the street. There is much to see. The lower parking levels of the high-rise are taking shape in a continuous cycle of excavation, shoring, carpentry and concrete manoeuvres. When the action on the site heats up, with the erection of new cranes or big deliveries, the thirty-five-year-old Abrams takes a closer look with the high-powered binoculars he was given for his bar mitzvah and keeps at the ready in his desk drawer.

"I'm not staring out at the building all day," Abrams protests. "If I'm dictating or want to stretch my back, I walk to the window and take a gander." The flurry of activity entrances the most indifferent onlookers. They watch the building's progress from the sidewalk peepholes, through the wide openings in the hoarding where dump trucks rumble in and out or from perches in high-rise towers such as Abrams's. Tourists stop by *en route* to nearby attractions like the CN Tower. Commuters steal a quick look on the sprint to the train or the subway at Union Station. Kids on their summer holidays riding mountain bikes or wearing Roller-blades pause for a rest, clinging for balance to the chain-link fence of the site's gates while they gape at the action. And bleary-eyed conventioneers flood here from trade shows in the Metro Toronto Convention Centre across the street in search of something more stimulating than keynote addresses and motivational seminars.

Standing in groups or one by one, these sidewalk superintendents puzzle over what they see. The more astute notice when someone climbs up the crane to take the operator a cup of coffee, which usually prompts heated discussions about whether the elevated job allows for bathroom breaks. Among the most appreciative in the crowd are the special-interest observers such as construction workers and managers. An architect visiting the city from New York is impressed that a construction site this big with so much activity has so little clutter. His wife is less impressed when the boom of the massive crane swings over the hoarding and the sidewalk where the couple stands. Her method of dealing with her husband's fascination with construction sites? "You walk away fast."

Barrie Ralph and Paul McGrory, who work as low-income housing coordinators in the gothic bell-tower of St. Andrew's Church, which is kitty-corner to the site and was built when this land housed the Parliament of Upper Canada, take in the scene as much as once a day. They slowly circle the hoarding at lunch time and stop at each peep-hole. "It's a way to pass a half an hour," says Ralph. "We don't hammer in nails, pour concrete or get our hands dirty for a living, so we live vicariously through those who do." He is especially fascinated by fine details, such as the laying of the conduits through which wiring and other services will eventually snake, a delicate process amid the chaos of heavy steel and concrete work. "Who's the master brain that knows where they're all going and what they're going to do?" he wonders.

McGrory is more interested in the big picture. He considers the scene "a pastoral landscape" for urban dwellers, a good place simply to clear his head. "It's a stress-reliever, it takes you to a different space," he says. "We're in an emotionally draining job, dealing with people who are very needy."

Then there is Bruce Whitehead, an electrical supplier and amateur palaeontologist itching to get into the hole before it is filled to see the fossils left behind on the bed of glacial Lake Iroquois. "None of this has been seen by man before," he says, eyes gleaming. Contractors often get requests from spectators who want to venture onto the site for various reasons, but they are reluctant to allow anyone in because tours take time and are disruptive. Exceptions can be made, although visitors must sign a form absolving Eastern from liability, be accompanied by someone from Eastern's staff and dress appropriately. Eastern will provide hard hats in a pinch, project manager Brian Gardner says, "but you'd be surprised how many women we get turning up in peekaboo shoes with four-inch heels. They just can't come in."

The groups that come best prepared are from schools. This highrise doubles as one big research project for students of construction techniques, design, engineering, scheduling and management. "It's good to be able to study a real live project from the bottom to the top," says Kianoosh Kharrazmi, a fourth-year student at Toronto's Ryerson Polytechnic University who is writing a thesis on Simcoe Place's planning process. Alistair MacKenzie, an assistant professor of project management at Ryerson who spent thirty years in the construction business himself, agrees. "This industry is so much straightforward nuts and bolts—or concrete and steel—that it's very difficult to get the whole flavour of it in the classroom." Each year, Ryerson's department of architectural science and landscape architecture grants degrees to about 120 students for its four-year program specializing in project management, architectural design or building science. Students especially learn by visiting sites and talking to the contractors.

First-hand observation is important at a time when there are few part-time or summer jobs in the flagging construction industry. There aren't even many projects in the city for the students to visit. George Kotanidis, a student in the final year of a three-year construction engineering technology course at George Brown College, hopes someday to head a project like this; meanwhile, he's already spent enough time at the site to fit in with the workers and general contractors. During Toronto's construction boom, Kotanidis interrupted his studies at George Brown and worked for three years building schools. With a tighter job market, he's returned to the classroom, mindful of the need to earn more qualifications. Simcoe Place is a major focus of his studies. He's part of a five-member team that has to report on the project's management and building techniques throughout the year. He is also preparing a technical thesis on the high-performance concrete that fortifies the structure.

Most of the people in his program are men. Indeed, men are noticeably over-represented among both those watching and those being watched at the construction site. One of the rare female observers asks why there are no women working, suggesting they could do some of the concrete-finishing jobs where the men appear to be sweeping the fresh material. "Women use brooms all the time," she says, referring to the huge bull-floats. There are no female labourers, carpenters, ironworkers or operating engineers on the site so far. Not only would most women find the heavy labour taxing, but there are few openings in the depressed building market for construction apprentices, particularly women.

But those spectators who like to sneak a peek at the male beefcake on display at construction sites are disappointed. There are no muscle shirts, skimpy shorts or bare chests in sight. Safety concerns and late-twentieth-century sensibilities about exposure to the sun's ultra-violet rays have ruled out such attire for workers in favour of a mandatory dress code that runs to elbow-length sleeves and long pants. As sensible as it may be, the cover-up hardly suits the scorching summer weather in the city. The typical central North American heat and humidity have reduced productivity on the site and can cause health problems such as sunstroke; plenty of drinking water is carted into the excavated hole in the sort of round plastic Thermos coolers brought to community picnics.

What a construction crew likes to see is a clear, sunny day, about 20°C, but perfect conditions are a rarity on an exposed construction site. Winter is the most challenging period for construction work, although summer extremes—the cycle of unrelenting heat, humidity, wind and liberating storms—can also play havoc with techniques and schedules. The hard-pressed contractors are devotees of long-range forecasts. They have programmed the phone number for the weather office on their telephones, and a chart on the wall of Eastern's trailer identifies sixteen different cloud formations and the weather they bring. The company has to be sure that a few hundred tonnes of concrete ordered for delivery the next day do not go to waste because of a freak storm or unexpected heat wave. Concrete-forming is especially difficult in the heat, because the cement in the mixture can harden before it is adequately placed and levelled. Precautions have to be taken so the water that is critical to concrete's chemical hydration does not evaporate too quickly. On a hot day, the surface of the newly placed concrete is either continually sprayed with a light veil of water or draped with wet burlap to keep damp.

Hot weather is even more of a concern with the temperamental high-strength concretes and their greater concentrations of cement. They may even start to set while still in the mixing trucks. Normally it is acceptable for ninety minutes to elapse between the time a truck is filled, or "charged," at the Dufferin Custom Concrete plant in the city's port and when the concrete is placed in a form at the site. But in 30°C heat, this safe period is cut in half; any longer and the concrete may spoil. The tickets stamped with the time that each truck was filled are scrutinized, and the concrete rejected if it is too old. The issue of who pays for the concrete turns on the reason for the delay.

Summer also brings storms to the site, with high winds that turn heavy plywood into sails and make the crane operators feel uncomfortable. If there is any sign they can't control their loads, the cranes are shut down. Showers pose more problems. Excavation is easiest when the ground is dry, and even the frozen earth of winter is no match for the powerful hydraulic backhoes, but rain and run-off turn the soil into mush and can destabilize the earthen ramps used by the heavy machinery and trucks. After a heavy rainstorm, the holes excavated in the rock for the building's footings became ponds. The hole for the foundation that supports the central core filled with water twice before it could be filled with concrete. Portable pumps were brought in to drain 250,000 litres of water each time, enough to fill a good-sized swimming pool.

A downpour can ruin finished areas in buildings that have not been sealed off. It also causes serious problems for new concrete. Pelting rain washes off the cement "fat" that the concrete crews and finishers worked so hard to bring to the surface and polish, making flat slabs intended for floors so rough that they must be ground smooth with giant rented polishers. It is an expensive and time-consuming procedure that subcontractors would rather avoid. Working outdoors is difficult too. If construction workers awake to heavy showers, they stay home without pay. If they are called in to work in threatening conditions and are then released before starting work because it has begun to rain heavily, they receive just two hours' wages, called show-up time. Otherwise they are paid for as long as the weather holds.

Weather is not the only thing that can wreak havoc with a project's schedule. Ask a construction boss whether a job is on track and the response you'll get is more than a simple yes or no. This is not an issue of etiquette or equivocation. Instead, what follows is a lesson straight from the business world's time-management lexicon—a tale of overviews and floats, milestones and critical paths. The short answer is that the Simcoe Place construction team expects to finish on the contract date, 116 weeks from when the project began. That is when Eastern agreed to "substantially perform" its contract—legalese from the province's Construction Lien Act for completing 99 per cent of the value of the work and handing over the keys for the building to its owners.

The effort that goes into meeting this deadline includes not just gruelling labour on the part of the construction workers, but also number-crunching and computer programming designed to make the massive project proceed like clockwork. This began when Eastern and two other contracting companies tendered bids to build the building, each of them suggesting a final cost and completion date. Working out that date involves educated guesswork on the part of contractors, who draw on their experience to consider the sequence, logic and duration of each stage of building.

Once Eastern was awarded the contract and a starting date was set, this rough schedule began to be blocked out in a construction overview covering the entire project. It established overlapping activities to be done at the same time—say, excavation, building the P-2 parking level and erecting one of the site's cranes. The overview is continually revised, and becomes more detailed as each separate job or time period starts and more information is known. A large chart on the wall in the trailer dealing specifically with the parking garage sets out the seventeen different times that concrete is incorporated into the P-2 level alone. To make sure they get the most out of labour, materials, machines and conditions, including the weather, a team of managers and subcontractors plots on a two-week timetable how operations such as concrete-forming will be carried out, sometimes down to the hour.

Computer programs simplify the mapping out of the building stages, allowing the contractor to try out different sequences and recalculate after adjustments have been made. In a more efficient world, every activity could overlap, but obviously light fixtures can't be installed until there are ceilings (and wiring and a permanent electrical supply, approved by inspectors).

The time a project will take is calculated by plotting the entire sequence of activities from beginning to end. This is known as the schedule's critical path. Within the path, there are time markers known as milestones, key dates by which activities such as enclosing the building in its outer wall or finishing the underground garage must be completed. However, a certain degree of flexibility, known as float, is built in. Brian Gardner is secretive about the amount of float he has allowed here, and he is not cavalier with it; if too much float is used, there will be none left for a truly rainy day. And there are those days, such as when the Simcoe Place workers discovered the brick sewer passing through the site. The happy news about the long and mostly favourable summer is that Gardner figures two of the four weeks lost in the excavation have been recovered.

Contractors and developers are mindful that set-backs can occur at any time, despite the best planning and preparation. At Simcoe Place, with only a few hours' warning, many of the construction workers walk off the job to protest against a rumoured plan to scrap the project before it reaches ground level. The walk-out means a delay, especially noticeable on a mild day that is perfect for working with concrete, but there are few complaints from the foremen and bosses around the site. Everyone involved in the project, from the labourers and subcontractors to the interior-design consultants and the developer, is nervously awaiting the reaction to a provincial auditor's report suggesting that the decision by the Workers' Compensation Board to build Simcoe Place as its headquarters did not follow government directives.

It's the first work he's had in a year and a half, but John Teixeira put down the tools he uses to build scaffolding at the site and joined his co-workers on the steps of the Ontario Legislature at Queen's Park to demand that the government let him keep his job. He carries a protest sign supplied by the Labourers' International Union with the message Create Work, Don't Stop It. "Who's going to feed my kids?" the twenty-eight-year-old general labourer asks, glaring from under the brim of his well-worn hard hat at the lofty pink sandstone arches of the government building. "How would the politicians like it if everyone who works in here was laid off?"

The beleaguered building trades in Toronto are glad to have a project that will employ more than four hundred people at its peak, but rumours continue to swirl through the site that political pressure will shut it down. Much like the second-guessing, redesigns and cost-cutting that occurred 150 years ago when the former legislature was built at Simcoe Place, instability and uncertainty plague this project. The five main unions at Simcoe Place, representing labourers, carpenters, ironworkers, operating engineers and electricians, loaded up a string of minivans and headed to the present legislature to make their point that cutting this project could be devastating. The auditor's report does not say the building should be stopped, and both the board and the provincial government insist the project's shortcomings have been overblown and its costs distorted. "We are firmly committed to completing it," says Linda Angove, director of the WCB's facilities-strategy project, a group of board employees responsible for finding the right quarters for the organization.

Such words reassure the construction workers, but the situation provokes worry all the same. Many of the men drive to the site each day past the Bay-Adelaide Centre, a downtown skyscraper development that stalled when it failed to attract enough tenants. That project was cancelled just as the building core and underground garage were being built, about the same stage that Simcoe Place is at now. It was capped off at ground level and a half-acre park is being installed on top, one of many public benefits that the developer is still required to provide despite the cancellation of the project. Ironically, the park was in exchange for the right to put up a much bigger building than should have been allowed on the site. Now it will stand as a monument to the excesses of the building boom.

So fears among the workers at Simcoe Place persist. No wonder, when the alternative stares them directly in the face: every day, streams of carpenters and steelworkers visit the site to ask for any kind of work, from their own, skilled jobs to hauling garbage.

"We have thousands of workers who are looking at welfare, food banks or suicide," says John Cartwright, manager of the Toronto Building Trades Council, which organized the demonstration at the legislature. At the peak of the building boom in the late 1980s, there were about 80,000 construction jobs in the city; today only 25,000 are working in the trades. The same number are unemployed and the rest have left the industry or fled the city in search of construction elsewhere. Unemployment rates range from 25 per cent among elevator workers to 65 per cent for millwrights. Young people and women brought in over the last decade to diversify the industry have been "starved out," Cartwright says.

The rally breaks up and workers in hard hats eventually head back to the site. There is quiet talk that the government will not cancel the project, especially because there would be huge penalties to pay to the developer now that the work is well under way. But the tradespeople hope that their pressure makes its cancellation even less likely.

Those left standing on the legislature steps include John Birnie, an unemployed forty-year-old sheet-metal worker who joined in the demonstration out of hope that Simcoe Place will soon put him back to work. Laid off from a car plant twenty months ago, Birnie has watched his name rise on the list of nine hundred unemployed journeymen in Local 30 of the Sheet Metal Workers International Association. He figures he could be called out any day now to work at Simcoe Place, as it comes time to install galvanized-steel ductwork for ventilation. Birnie lives on welfare payments of $569 a month, which pays for his two-room apartment, a public-transit pass, union dues and a little tobacco. To eat, he picks through the offerings at a food bank that in better times he helped set up at his union hall. He realizes that Simcoe Place is not a make-work project, and in fact the city hardly needs another high-rise tower. Working on the twenty-eighth floor of a downtown building three years ago, he looked at the high-rises around him and saw nothing but vacant offices.

Once paid thirty-five dollars an hour for unionized sheet-metal work, Birnie has lately been turned down for jobs unloading trucks at a few dollars an hour because of competition. One position that he applied for as a health and safety coordinator on a job site attracted six hundred other candidates. He didn't get it. Lately he has started looking for construction work as far away as Saudi Arabia and Russia. Construction workers have turned into economic migrants, travelling especially to Dubai in the Persian Gulf, where work can be lucrative and income-tax-free. In the booming eighties, Toronto had more construction jobs available than people qualified to do them, which led to inflated wages and ugly bidding wars between contractors for workers. Those lucky enough to have construction jobs in the early nineties are often overqualified and earn substantially less than they did before.

The same difficulties are faced by the professionals who have a hand in Simcoe Place. Gary Dunlop, who until recently oversaw the project for Cadillac Fairview, left to take a job as project manager for the massive redevelopment of Toronto's Lester B. Pearson Airport. But the whole airport scheme was cancelled because of political controversy over the privatization of the facility, and after just six weeks on the job, Dunlop found himself out of work. There is little available employment out there, as development companies cut back or close altogether. It would be six months before Dunlop was working again.

Entire companies have the same instinct to travel that individual workers do. Looking to far-flung markets is often the only option for companies trying to survive. Most of them have dabbled in overseas work in the past, but now they are stepping up their efforts, aggressively marketing their services and the benefits of Canadian technology and know-how. Interestingly, a century after waves of Chinese people migrated to Canada to build the country's network of railways and roads, the tide has turned. Today, the construction industry here especially looks longingly at China.

"We don't have any option. There's just not enough work in Canada," says Grant Milligan, whose company, Quinn Dressel, has found a lifeline in China. There the work for the structural engineers has ranged from two towers being constructed for the Shanghai Securities Exchange to a giant 110-storey office building in Chongqing. The effect of the crash in the Canadian building market has been noticeable at Quinn Dressel. In the late 1980s, the company had fifty employees and occupied one and a half floors of a brick building in Toronto's tony Yorkville area. Now there are just fifteen staff members working on large projects abroad and the office space has been pared back to one floor. When Milligan first joined the firm in 1979, it worked on schools and shopping plazas, but now, he said, Quinn Dressel is seen as a "designer of big buildings" and is not considered for—or can't afford to do—smaller work. "We made a tactical error," he said.

It's a common story in the development industry. Successful companies get bigger, taking on reputations and overheads that preclude them from doing small projects that do not offer substantial pay. It's hard to beat the price of a single man with a pick-up truck, a cellular telephone and a computer at home for bookkeeping when you're paying for offices, receptionists and accountants. Tony Patullo says Avenue Structures has sadly had to turn away from the residential-housing market, once its mainstay and the place where it developed its advanced concrete-forming techniques. "It's difficult for us to compete on simpler, straightforward jobs, because smaller operations have less overhead and they beat us on price," he said. "We are depending on the more complex and larger jobs to be able to survive." Even heavy construction work can be made portable in the face of a recession. The Patullo brothers, for instance, have taken their concrete forms and crews to a hospital addition in Erie, Pennsylvania, and have just finished work on a student residence at Colgate University, south of Syracuse, New York.

The extra work comes at a price, says Grant Milligan, even for companies such as his that have greater mobility. Working on a thirty-storey building in the middle of Toronto is already an enormous challenge; more daunting still is to do it tens of thousands of kilometres away, where the language, culture, climate, techniques, contracting practices and subcontracting partners are almost completely alien. Partnerships with local firms are often sought so that day-to-day problems and cultural differences can be dealt with more readily. Amid his work on Simcoe Place, Milligan has made three exhausting trips to Shanghai on the Securities Exchange project, at a cost of $25,000.

By turning to Canadian companies, the Chinese get extensive high-rise experience, but there are signs they have also caught North America's edifice complex. Shanghai has taken on a concrete-and-glass look that eclipses indigenous architecture and has transformed whole sections of the city. But skyscrapers are seen as the paragons of progress, and Milligan acknowledges that local resistance to knocking down ancient buildings is nothing like it would be today in a North American city.

The architects at NORR Partnership are also caught up in the overseas building boom. NORR has moved thirty-eight employees to offices in Abu Dhabi and Dubai, wealthy oil and banking strongholds in the United Arab Emirates of the Middle East. Since building Toronto's first modern airport terminal in the 1970s, the company has acquired an international reputation for designing such facilities. It has planned or done consulting work on airport projects in Kathmandu, Jakarta, Rio de Janeiro and Copenhagen, as well as elsewhere in Canada. Bill Neish says the company is looking for work throughout the Middle East and especially in Beirut, which is eyed hungrily because it is considered ripe for development after years of war and instability.

Pursuing opportunities outside Canada takes an aggressive nature, since companies are up against competition from the rest of the developed world. "It isn't for everybody," Neish says. But when companies do secure work abroad, there are usually spin-offs for other Canadians, such as suppliers of materials and equipment. Antamex, which will make Simcoe Place's exterior wall, did the same job for the massive Canary Wharf office development in London's docklands, which was built by the Canadian firm of Olympia & York Developments. Architectural Dimensions, which built the promotional models of Simcoe Place, was introduced to the international development industry in the last decade by Canadian companies ordering models for their overseas projects. Company partner Ted Bassken says he now does 85 per cent of his business outside the country. "If you're drawing on a worldwide marketplace, you have so much to choose from."

While they may keep some companies in the development industry alive, the foreign projects mean fewer jobs for heavy contractors who do not have portable operations, less employment for construction workers who cannot follow the work and a dearth of construction sites for the sidewalk superintendents who so keenly follow the development of the city around them. "I like to see the landscape change all the time," says Paul McGrory, who has watched an endless string of developments go up around his social agency office in the last decade. "It's nice to see something positive, new and exciting. I'd miss it if nothing else was built around here."

SEVEN

A CITY WITHIN A CITY

New buildings seem to appear overnight, planted on street corners or drawn effortlessly on city skylines. But the process of building is not that simple. As a new element is added to the urban landscape, a microcosm of the city is established with a life, culture and technology vastly different from the one surrounding its plywood barriers. Construction workers arrive, often before dawn, lugging mammoth lunch coolers and sporting hard hats and work boots. Office workers come at a later hour carrying briefcases and wearing suits or white sports shoes for the rush-hour dash to the subway. All day the construction workers, almost all men, use their hands and a myriad of heavy, noisy tools, not the clicking word processors and discreet telephone head-sets that have come to dominate the egalitarian workplaces of the information age. The construction workers and the equipment they use to build the building require services that are alien to the people downtown: portable toilets, mobile lunch trucks, trailer offices, rudimentary roads, simple heaters fueled by gas, electricity delivered by serpentine cables and temporary water service.

Simcoe Place's city within a city is more apparent now that the construction project is in full swing. The concrete structure is growing to occupy a greater and greater part of the site. Walls, slabs and columns are fitting together into the huge underground parking garage that makes up the building's lowest level. An increasing number of tradesmen come to "rough in" the electrical and mechanical services that will make up the finished building's vital systems. First, though, working in a place that until recently was a parking lot entails establishing temporary conveniences that will disappear when the new building finally opens.

The most critical of these is the least talked about around the site: washrooms. Toilets tend to be a taboo subject anyway, but here the sensitivity is not a matter of squeamishness or politeness. Instead, the Simcoe Place project is at the centre of a major dispute concerning temporary toilets. Prompted by the situation at the site, a nineteen-member steering committee of the provincial government has recently started studying construction privies. Stern missives about toilets have flown between the Ministry of Labour and managers at Eastern. Tempers are raging.

It is about defining a toilet, but this is more than scatological semantics. It's a story of new technology and ever-more stringent labour regulations faced by builders. A couple of decades ago, the only option for workers who wanted to relieve themselves on a construction project was an open-hole portable toilet plunked some-where in the middle of the site. Campers know this variety: a plain cubicle made of green or brown plastic. Inside is a humble hole in the middle of a plastic box, sometimes topped with a traditional toilet seat to simulate the comforts of home. Below the hole is an open holding tank; as it fills, there is an unfortunate tendency for its contents to decorate the backside of the user, a phenomenon known as backsplash. High-rise builders invented an even more portable open-hole urinal with cut-away walls, called a roll-on, that afforded little privacy to the user (after all, most were men) but could be carried up and down construction elevators and shared among the floors of a growing building.

Considered unhygienic and even uncivilized, both of these open-hole toilets are rarely permitted on construction sites any more. Instead, outhouse technology has expanded to include fully enclosed chemical or recirculating toilets, which come with both urinals and bowls that are flushed with a thick chemical disinfec-tant by pumping a handle. The solids are filtered out by a screen and the solution, combined with added urine, reused. Even more high-tech is a chemical toilet with a flap that separates the holding tank from the bowl, eliminating backsplash altogether. The acme of portable-toilet technology is a self-contained unit, which comes with its own fresh-water supply in a reservoir for flushing the bowl or urinal as well as for washing hands in a tiny basin built into its wall. More luxurious still are larger self-contained units, commonly known to workers and managers as Cadillacs, which provide a steady supply of hot water for hand-washing.

A large and lucrative outhouse industry has grown up around the new devices because they cost more to buy or rent than the old versions and require frequent emptying and maintenance. Stamped on the doors of the toilets are appropriately suggestive names— Nature's Call, At-A-Way-To-Go, Port-O-Let, Johnny-on-the-Spot, Jerry-on-the-Job, Poly-John, Here's Johnny—and accompanying images of bears, pine trees, elephants and life preservers.

Loo levity notwithstanding, toilets on construction sites are a serious business. The difficulty for contractors such as Eastern arises from a provincial regulation issued with the revised Occupational Health and Safety Act four years ago, which requires construction sites to provide "flush" toilets but does not distinguish between all of the different varieties of portable devices that flush or state whether a urinal is in fact a toilet. Simcoe Place offers its workers portable chemical toilets from Nature's Call, which are hoisted into place with the crane and brought to ground level for cleaning twice a week.

It's the servicing that is at the root of the controversy here. The job of clearing the sewage out of the cubicles is one of the least palatable on the site, but Ross Carter doesn't mind, especially because he makes thirteen dollars an hour and has had steady work with Nature's Call for five years. He uses a vacuum hose to suck the material into a waiting pumper truck, which he drives between various sites. Carter then cleans the cubicles with water and a sponge, replaces the roll of toilet paper and adds a litre of what is euphemistically called blue solution—formaldehyde that disinfects and won't freeze. When his pumper truck is full—it holds about 2,700 litres—he dumps the sewage at a treatment plant.

The job has its benefits, especially when Carter is asked to install and maintain toilets at car races, fairs and backstage at rock concerts—even once when the Rolling Stones played at SkyDome.

He and his colleagues got a little lift out of thinking that their hoses might have been picking up urine from Mick Jagger or Keith Richards. "We thought," he jokes, "that we should bottle the stuff and sell it."

The problem comes when Carter's truck doesn't get to the site frequently enough or the toilet can't get to it, via the crane. This can happen when a crane breaks down or cannot work because of wind. The Ministry of Labour recently received an anonymous complaint from a worker at Simcoe Place about a chemical toilet that was over-filled and dirty because a crane was out of service. Eastern has been ordered to provide more flush toilets and place them closer to work-ers. The contractor complied with the order, but has appealed it on the grounds that the regulations are not clear. The appeal has prompted the province to set up the committee made up of repre-sentatives from labour, management, toilet suppliers and the govern-ment to write better standards.

Meanwhile, the situation has led to tension among the workers and managers at the site. Some have been doing what comes natu-rally in whatever corner of the grounds—or even the new building—is convenient. Signs posted by Eastern carry a stern warning: "Workers found urinating in areas other than construction wash-rooms will be banned from the project." Construction-site wags have defaced the notices, replacing "urinating" with "mating" or adding postscripts. "Public caning would be better," one annotation reads.

Eastern plans to increase its toilet facilities as the structure and the number of workers on-site grow. It will open up some of the build-ing's new washrooms for workers as floors are built and the water is turned on. The fancy tiles and granite will be covered up and the toilet partitions will be temporary ones made of plywood so that they are not damaged by work boots or covered in the jokes, poems, comments and complaints common to public washrooms. All of the facilities are considered unisex, although there is still only one woman on the site, Eastern's Rosy Pereira, and she uses one of the two small bathrooms in the contractor's trailer. For now, construction workers can also get some comfort from the flush toilets, urinals and sinks with running water located in a humble trailer at the western corner of the site. From there, the sewage moves up in the world, draining into the pipes of the Broadcast Centre next door.

Those that will eventually carry sewage from Simcoe Place remain capped as the contractors work out how to connect them to the city's permanent water and sewer system. A few decades ago, the century-old municipal sewer that the backhoe shovels hit when they began excavating the site would have been considered a godsend instead of a problem. The new building's drainage system would probably have been hooked right up to the old brick conduit, with its tried and tested arch design dating back to the Romans. Today, however, the matter of taking away the sewage produced in the high-rise as well as the rain and snow produced by Mother Nature is a much more delicate and closely monitored process.

The planning began long before construction started. Indeed, a decade ago the city's public works department was alerted that there would eventually be a building on this site. Once Simcoe Place was designed, mechanical engineers Smith and Andersen Consulting Engineering began figuring out what sort of water and sewage services the building would require. The eventual design allowed for 261 toilets, 101 urinals, 227 faucets, 60 drinking fountains and 5 showers. Two years ago, the city's public works department was given the calculations showing the size and location of the pipes that would be needed to carry all of the fresh water to the building and drain its sanitary sewage and surface water. The city checked the figures, determined where and how to hook up to the labyrinth of pipes under streets and sidewalks, and decided to charge the developer $91,000 to extend the services two metres from the water-main under the road to the edge of the lot.

Despite the proven durability of brick pipelines like the one found underground, plastic and concrete are now the passageway of choice for water and sewage. To keep the two systems separate, all of the water pipes are buried 1.5 metres below street level, while the sewers are 1.8 metres deep. The city completed the job when the project got under way.

The water will come in through two twenty-centimetre pipes branching off the water main under Front Street, mostly flowing from Metro Toronto's R. C. Harris water-treatment plant on the east side of the city. At the site it is divided into its two separate functions. While one set of pipes serves the building's bathrooms, restaurant kitchens and drinking fountains—the "domestic" side—another carries water to fire-fighting sprinklers and standpipes for hoses. The building is so tall that booster pumps are needed to distribute the water. And as an added safety measure, there are two water-storage holding tanks for fire-fighting up in the penthouse.

Most of the sewage generated above ground at Simcoe Place will flow directly to the city sewer pipes below the street, but the effluent from the building's underground will go down to the bottom of the building, where it will be collected in massive concrete sumps and pumped up to those pipes. The sewage will leave Simcoe Place through a thirty-centimetre pipe under Simcoe Street to be dealt with at the main sewage-treatment plant at Ashbridge's Bay on the shore of Lake Ontario.

The precipitation that falls on the site, called surface water, will flow through two fifty-centimetre pipes, to be discharged into Toronto's inner harbour at the foot of Simcoe Street. Groundwater, such as the moisture that continues to percolate through the soil where the ancient sewer was found, could cause damage if allowed to build up. So it is already being channelled through vertical sheets of plastic, called chimney drains, draped along the outside of the building's concrete wall to collect in weeping tiles under the building. It is finally pumped out along with the rain water to the harbour.

In a small plywood enclosure, situated over top of the sewage pipes along Simcoe Street, the air is buzzing. This is hardly surprising; 13,800 volts of energy are coursing through equipment crammed into a space the size of a galley kitchen. The humming metal boxes, switches and transformers in this temporary room have a big job: they run the cranes, power tools, pumps and compressors, as well as the computers, lights and air conditioners in the contractors' trailers and even the light fixtures that illuminate the underside of the wooden hoarding surrounding the site.

For the first few months of construction, most of this equipment was fed by portable diesel generators and air compressors, but by the time the first crane came to life, a larger supply of electricity was needed. A crane's swivelling and hoisting takes a lot of energy, and once the site's third crane was up and running, the generators would have been overmatched. Even though the construction site's electric service is temporary—it will be replaced by a system in the completed building three times as big—there is enough power here to serve a good-sized town. Wires, panels and cables are strung throughout the site, the larger 600-volt ones heading for heavy equipment such as the cranes. Garden-variety 120-volt outlets—the kind a toaster is plugged into—are available to run saws, drills and lights.

This temporary electricity is now making itself obsolete by helping workers to create the building's own power system. The main electrical room is about to occupy a space on the concourse level, one floor below ground. Meanwhile, manufacturing plants are fabricating everything from the ducts that will carry power cables to the big electrical equipment that runs them, referred to in the business as switch gear. Two 13,800-volt cables from Toronto Hydro will eventually be pulled through the ducts in the wall to serve the building's power, communications and emergency systems.

These high-voltage cables will first be directed through a switchboard and metering cabinet, so the building's power can be easily shut off in an emergency and the power company can measure and charge for the amount of electricity the building uses. Then the power is divided into several sections and carried through a series of three transformers, which lower its voltage. It heads next through more switchboards and is transported to the building's different electrical systems along huge insulated slabs of copper called bus ducts, finally ending in wires that head to wall outlets and light fixtures.

Toronto Hydro will not turn on the power until it is satisfied that the building's system is safe and does not make such huge demands that it disrupts its neighbours. The electrical consultant to the project, Mulvey and Banani International, figures the building at its peak will require seven thousand kilowatts of power at any one time, with an average of five thousand kilowatts. On the assumption that Simcoe Place will be active for about three thousand hours a year, this means it will use 15 million kilowatt hours of power a year. Compared with buildings that company president Husayn Banani worked on in the

1960s and 1970s, this one is a miser, even with its hungry network of computers, printers and fax machines. This is because of energy-saving techniques and devices, including occupancy sensors in the ceilings that turn appliances and lights off if there is no motion or body heat. "It's getting more and more complicated to switch on the lights," says Banani. Evolving telecommunications and computer technology will mean constant changes to the electrical system even after Simcoe Place is built.

The electrical plans also take acts of God into account. If the power goes out, a 1,500-kilowatt diesel generator, which will be installed on a penthouse floor, will provide emergency power to the building's elevators, some lights and especially to smoke-ventilation equipment throughout the building. Other generators in the penthouse will keep computers on-line.

If mention of a penthouse evokes images of sunken living rooms, hot tubs and panoramic views, think again. The three on top of Simcoe Place are called mechanical and electrical penthouses, because they will be home to these rumbling emergency diesel generators as well as gas-fired boilers and their exhaust stacks, the two water-storage tanks filled with ten thousand gallons of water for fire-fighting, chillers for air-conditioning and their accompanying labyrinth of pipes, cables and other hardware. All of these are put at the top of the building because of the noise, exhaust fumes and vibration they produce. They also take up a lot of room and would be difficult to fit lower down.

The roof of the building is another area of concern for Mulvey and Banani, because of electrical excesses in the form of lightning. Any strikes have to be channelled benignly down to the ground without ravaging the building's electrical system, plumbing and structure. Braided copper cables being strung through ten of the tower's main columns connect 106 copper and steel lightning rods that will be positioned around the roof to long copper spikes that were long ago driven into the ground below the building's foundation.

The gas company will be the next to attack the streets surrounding Simcoe Place to hook it up to the rest of the city. People who live or work around a construction project are aware of the periodic disruptions that it can cause. Each time it is connected to a new underground municipal system, lanes of traffic are blocked by utility trucks, services are temporarily cut off or the road and sidewalks are torn up. Now Consumers Gas Co. needs to lay down a new, high-pressure natural-gas main, not only eventually to feed the building's heaters but also to supply gas to the construction project.

Starting in the summer, meetings were held between the company and Eastern Construction to determine how much fuel and temporary equipment the project will require to keep freshly laid concrete and work areas warm over the coming two winters. The cast-iron gas main that currently runs under the site is a relic, delivering gas at only two to twelve pounds per square inch. This is inadequate pressure and volume for the temporary heaters required by the builders, let alone the finished high-rise. For the last several years Consumers has been replacing these old medium-pressure cast-iron pipes throughout the city with intermediate-pressure plastic or steel ones that carry gas at sixty pounds per square inch. The arrival of a new building is a reason to do the work here.

The planned service requires Consumers to install a new steel gas main stretching eight blocks to the west. The existing gas main should suffice for the first few construction heaters fired up in early winter on the lower floors of the building, but greater pressure will be needed as the tower grows. The construction heaters alone are expected to use a total of 21.6 million cubic feet of gas over the next two winters, with the bill to be paid by the contractor. When Simcoe Place is finally completed, it will use 55,000 cubic feet of gas an hour. That fuel will flow into a gas-meter room on the building's concourse level, where it will split into two branches, each going through a valve to reduce the pressure, as well as through a regulator and a meter to once again measure its flow. One branch will go up the building to the three boilers in the second penthouse that will supply heat to all of the radiators in the building. The other will be piped directly to the ten concessions in the concourse's food court.

It will be some time before pizza and hamburgers are being served down there. But you can find plenty to eat in this miniature city.

Given the construction workers' inclination for plain talk, the favourite source of food is called the gut wagon. For the bleary-eyed workers staggering onto the construction project early in the morning, Norma Davis's idling snack truck is a sweet sight. Beginning at 6:30 a.m., they fill up on coffee that comes already laced with sugar at her Yorktown Catering mobile kitchen. Dressed in sneakers and a long windbreaker, with a dark blue hard hat atop her long black hair, Davis makes four appearances a day at the construction site. She serves up drinks, snacks, hot meals and sandwiches—as well as a friendly chat and the requisite packs of Rolaids—from the back of her stainless-steel catering truck.

The physical demands of erecting a high-rise building could not be met without all of this high-energy food, but mobile trucks that call on construction projects are facing tough competition from wallet-friendly hot-dog stands, steaming chip wagons and, of course, lunches packed at home. "Today, with the economy, people don't eat much off the truck," complains Ab Chomski, who owns Yorktown Catering and has been in the mobile-food business for forty years. "They might not have a job next month." During the booming eighties, Chomski kept ten snack trucks on the road. He required three alone to feed the throngs of workers at the massive SkyDome project kitty-corner to this site. In 1993 there were only two Yorktown trucks in the entire city, and the construction projects they are contracted to serve are few and far between. This one is the largest. Others on the circuit include a new hospital that is nearing completion on a downtown boulevard and a public-housing project on the city's east side.

Davis stocks her truck early each morning at City Wide Catering, a commercial commissary in suburban Mississauga, west of the city. There are thick sandwiches, the presweetened coffee (mixed at a rate of one cup of sugar to a gallon of coffee), little cans of Dinty Moore stew and a five-dollar hot special each day, such as cabbage rolls, spicy veal or chicken and wedge chips. Davis keeps these warm for hours with a small propane heater.

Her stiffest competition comes not from the nearby street vendors, with their limited repertoire of grease-soaked fries and bratwurst on a bun, but from the insulated coolers that men carry with them to the site. The workaday lunch-pail is largely a thing of the past. Most workers instead tote massive Coleman and Thermos boxes, which not only are ideal for keeping food cold or hot but also give the men a clean and dry surface to sit on when they eat. Otherwise, dining alfresco on a construction site means sitting among tools, plywood sheets and gravel. As Simcoe Place grows, there are more and more comfortable and protected places to eat, although eventually there will be designated lunch spots because of worries about Coca-Cola and pasta sauce splattering on new drywall or freshly laid carpets.

Standard home-made fare brought to the site includes slices of last Sunday's roast, leftover lasagne, soup kept hot in Thermos bottles or a stack of hearty sandwiches, as well as fruit and several drinks per person. Even the largest carbohydrate fixes don't seem to go far with work as physical as this. Don Hare, a slim, twenty-four-year-old ironworker who spends his days weaving hefty pieces of reinforcing steel into the building's footings and columns, looks sheepish as he buys chicken parmesan on a kaiser roll and a can of root beer at the catering truck during the half-hour lunch period. Hare already devoted his coffee break to the baloney and two tuna sandwiches, two cans of pop and two bananas that his fiancée, Maria Schrembi, assembled for him last night. It's not lost on Maria, Hare says, that her repast is just a snack in the long working day. "She knows that I eat more than what she makes me," he explains, and goes off to eat his meal before work resumes.

Norma Davis is happy to have the extra business and enjoys such regular clientele. She worked as a laboratory technician until, longing to have more contact with people, she switched to the catering job last year at the age of forty. At first she was nervous about being one of the only women on each construction site she visited, but she gets along well with the workers. Some ask her for credit and are ready with the money the next day. In these early stages of construction, most of her trade is with "runners," men who fetch food for colleagues working in remote parts of the site, usually far down in the excavated hole. The constant faces include John Briolo, a sixty-four-year-old labourer who, as he nears retirement, is happy to spend less of his day carrying plywood and nails. For the rest of his shift he takes money, fills orders and delivers coffee, drinks and treats from a tattered plastic milk crate that he fills up at the catering truck each time Davis makes an appearance. The process is time-consuming and complex. A typical mid-afternoon order includes thirteen coffees, four teas, three hot chocolates, a Danish pastry, several cans of pop and an iced tea at a cost of $21.35.

Davis hopes her business will pick up now that the building has reached the all-important street level. At last many of the hungry, thirsty workers can see her truck or hear the blast from its air horn announcing her arrival and departure from the site. Eventually, the mobile snack truck will no longer be needed, as food joins the list of services seamlessly incorporated into the city's network of roads, side-walks, public transit, electricity, natural gas, water and sewage. Those inside the new building will be able to choose from the dozen fast-food outlets, coffee shops and restaurants at its base, or travel under-ground to other developments with their own food courts. The construction workers and their city will vanish, the new building at one with its surroundings.

EIGHT

FINAL EXCAVATION:
THE END OF THE BEGINNING

The construction of a building is studded with milestones. Careful observers walking past the site can see one now. The structure, or at least a few of its columns, has finally begun to poke above the hoarding at the site's eastern entrance. At the other end, the work seems barely started, although here another milestone is being marked too: The last loads of shale bedrock are being dug up and trucked away.

It's another illustration of how construction is staggered and layered. While the building's main tower is given full attention, work on the rest of the underground parking garage and concourse lags far behind. But now only a ramp, made of loose rock piled in the southwest corner of the lot, remains to give trucks access to the bottom of the pit. This will have to stay while a monstrous backhoe finishes making holes for the seventy-two foundation footings there that give the parking garage that will fill this area its stability.

The foundation has to do more than just withstand the stresses and strains from the structure above; it also must deal with the natural forces of wind, groundwater, earth tremors and the rumble of traffic that will make its way along the surrounding streets. Nowhere is that principle more apparent than at this west end of the site, where Simcoe Place encounters its new neighbour, the Broadcast Centre. Footings—the concrete-and-steel anchors placed in the ground below each of the building's columns—spread the load that is borne by the column over a greater area. Their size, shape and depth are determined by structural engineer Grant Milligan who considers the weight they must bear as well as such factors as the stability of the ground. Following Milligan's instructions, the backhoe's ripper tooth makes a 1.5-metre cubic hole in the rock for every footing. (Under the main tower, especially in the building's all-important and weighty core area, some measure several times this.) Once the hole is dug, reinforcing steel is woven across it. Next, a series of dowels—pieces of steel in the shape of Ls—are secured in the middle of each hole, with the short ends down and the long ends extending up above the top of the hole. Finally, the hole is filled with concrete to secure the bottom of each dowel. The top will eventually overlap with the reinforcing steel in the column that extends above.

Footings make a structure at one with the earth in which they sit. However, this means the slightest vibration in the rock beneath or around the building may be felt inside it. Such subtle movements will barely be noticed by the office workers, shopkeepers and short-order cooks in Simcoe Place, but could be devastating for those in the sophisticated recording studios and performance halls next door. For this reason, the Broadcast Centre's footings are unique. Instead of adhering to the rock, they isolate the whole building from the ground beneath it. A firm of acoustical engineers called Vibron Ltd. was brought in to design 150 sophisticated pads to sit beneath each of the footings so they do not even touch the rock. They are large—four metres square and two metres deep—to spread the load, and are made up of a combination of rubber and insulation foam.

Tom Paige, a senior project engineer at Vibron, says such acoustical features are more common as cities grow noisier and building uses become more sensitive. The isolation technique was employed at the Broadcast Centre mostly because Metropolitan Toronto threatens to build a subway line beneath the building one day. Paige says the last of the backhoes now at work deep in the Simcoe Place site are putting the foundation he designed to the test. What's more, special care must be taken in connecting the basements of the two buildings so the newcomer doesn't end up passing along bad vibrations to its sensitive neighbour.

Back under the main building, a crew is putting the finishing touches on the lowest level of the garage. The wait is brief, but the sense of anticipation is palpable in the murky depths of the building. "Start her up!" calls out a supervisor illuminated by a single spotlight. A cigarette dangles from the corner of his mouth as he crouches and rests a hand on a fat metal pipe that the men standing around him have spent the morning assembling along the ground. He walks a few metres farther and again slowly bends and touches the pipe. He feels a satisfying rumbling coming from under the plastic shell and his face brightens. It's coming. Finally a soft whooshing can be heard—not a constant sound, but one that rises and falls as if the pipe were breathing. A few more exhalations and the end snorts out a lumpy grey ooze, a slowly flowing river of concrete.

The sight is a welcome one. The concrete will form what is called the building's slab-on-grade, essentially a basement floor laid directly on the bedrock earth of the third underground parking level. This out-of-the-way area has been left unfinished while the main work on the tower proceeded up above. But once it came back to finish the floor, the construction crew faced a problem of its own devising. The conventional way of placing concrete—filling buckets and lowering them with the crane—is out of the question because four floors of the building are in the way and the crane's hook and huge concrete bucket cannot get near.

This is a job for the hydraulic concrete pump, an innovation in construction that transports concrete from the mixing trucks to where it is needed. The pump sits on a vehicle topped by a huge boom, resembling an aerial fire truck. Each load of concrete is dumped into a hopper on the back of the pump truck, then forced by a set of sturdy hydraulic pistons in a surging motion through the pipe that extends along the machine's huge boom and far beyond.

Unfortunately, the technology has several shortcomings that the contractors could not ignore. The pump does not do well at sending concrete downward, because the pull of gravity can cause unwanted air gaps that affect its flow. It is more comfortable pumping concrete at a constant pressure upward. Even worse, a parking-lot floor like this one requires coarse concrete, with gravel that is twice the standard size. There was a good possibility the material would get stuck in the pipe, even one that was enlarged from the usual ten centimetres to twelve centimetres across for the occasion. "There was some discussion as to whether this stuff was pumpable," says Brian Gardner in an obvious understatement as he nervously watches the scene. "We just had to try and see what happened."

The moment of truth passes quickly and happily for Gardner and the crew underground. Then, working under a string of bright lights positioned on poles that look as if they belong on a movie set, the workers hurry to keep up with the relentless flow of concrete spurting through the pipe, enough in one day to make a floor 1,100 metres square and 12 centimetres deep. As its name implies, the slab-on-grade goes directly on top of the rock at the bottom of the excavated hole, with only a layer of gravel beneath for drainage. There is no need for the usual wooden formwork or reinforcing steel on the suspended-slab floors above, just a single layer of wire mesh, much like a chain-link fence, that was rolled out to cover the gravel before the concrete arrived. The mesh is pulled up into the concrete for added strength as it is placed.

The concrete with the larger gravel resembles the material that roads are made of, and for much the same reason. As it cures, all concrete shrinks and inevitably cracks. The greater the expanse of concrete, the more noticeable this is. Even worse, if the top of the concrete is exposed to the air and the bottom sits on moist rock, as it does here or on a road, it cures unevenly. When the slabs on all the other floors are made, temporary gaps are deliberately left to account for this shrinkage. These will eventually be covered with waterproofing that stops moisture from getting in and hides the unsightly cracks. The slab-on-grade, on the other hand, must be made all at once, without gaps, and will not be refined later. Some shrinkage is inevitable, but its effect can be minimized with the use of larger gravel. Later today, the concrete finishers will also criss-cross their freshly made masterpiece with saws, scoring the floor every five metres to make a weak point that controls where spaces will eventually occur. When the garage opens, only this decorative cross-hatching left by the saws will show, not the cracks that form harmlessly below.

Not that the drivers negotiating the twists and turns of the parking lot will notice. Who hasn't spent what feels like hours wandering through the labyrinth of dead-end passages and heading in the wrong direction up the one-way ramps of an underground parking garage? Architects, designers, sign consultants and garage operators share the frustration, and they are banding together to design garages that should make motorists feel a bit less like rats caught in a maze. Far away from the construction site, on drawing-boards and in marathon boardroom discussions, a plan is taking shape for moving hundreds of vehicles a day in and out of this garage. Gardner says the garage's design is art and science. The trick is to engineer simple and consistent parking areas and turns while striving to brighten a traditionally gloomy place and arranging for directional signs in the right colours, sizes, shapes and locations so they will be easily seen by harried drivers in the tight space. "Most people get into a garage and they don't know what the hell's going on," he laments, his words obviously reflecting his own experience.

The project's earliest plans called for four generous levels of parking, but municipal planners cut the garage back to three. Not so long ago, developers were forced to put in more and more parking spaces to accommodate visitors and tenants. They happily complied, of course profiting from the steep prices paid for the privilege of parking in the bustling downtown core. But today a new thinking is afoot: limit the supply of parking so its cost rises. Then fewer people will drive their cars here in the first place, opting instead for public transit. Since the new rules were introduced, demand for downtown parking has indeed dropped, although not because of prices, which have actually fallen. Instead, the ailing economy has put people who traditionally drove downtown out of work.

What is left of the parking garage at Simcoe Place extends underground all the way from the building's main tower through to the other end of the lot, where its concrete structure will be topped by the park. The lot's entrance and exit will be in the middle of the south side of the site on Front Street. Several subcontractors have already been chosen to supply the garage's security gates, card-readers for drivers with monthly passes and the machines, ingloriously called ticket-spitters, that issue tickets to daily visitors. At the exit, there will be kiosks for several cashiers and another machine to read passes. As well, the ramp must be heated with electrical coils embedded in the ground to stop it from freezing in the winter. The concrete crews working on the garage floor and walls leave conduits—the empty pipes through which the wires for all of this equipment will later be threaded. Spaces must also be left in the ground next to the ticket-spitters and the gates that rise to let cars in and out. Here, electrical sensors will be embedded to alert the machines that a car has arrived.

All of these wires make parking gurus nervous, mostly because of the corrosive road salt that cars will inevitably deposit on the concrete. Any middle-aged parking garage or concrete road structure such as an elevated expressway displays evidence of the devastation that salt brings. It combines with water in the clumps of snow and ice that build up under a car and then melts in the underground warmth. The mixture seeps into the naturally porous concrete and goes to work on anything metal within, such as electrical wiring and even the steel reinforcing bars that give the structure its strength. The metal rusts and expands, literally blowing apart, and, in turn, the concrete around it cracks and flakes, leaving an unsightly and eventually unsafe mess.

Recent technology should give this garage a better chance against the salt. All of the steel used in the substructure is coated with epoxy, a fine pea-green powder baked onto the metal that is intended to slow the salt water's penetration. Steel bars coated with the material cost 30 to 50 per cent more than standard ones, so they are used only in places such as garages where salt is likely to be a problem. In many parts of garages, especially where the sensors and wiring are embedded in the pavement, a thin waterproofing membrane of urethane or rubberized asphalt is applied to the concrete for extra protection against the salt water. And almost any wiring that does not have to be embedded in it, such as the electrical system for the garage's lights and illuminated exit signs, sits on the surface. There it can be cleaned and repaired without going to the trouble of ripping up walls and floors.

The garage's steel bars come in sizes from ten to fifty-five millimetres in diameter, but are measured in lengths of ten to thirty feet. The concrete placed around them each day is delivered to the site in cubic yards but first mixed in kilograms at the plant and ordered in cubic metres by the contractor. The crushed limestone rock under the garage floor is measured by the tonne, but the mixture of gravel and sand used for fill around the building's perimeter walls comes by the cubic yard. Confused? The stalling of the country's conversion to metric is not just causing turmoil at the grocery-store produce counter and generational misunderstandings between schoolchildren and their imperial-minded parents.

This is known in the business as an imperial construction job, meaning that all the architectural working drawings and contractors' technical shop drawings are in feet, yards, tons and gallons. But a good number of suppliers, contractors and consultants contributing to the building long ago began to think metric. "We're totally screwed up," shrugs Brian Gardner, who says that dealing with the two systems of measurement is like speaking two languages—with serious consequences for the wrong translation.

When the country was turning metric in the early 1980s, there were decrees from all levels of government to adopt the new system. Government projects went metric, and construction codes and laws were rewritten; only work that had already started could remain imperial. Cesar Ramires, a building-plan examiner for the City of Toronto, says that things have relaxed considerably since then—with predictable results. The buildings department will accept architectural plans in both systems of measurement and finds that most large projects use metric—with some sizeable exceptions, like Simcoe Place. The situation has been made even more confusing by regulators trying to help. Toronto's zoning by-law is totally metric, showing all lengths in metres. The Ontario Building Code is metric, with all lengths in millimetres and imperial units included in brackets. "We jump all over the place," Ramires says.

The measurement mix can favour or penalize builders, he says. Buildings must be set back 0.9 metres, or 3 feet, from the edge of lots. If you want to be picky, 0.9 metres is actually 2 feet, 11 inches, meaning that those who stick to imperial gain an inch. "It's just the tape measure you carry." Gilbert Steel, which fabricates and manufactures all the rebar for Simcoe Place, converted its plant near Toronto's airport when all the steel mills went metric in the early 1970s. Rebar was once measured in eighths of an inch and referred to by a number, which identified the material's diameter. Asking for a "number four" meant you wanted rebar that was four-eighths of an inch thick. Today, says Anton Plobner, an administrator at the company, the bars range from "10m" to "55m," a reference to their diameter in millimetres. (Most metric lengths in construction are referred to in millimetres, never centimetres or metres, hence the single *m*. Metric tonnes are called "tonnies," to avoid confusion with tons.)

Even though the metric and imperial sizes are roughly equivalent, the slight difference in the diameter and the weight of the bars does make a difference, and only two or three find exact matches in the old imperial system, Plobner says. Structural engineers in Canada, even those who work on imperial jobs like Simcoe Place, have become used to the metric rebar and do not want to play around with old imperial thicknesses because they might not be the right strength or weight for the designs. Converting to metric has proved to be a boon of sorts for the steel industry in the recession, Plobner says. He even has concerns about getting enough rebar for Simcoe Place because steel mills in Ontario are so busy shipping the bars to construction projects in booming China and for work on Hibernia, all metric jobs. Meanwhile, the United States has a glut of steel because all its production is in imperial units.

Back down at the west end of the site, meanwhile, the steel has yet to arrive and the excavation is just nearing an end. Anyone who has pushed a broom has been swayed by the temptation to sweep the last bit of dirt under the corner of a convenient rug. The builders here aren't so lucky. "There's no carpet to put it under," shrugs John Gerhardt, a foreman for excavator Rumble Contracting, watching from the edge of the site as a massive backhoe slowly brings up rock from the hole. The excavation has finally dwindled to the point where the ramp has to be dismantled. The feature was intentionally made of rock brought from other parts of the site so it could be more easily scooped up and removed when the time came for it to go, but this final bit of an excavation is anything but easy.

A backhoe tag-team, one large and one small, takes the lead role in this disappearing act. Earlier on, the large machine was in charge of taking apart the middle and upper part of the ramp and then loading all of the material into dump trucks that backed down what was left of it. The smaller backhoe worked down below, piling the material next to its larger counterpart, which passed it on to the trucks. As the ramp grew smaller, it was reduced to several piles of rock separated by dug-out holes. The relationship between the two machines became more critical. After removing much of the rock within its reach, the large backhoe rolled up to take a new position on the street above, blocking the sidewalk and a lane of traffic. Its seven-metre arm, fitted with a two-metre extension, cleared away all of the rock it could reach on what remained of the ramp directly below it.

For the last week, this large backhoe has been reduced to dropping its bucket straight down to be filled by the small one, which is sitting on the last pile of rock fourteen metres down. Each time the large bucket is full, the backhoe slowly lifts it and drops the material into the waiting dump trucks. The process is called spoon-feeding, and it's as delicate and frustrating as it sounds. "This part is very slow," says Gerhardt as he leans over the precipice to direct the operation. His intervention is vital: separated by the site's sheer wall, the two backhoe operators cannot see each other.

The machine perched on the upper edge of the hole is a good test of the temporary steel-and-wood shoring around the site. The backhoe itself weighs forty-four tonnes, including an added half-tonne slab of metal that sits on top as a counterweight to stop it from tipping over as it lifts four tonnes of rock at a time. Gerhardt seems to have faith in the shoring. He has clipped his red canvas safety harness—required equipment for anyone working so close to the edge of the hole—to a loop of metal on the side of the huge machine itself. "If it goes over, then we're all in trouble," he says, squinting and turning away as rock and billowing dust cascades from the bucket into a dump truck.

The stream of trucks, which once took away several hundred loads a day, has slowed to a trickle. As work progresses, the backhoe tag-team takes more and more time to dig up each load of dirt. Just five trucks are left to make the eighty-minute round trip from Simcoe

Place to the construction site north of the city where the rock continues to find new life on the ramps of the cloverleaf interchange.

Although the excavation crew is under pressure to remove the last bit of rock as soon as possible, the day is shortened by the contractor's street-occupancy permit, required to close off the lane of traffic. Under its terms, work has to come to an end by the time the afternoon rush hour starts. Just after 3 o'clock, the large backhoe is driven around to a safe spot in the loading area at the side of the construction site and the material that has fallen on the road around it is bulldozed and swept back down into the site.

Meanwhile, observers of the scene are being treated to a surprising sight: an entire flank of the basement wall of the Broadcast Centre has been exposed. In fact, when the soil and rock was excavated, even the contractors at Simcoe Place were taken aback by what they saw: a part of the CBC wall was leaning into the space where they planned to put their own wall. But the CBC building is not falling down; in fact, its wall is a sturdy forty-five centimetres of concrete and reinforcing steel. But there is a problem about ten metres below ground level, where the wall has bulged out across the lot line because it was made right up against a wall of shale bedrock. Thus the upper part of the CBC, built with wooden formwork, is perfectly uniform, but some of the concrete below oozed out into the rock's nooks and crannies, like a Christmas pudding taking the shape of its mould.

It's more economical and efficient to make a wall right up against rock because the alternative, a uniform free-standing wall, would require the contractors to build an extra layer of formwork around the outside of the wall. This would entail an expensive excavation of another metre of rock all the way around the building to make room for the forms. In any case, most contractors don't worry much about what the outside of an underground wall looks like. But when the architects and structural engineers finally designed the underground garage at the west end of Simcoe Place, they decided to put its foundation smack up against the CBC. The two walls would be separated by only a thin layer of insulation, to ensure that the rumblings in the new building did not affect the CBC's sensitive microphones and cameras.

The bulging wall is just one of many unanticipated problems that can arise with neighbours in a project of this size. Such situations can sometimes end up in court. But the fact that the developer, contractor and structural engineer were the same for both projects meant that there was a good chance of compromise in this case. Over the last six weeks, Cadillac, Eastern and Quinn Dressel met several times, each putting forward solutions to speed along the work.

The obvious remedy is for the contractor to cut back the parts of the wall that jut over the lot line using a large hydraulic jackhammer mounted on a backhoe, called a hoeram. But using the machine to shave back fifteen centimetres or more of concrete could be expensive, take several weeks and seriously disrupt the CBC. The other idea—completely redesigning the Simcoe Place garage wall—means not only a lot of last-minute work for the structural engineer and architect, but also the loss of parking spots and valuable rental space in the concourse. The compromise has the contractor bringing in the hoeram to take just seven centimetres off the wall, which should take about a week. Meanwhile, the Simcoe Place wall is being redesigned to be seven centimetres thinner. All parties are satisfied.

The big test of this scheme comes at 9 a.m. on a crisp November day, just after the CBC's "Metro Morning" radio show—twenty-five metres away through the wall—goes off the air. Watched closely by the developer, consultants, contractors and CBC officials, the hoeram hammers away at the wall. All is serene in the studio: the vibrations outside are not being transmitted inside.

Neighbours have long recognized the savings to be found in joint action, whether it's homeowners renting equipment together to clean out eavestroughs or cottagers hiring contractors to pump several septic tanks at once. Thrifty urban construction crews think the same way. When the builders brought in a mobile crane to haul the last small backhoe out of the excavated hole, the timing couldn't have been better for the CBC, which needs to add finishing touches to its roof. The two went Dutch to hire a 150-tonne crane for the day. Such collaboration helps when a piece of equipment costs $335 an hour, but it also strikes the right note of neighbourliness after the problems

with the wall and dealing with noise, fumes, dust and other imposi-
tions of sitting next to a construction site.

The plan is not without its complications. In order for B. W.
Haggart Crane Service to complete all of the chores in one day—and
to alleviate the city's worries about closing several lanes of Front
Street—the work starts in the dead of night. Mounted on a massive
trailer, the crane arrives at 4 a.m., illuminated only by street lights,
nearby neon signs and flashing orange warning lights on the partly
closed street. Slowly the vehicle is driven into place at the edge of the
site, and the crane begins its long preparations to hoist the backhoe.

At the push of a button, four legs called outriggers extend from the
sides of the truck to sit on steel plates that distribute the crane's vast
weight on the pavement. When the operator pushes a second button,
a large lead counterweight emerges from the back of the cab to keep
the machine from tipping over. Anchoring the crane this way is critical. The backhoe waiting for a lift fourteen metres below ground level
may be only that small variety used to tidy up the final excavation,
but it still weighs in at thirty tonnes, and can be brought up only with
heavy steel slings hanging from the crane's massive hook.

As the moon fades overhead and the morning-show radio personalities shuffle into work next door, the two slings are lowered into the
hole from the crane's boom and guided by workers to extend around
the bottom of the backhoe's tracks. When the crane's hook is raised,
the backhoe slowly comes with it, as if resting on a giant swing. The
boom swivels and slowly the backhoe is set on the street, where it is
unhooked from the cable, driven onto a flatbed trailer and towed
away.

The roar of the crane engine in the still morning hours is deafen-
ing, but there are surprisingly few complaints from the neighbouring Crowne Plaza Hotel, and the noise doesn't seem to bother civic
officials (not that there are any here at the break of day). But the city
officials had been disturbed by the idea of elephantine machines
blocking pre-dawn traffic and hoisting oversized objects over the
street and sidewalk, so the contractor had to pay three uniformed,
off-duty traffic police officers $38.50 an hour—one-and-a-half times
their normal rate—to ensure public safety.

Constable Stuart Parsons, responsible for directing the less than teeming masses on the empty sidewalk, shifts his weight from foot to foot, shoves his hands in his pockets for warmth on the frosty morning and peers over the edge of the site. Between 4 a.m. and 7 a.m., when the backhoe operation is finished, the only pedestrians he encounters are some indifferent construction workers. "At $38.50 an hour, I'll be happy to get bored all day long," he chuckles, admitting nonetheless to having last-minute regrets about taking the assignment. "At 2:30 a.m. when I got up, it didn't seem like such a good idea." Officers at his division, which is responsible for downtown traffic enforcement, are on a rotation for paid-duty work that can involve escorting funeral processions, sorting out busy parking lots or watching over construction sites. After earning his pay at Simcoe Place, Constable Parsons, still off-duty, leaves for a 9 a.m. date at traffic court, where he also makes time-and-a-half for testifying about a speeding ticket he issued.

By that time, the mobile-crane crew has turned its attention skyward, where railings are being installed at the edge of the Broadcast Centre roof. These have a dual purpose: to allow the network's camera operators to take shots safely from the top of the ten-storey building and to anchor acrobatic window-washers. For the job, the huge crane is extended to its full height of eighty metres and hoists lengths of galvanized steel up to the roof. The machine is moved to three different points around the Broadcast Centre and more paid off-duty police are brought in. At Simcoe Place, a team of carpenters and labourers, finally freed from the encumbrance of the rock and equipment in the last corner of the site, move in to begin forming the final part of the garage, the excavation finally over.

NINE

A WINTER'S TALE

A freezing fog suddenly hangs over the city, as cold as it is damp. The striped umbrellas of hot-dog vendors are covered with frost. Pedestrians brace against the bitter air and children cover their faces with scarves. But inside a tarp made of opaque plastic that has been drawn across the second level of Simcoe Place, the temperature has climbed to a steamy 30°C. It isn't being heated to give comfort to workers. In fact, the space is empty. The heating allows work to proceed on the floor above, so that the water in setting concrete does not freeze.

Letting a slab of concrete freeze is the construction equivalent of a ship's captain running his vessel aground. Brian Gardner shudders to think of the consequences: costly delays, angry consultations with structural engineers, tests of the concrete and a nervous wait to see if, by some happy miracle, it will achieve its desired strength. Ultimately, a whole slab or column may have to be demolished; a section of concrete that is not up to scratch may not support the structure.

The seasonal procedure known simply as winter protection and temporary heating began in late fall, when Simcoe Place was connected to the new high-pressure service from Consumers Gas. A network of temporary steel pipes and gas heaters was hooked up to the supply, snaking to the top level of the growing structure. Now, each time the thermostat drops, a steady flow of gas goes to heaters set up directly below where concrete is about to be put. Tarps are also hung around this lower floor as temporary walls to hold in the warmth. In order to make a section of the third-floor slab, the heaters are on the second floor, allowing the heat to rise up and warm the structure above. Older workers call these heaters salamanders, recalling the huge, portable furnaces once fuelled with coke, a form of processed coal.

In those days, the protective tarps were made of canvas so heavy they could barely be lifted. The ones here are made of thinly woven polyethylene and are easily tied or nailed into place and later removed. In cold conditions—it's work as usual down to -20°C—the heaters are started at least a day before the concrete arrives. This warms up the wooden formwork and structural steel that will receive the concrete, for the same reason that boiling water is poured into a pot before tea is made: left cold, the forms and steel would rob the fresh concrete of the valuable heat generated by its chemical reaction. The technique also melts any snow and ice that have built up, which can also cool the concrete and frustrate crews trying to coax it into tight spaces.

When the concrete comes, it has already been given a boost of heat at the plant. The tickets that accompany each load and show the time they were mixed are just as closely scrutinized as they were in the sweltering summer. Back then there were concerns about the 30°C heat speeding up the solidifying process. In the winter, an old batch of concrete could cool off so much that it will not set properly. Once the concrete has been placed and has hardened enough to be walked on, it is covered with two polyethylene sheets, which the builders call blankets, that have pillows of air or foam between them to hold in the heat. These, plus the heaters and the tarps, are left in place for about three days, until the concrete has reached three-quarters of its strength. The part of the building with the new concrete becomes a favourite destination for workers, who gravitate to the warm, empty space to eat lunch, take coffee breaks or just warm up.

After midnight, when the late concrete crew leaves and the temperature drops, the dangers can increase. In very cold weather, even a thick slab of concrete can be ruined. To assure the contractor a good night's sleep, a security guard watches over the heaters and makes sure everything is nice and warm within the plastic tarps.

Meanwhile, in the Broadcast Centre, Simcoe Place's inner circle of contractors, consultants, architects and developers has gathered for its biweekly progress meeting. The sessions take place in a large, unfinished and—unhappily for Cadillac Fairview, the developer of both buildings—unrented store that conveniently looks out on the site. On jobs where there is no such instant boardroom close to hand, meetings are held in one of the cramped site trailers. The contractors' goal, assuming this space will eventually be rented, is to move to a finished part of the new development that can be closed off with tarps, warmed with heaters and illuminated with temporary lighting.

This is the meeting where financiers, designers, hard hats and artisans find common ground, where praise is given, progress is noted, decisions are made, samples are perused and problems are raised, argued about and eventually resolved. Led by the three senior managers for Eastern—Gardner, Renato Tacconelli and Robert Leonardelli—the group of thirteen men moves swiftly through twenty-four outstanding items from their previous encounter and a handful of new ones.

The meeting lasts a little over an hour and follows the usual bad news/good news format familiar to anyone who has sat on a committee. Despite some catching up, the project is at least two weeks behind schedule as the weather worsens. But the contractors report that the crews hope to gain ground by following a second, revised schedule. The building's third floor is complete and the fourth will be finished soon; masonry walls on the underground concourse are progressing; the parking garage will soon receive its elevator equipment and even get a splash of colour if paint samples can be approved. Some matters are dispensed with in a few words. In fact, not much is said by the men around the table as even contentious issues are raised; these are better examined in detail in a meeting between the players involved.

There are countless smaller, less formal and more productive sessions than this. The Eastern staff holds a meeting in their trailer every week, but each day they get together, usually over lunch. Sitting around Gardner's desk, talk drifts between the morning's activities on the site, last night's hockey game, problems with subcontractors and the daily crossword puzzle, which becomes a collective brainstorming and tension-releasing exercise. Clues and prospective spellings are continually shouted out, prompting quizzical looks from visitors who happen by. Any words that continue to perplex the men are the responsibility of George Kotanidis, who just a few months ago was a college student doing a project on Simcoe Place but now is an eager expediter in the trailer, working out paperwork and finances for the project. Kotanidis uses the thesaurus programmed on his desktop computer to complete the puzzle each afternoon. These are people who don't like unfinished business.

The tone of the formal fortnightly meetings is friendly, although the style is more professional. Most of the players know each other from previous projects and will come together like this at least sixty-five times over the course of this job. There is little sense of distance between the consultants with degrees and those who come from the hands-on trades. Brightly coloured take-out coffee cups and sandwich wrappers litter the table. Some of the men tilt back precariously in chairs as the meeting progresses. There are jokes about whether a consultant known to be renovating his basement is hanging on to samples of door hinges he is supposed to be evaluating for the project.

The serious talk is saved for the project's scheduling problems and other issues. Municipal building inspectors have raised costly concerns about the layout and efficiency of the sprinkler system planned for the concourse. Decisions have to be made right away about the colour and degree of lustre of the floor tiles in the building's bathrooms. Stress tests in Miami of the tower's exterior curtain wall have finished. Work is still underway on the Broadcast Centre's bulging underground concrete wall. On the lighter side, Christmas lights have been strung on the tops of the project's three tower cranes. There is envious talk of the expedition by a few designers to a quarry in Spain to look over slabs of cream-coloured marble that will line the building's lobby.

The items under discussion are numbered according to the session in which they first were raised. For instance, 5.1, the project's schedule, was the first issue brought up at the group's fifth meeting. The bathroom-floor tiles, item 6.4, came to the attention of the inner circle as the fourth item at the meeting two weeks later. The numbers are a good reminder of how long a problem has persisted. This is the project's twentieth meeting. The goal is to eliminate each outstanding difficulty from the list as quickly as possible, but it is obvious from a few heated discussions around the table that several are insoluble.

The one that raises the most debate is 7.3, dealing with the large custom-made ceiling light fixtures. Their Winnipeg manufacturer has provided a sample to show roughly what they will look like and how they will fit into the mechanical and electrical layout above. Today, though, there is an announcement from the project's electrical contractor that a sample of the finished product will not be available for several months, when all of the fixtures will be produced at the plant. In construction, as the ensuing discussion shows, even something this commonplace has a spin-off effect on the work of countless consultants, subcontractors and suppliers. Half of the group is eventually embroiled in the discussion of why they can't wait that long to see the fixtures. They decide an earlier date must be arranged and the item, 20.5, is carried over to the next meeting.

One man at the table keeps tabs on every item on the agenda. Jack Cusimano pays Simcoe Place's bills. At the end of each month, a fat courier envelope lands on his desk, filled with an invoice from Eastern. Cusimano checks the accuracy of the bill so the contractor can be reimbursed by the end of the next month. It may sound like a long time to add up a few columns of numbers, but to appreciate the work involved in verifying a construction invoice of a million dollars or more a month, it helps to know that Cusimano is not an accountant but a civil-engineering technologist. The number-crunchers will get at the bill later. Cusimano works for NORR Partnership, which not only drew up the concept and plans for the building but also has to make sure those designs are carried out. This means helping the contractor and subcontractors interpret the documents, sorting out problems and changes and then checking the bills, a process known as payment certification. It's a role that has been assigned to architects since the early Greeks, when designers were supervisors of construction and masters of detail, required to keep workers on track and to see that all the pieces of the project were in place.

Cusimano spends ten days with his team at NORR after each monthly bill arrives, investigating how the money has been spent. The project's three specialized consultants—structural, mechanical and electrical—join him. Then a battery of consultants for the project's owners—Cadillac, the Workers' Compensation Board and the Toronto Dominion Bank—pore over the bill.

The difference between a contract for $100 million to build a high-rise and a deal to add a new bathroom to a family home is not only the quantity of money involved but also how it is is paid. On smaller projects, most contractors ask for a deposit as a sign of goodwill or to pay for materials; more money is paid in the middle of the job, and the balance when it's finally complete. But on a large job, the building developer or owner is careful to pay only for finished work as it is done. This way, contractors get their money within a reasonable timeframe and developers are safeguarded against "front-end loading" by unscrupulous or disorganized workmen who might be paid at the beginning of a job but run out of money before it is over.

The high stakes and cost of developing high-rise buildings have led to legislation and practices that protect developers, contractors and subcontractors. The Construction Lien Act requires owners to withhold 10 per cent of payments until forty-five days after a general contractor finishes work, in case of claims by employees or suppliers. Building owners also insist that a contractor be insured so the job will be completed if he goes bankrupt. A contractor can be paid two ways: either by what is called a unit-price contract—adding up each piece of material and hour of work as the project goes along—or by a lump-sum, stipulated-price contract, the method here. Eastern will eventually get the agreed price of $100 million, but not all at once. Instead, the twenty-four-page contract requires the company to submit an invoice each month for work completed. The bill is called the progress draw, because it reflects the progress on the project and draws on the total contract price. The owners already have a good idea what each draw will be from a month-by-month breakdown the contractor presented when the project began. In it, the monthly invoices range from $200,000 to $5 million.

When a draft bill ripples across Cusimano's fax machine on the twenty-fifth of the month, he sends out copies to the project's structural, mechanical and electrical engineers. An expanded version and proof that Eastern has paid its subcontractors and suppliers for the previous month's work comes by courier the next day. The consultants have five days to comment on the bill while it is still at the draft stage and another five to look at the finished version, checking the site to make sure the work claimed has indeed been done. For the next twenty-five days, the building's co-owners have a crack at the bill. They evaluate the cost of the work done, calculate the amount that any changes to the drawings or specifications have added to the total price and decide how much they should each pay. The Workers' Compensation Board, for example, is not financially involved in the concourse, with its shops and restaurants, but is required to pay for part of the columns in the area because they support the offices above. A cheque, minus the 10-per-cent lien holdback, is sent to the contractor at the end of the month.

Being the man in the middle of this process can be hard, but Cusimano sees the rewards. "It's a damned good feeling to drive down a street and look at a building or drive over a bridge that you worked on and say, 'I was part of that.' There's a lot of pride there."

January is blamed for absenteeism, cabin fever and hibernation. But if anyone has a bad case of winter woes, it's the contractors, construction workers and developers at Simcoe Place. Record cold temperatures and snowstorms have brought construction almost to a halt. In two weeks, there have been only two productive days of work on the tower's concrete skeleton.

A construction site without construction is sad to behold. Tower cranes sit idle. Eddies of snow swirl around empty concrete buckets and rusting piles of reinforcing steel delivered weeks ago in anticipation of better weather. Somewhat sheltered below ground in the unheated parking and concourse levels, shrouded in the mist of their own breath, a handful of inside workers install ductwork, wiring and pipes for the sprinkler system. Most of the site's workers, those involved in steel and concrete, have been told to stay home—and are not paid.

The most comfortable spot is inside the contractor's trailer. Here, Eastern officials, along with consultants and subcontractors looking for a warm place on visits to the site, catch up on paperwork, try to

squeeze extra time out of schedules and phone for updates of the forecast. An afternoon sampling of a typical message from the airport
weather office chills even the most ardent winter enthusiast:
"Currently -19°C with a wind-chill equivalent temperature of -33°C
. . . Northeasterly gusts to 46 kilometres an hour . . . Snow developing tomorrow, then changing to ice pellets." For further emphasis,
the average temperature for the day punctuates the recording: a high
of -3°C and a low of -11°C.

The news is all bad. The techniques that the builders use to work
in cold weather are no help when temperatures dip this low. Not only
is it impossible for workers to stay outside for very long, metal
becomes brittle and snaps, sensitive equipment breaks and the risk
grows that any newly laid concrete will freeze. Even worse, cranes are
unstable in the wind and, down at ground level, icy gusts rip away
the blankets and tarps tacked up to warm the concrete or placed over
materials for protection. Cold and wind are not the only problems.
After a heavy snowfall, it takes hours or even days to clear away the
snow and to scatter sand—salt is too corrosive on the new material—
necessary for construction to proceed safely.

The morale among the workers who do come to the site sinks with
the barometric pressure. When it's possible to work, bodies ache with
cold. Days off interrupt the momentum and scheduling of setting up
formwork, laying down reinforcing steel and placing concrete. The
cyclical pattern of cold and storm means a week can go by without
any real progress on the structure. The temperature rises and it snows,
then just when the workers have cleared the site, the temperature
plummets and they are paralyzed again.

Workers and contractors are not the only ones frustrated. Cadillac
and its partners are anticipating reports from Eastern about how the
weather has affected the whole schedule. Construction was supposed
to have progressed long ago from the building's large, five-storey
podium to the floors of its main tower. Instead, the crews are just
struggling through the uppermost level of the huge podium, the
mechanical floor that houses the building's heating, cooling, electrical and fire-fighting equipment.

With such harsh winter weather, Cadillac expects a delay claim from Eastern, but is unwilling to reschedule the completion date. "I still feel confident that we're on track," says John Doyle, the new project manager for Cadillac who, like his predecessor, Gary Dunlop, does not easily concede defeat. "We just hope the weather breaks."

The forecast is also bad news for the construction elevator newly fixed to the outside of the building. Much like the crane, the hoist must be shut down in bad weather, its steel structure susceptible to the wind and cold. When Simcoe Place is finished, banks of rosewood-lined interior elevators will whisk stair-shirkers from the third underground parking level to the mechanical penthouse above the thirtieth floor. But until then, getting to the top of the growing building comfortably means a ride in the cage of the rudimentary man-and-materials hoist.

Political correctness has not yet successfully penetrated the construction site. There are no apologies for the sexism inherent in the machine's name or the large metal plate fixed to its wall: "Capacity 2,178 kg or 24 men." "I'd pack twenty-four ladies in here if I could," grins operator Doug Maxted as he swings open the safety gates to take on a group of labourers and a couple of trolleys waiting at the busy ground-floor loading dock. Maxted works for Guy Boire, who owns East-West Elevator and Crane Ltd., the company responsible for the two construction hoists. The first of them has just started operating and a second will be put together soon. Both will grow a few floors at a time, as needed, until they extend to the top of the building.

Boire assembles and services the elevators and, without much work in these slow economic times, also doubles as a hoisting engineer, running the lifts through twelve-hour days. A forty-two-year-old native of Montreal, he has operated hoists for twenty-two years, moving to Ottawa, Edmonton, Vancouver—"wherever the boom was"—until he started the Toronto company six years ago. It's also a family affair. His elder son Sebastien, at nineteen, is training to become an operating engineer, and will spend most days running the second hoist at Simcoe Place. Son Dominic, just sixteen, also wants to be an operator, but for now helps out after school with repairs in the yard north of the city where the machinery is kept. Boire's wife, Luce, takes care of the office administration, beginning the day at 5:30 a.m. by sending her husband off to work with a plastic bag containing both lunch and supper, which he hangs next to the hoist's controls.

The main elevators inside the building will take over the lifting task in about a year, but until then, Boire and Maxted are becoming familiar with each worker on the project, as well as almost every piece of ductwork, sheet of drywall and box of bathroom faucets that goes into it. In the building's early days, the tower cranes lifted most of these objects to the lower floors; now those machines are reserved for handling the vital steel and concrete needed to build the new floors.

The man-and-materials hoist is a close cousin of the crane. Its central feature is a mast of latticed steel. This has been fixed to the building every few floors by braces, and an elevator car is attached to one of its sides. A rack-and-pinion system is responsible for the car's movement. A wheel with cogs on it, attached to the car, climbs a toothed bar on the mast. Two motors in the car, one for going up and the other for going down, turn the wheels in the appropriate direction with the flick of a lever. The motors stop—and the elevator brakes—whenever the lever is released, one of its built-in safety features.

As in the crane, a counterweight helps the motor do its lifting, especially when the car is carrying twenty-four men or a shipment of steel. A cable runs from the top of the car, up and around a pulley on top of the mast and connects with heavy metal blocks that fall as the car rises. If the car is overloaded, it will not rise at all. The extra weight pulls the cage downward until a small metal bar catches a device on the tower, immobilizing it.

This hoist is not known for its speed. At most it will go forty-five metres a minute; when the building reaches its full height of 120 metres, a top-to-bottom trip in the plodding cage will take almost three minutes. Eastern had the choice of using a single hoist that moves twice as fast, one hundred metres a minute, but for the same price opted for the two slower lifts, one of which will eventually go to the top of the building while the other stops at the twentieth floor. That way the two can spell each other in the event of a breakdown or when they require maintenance.

It takes a day or two to bolt a hoist together, and then testing is required before it can go to work. Sensitive to the importance of safety features in the wake of hoist accidents, such as one at a nearby skyscraper under construction five years ago that killed two workers, Ontario government inspectors put the device through a gruelling day of trials before awarding Boire an operating permit. The inspectors are also called in each time a new level is added to the hoist, known in the business as jumping. The pulley is taken off the top of the mast and several new sections are bolted into place and once again braced to the building. A length of cable is added to the counterweight and the device is ready to hoist more materials—and men.

Another safety measure is particularly critical at this time of the year. Like the crane, the construction hoist is susceptible to winter wind, so Boire carries a small wind-speed indicator with him to check on its velocity. Gusts above sixty kilometres an hour can twist and crumple the device's mast, so it must be shut down. This keeps materials moored at ground level and means men have to walk up stairs long distances to get to where they are working. The absence of the elevator adds to the grumbling about the winter conditions, but most men don't mind the warming walk in the bitter chill.

TEN

ONE FALSE STEP

The call crackles across Eastern's two-way radio system at 9:58 a.m. "We have an emergency situation. Call 911. Someone has fallen here." The voice of field engineer D'Arcy Gorman softens and the final two words of his message send a shockwave through the busy contractor's trailer. "It's Corrado."

Conversation stops. Drafting tables and schedules are abandoned. Managers appear from their tiny offices. Rosy Pereira picks up the telephone receiver from the large console on her desk and quickly dials the three digits. Corrado Patullo is a familiar face and a beloved colleague on the project, especially around this office. He and his brothers have worked on countless other sites with the people gathered in the trailer. By the time the emergency service answers the call, everyone has donned hard hats and coats, grabbed portable radios and hurried out, slamming the trailer's heavy metal door. Rosy is the only one left inside, awaiting further information at her base station to relay by telephone to the 911 operator.

Details of the accident come thick and fast across the air waves, all of them delivered by Gorman, who was the first to find Patullo. He solicits information from those nearby who might have seen what happened. Corrado had been working on a fly-form in a section of the ground floor of the building just outside what will eventually become its day-care centre. Partly sheltered from the cold on the bitter February day, it is also the only space on the site big enough to construct the massive temporary structures that are Corrado's specialty.

An individual fly-form looks much like a giant table or a stage set up in a school gymnasium: a flat piece of plywood, sometimes with fiber-glass troughs for beams or guard-rails at the edges, bolted on top of criss-crossed metal to sit high above the floor. Although temporary, each is a structure in its own right, built with blueprints and given an engineer's stamp of approval much like the hoarding that surrounds the site.

After months of frustrating delays, it will soon be time for the builders to move above the parking garage and huge five-storey podium to the building's "typical floors," so called because each is an exact dupli-cate of the one below. This means creating some forty-five of these fly-forms that can be secured to heavy aluminum trusses and pieced together into one unit to make an entire 25,000-square-foot floor of the building. Technically known as a panelized flying system, each form will be reused in the exact same position on each floor, the trusses retracted so it can be easily pushed, still intact, out to the edge of the building and hoisted or "flown" with the help of the crane to the level above.

Corrado had last been observed walking on top of just such a form, its trusses retracted but still two and a half metres high, enough for a nasty fall. Suddenly he was crumpled on the concrete floor below, breathing but unconscious, bleeding from his forehead and nose. The details of the accident are relayed to Rosy and again by her to the emergency operator, who orders fire, ambulance and police services to head to the site's southern gate, the one closest to the scene. An Eastern worker is dispatched to the opening equipped with an orange safety vest and a stop sign on a pole to clear away any concrete trucks and direct the ambulance to the accident.

Corrado is lying with his bloodied face down, but begins to stir as a growing crowd of workers gathers around him. Someone calls for blankets to keep him warm, but the injured man is quickly covered by a pile of men's coats proffered in the -10°C chill. Gorman bends down to the ground, looks into Corrado's face and reassures him that help is here and more is on its way. He loudly asks him what has happened and where he is, the standard way to assess the condition of someone with any sort of head injury. The fallen man stares blankly and struggles with a response. The same questions are posed by fire-fighters—first to arrive on-site because their station is just two blocks away—and then by ambulance attendants, who come within four minutes of the call and begin a more thorough physical examination to assess Corrado's condition.

They swiftly check for shock, trauma, fractures and back injuries. Hands carefully feel for broken bones, and the men ask about Corrado's physical shape and whether he is taking any medication. The coats are returned to their shivering owners and Corrado is carefully rolled onto a board and covered by an orange woolen blanket brought from the ambulance. The board with him on it is lifted, with the help of several of the men, onto a stretcher and then again into the idling ambulance, which slowly pulls up a ramp and out of the gate, the circle of workers staring after its flashing lights and siren long after they have faded into the distance towards St. Michael's Hospital. A newspaper photographer who heard the emergency call on a radio scanner and came onto the site to snap several shots of the scene is told loudly to "get lost" by one of the overwrought engineers and is escorted gruffly through the gate as he approaches to ask for the injured worker's name, history and other information about the mishap.

Just one week shy of his sixtieth birthday, Corrado has never had an accident. In fact, all of the Patullo brothers have spent four decades working in heavy construction, and this will be the first time any of them has been inside a hospital, save for visits after the birth of their children and following their mother's operation for kidney stones. They will suddenly be forced to reflect on the risks of their chosen profession while dealing with the disruption to family life.

The mood at the site is subdued. Everyone from the men who work for Corrado placing concrete or stripping formwork to the most senior managers is troubled by the image of the stricken man lying on the ground in a pool of blood beneath his life's work. There is sorrow, shock and a touch of realism in such incidents. "It could happen to any of us," says Brian Gardner. "There but for the grace of God go I." Talk around the site is of little else, and word of Corrado's condition and questions about the possible causes of his fall travel fast. A year into the project, this is Simcoe Place's worst accident. It couldn't have happened to a nicer person, someone known, despite his position as a boss, as a colleague who works hard and has many life-long friends among his staff. But from a practical point of view, the accident also could not have come at a worse time. Construction is bogged down by bad weather and other delays. Sensitivity over the event is noticeable; accidents can slow down work on a site and bring negative publicity, legal problems, criminal charges, questions about a construction company's work and concerns about the efficiency and cost of a project.

Cadillac Fairview's John Doyle swiftly telephones a reporter who has called about the incident. "This is not an unsafe job," he protests, trying to tone down the severity of the accident. "Sometimes these things do happen—there's not much you can do to control them. You make sure they're attended to quickly." But he acknowledges that on-site "everybody's skittish. . . . It's a risky job, but we want to limit the risk." Development and contracting companies trade on their safety history, publishing their low accident rates in annual reports and touting them to potential clients. Brass plaques certifying exemplary records and laminated awards from safety organizations are prominently displayed in offices. The goal is "zero accident frequency," Gardner says, although "the odds seem to be against us achieving it. You can't build a building of this size without any injuries at all."

Making sure the site's workers do their best to adhere to the giant red sign proclaiming Safety First, which hangs on the plywood hoarding at the west end of the site, is the responsibility of Maurice Dupuis, the safety manager on Eastern's staff. Wearing a grey hard hat with a green cross stamped on the side to indicate he is one of a handful of safety specialists on the site, he makes tours with the seriousness of a priest, looking for such sins as material scattered about or covers left off dangerous gaps in the growing building's floors. He keeps an eye on the workers' safety techniques and their use of equipment designed to protect them. On occasion, he preaches about the benefits of warm-up exercises to prepare bones and muscles for hoisting, hauling and hammering.

There may be little levity in Dupuis's demeanour, but he has to contend with some pretty grim statistics. In 1993, there were 112 critical injuries and 17 deaths on construction sites in Ontario, according to the province's Ministry of Labour. There were many more accidents among jobs throughout industry, especially manufacturing—449 critical injuries and 38 fatalities—but then seventeen times more people work in industry. The accident numbers in construction are getting marginally better, especially with the recent appearance of safety managers on the site. Dupuis says the overall mood and confidence can be overwhelmingly affected when there is an accident such as Corrado's, not to mention the personal concern people feel for the victim and his family. But there is also a practical side to limiting injuries. "Safety is a big business," he says in a flat tone, pointing to a well-thumbed copy of Ontario's 1991 *Occupational Health and Safety Act* regulations, a thick green book he carries with him and refers to as a bible. "Accidents cost a lot of money. It becomes economical to ensure they don't happen."

As the number of construction workers building Simcoe Place grows, the job gets a little more hectic. Dupuis is directly responsible for the twenty men working for Eastern (there are also safety representatives in the other companies), who are subject to even more stringent safety rules than are required by law. According to Eastern policy, they must wear safety glasses at all times while on-site, for instance, and are encouraged to use ear plugs to protect their hearing and gloves to protect their hands, on top of the usual safety boots and hard hats.

Dupuis is also in charge of general safety across the site. He is a professional engineer, and has worked for Eastern in the past as a project manager, running entire construction jobs. But with little on the go in these tough economic times, he's happy to still be employed—and to put to use the extensive St. John Ambulance first-aid training and retraining that construction managers receive. Most of the job is set out in his green bible. The *Occupational Health and Safety Act* ushered in a raft of new safety measures, defined the safety duties of everyone from chairmen of the boards of development companies to each individual worker and established a lengthy certification process for safety managers that Dupuis has just completed. The role is particularly important on this site because the building is, after all, the future home of the Workers' Compensation Board, the guardian of workplace safety. When time allows, Dupuis quietly takes on the contracting duties around the project that are his specialty, but these are not mentioned to the board.

Safety keeps him busy, though. He is co-chairman of the site's joint health and safety committee, a group of four people split between management and labour who each wear the special grey safety hard hat with the green cross. The committee is required to get together at least once every three months—although this one currently meets monthly because there are so many issues to deal with—to discuss safety equipment, report outstanding hazards and go over the project's emergency evacuation plan, which is amended with each change in the configuration of the building and layout of the huge site.

Under the terms of the act, Dupuis keeps track of all accidents, large and small. As well, Workers' Compensation must be notified by individual subcontractors if their own employees are involved in lost-time accidents, known as LTAs. Until Corrado Patullo's fall, there were just four such LTAs among the formwork crews. In one, a carpenter cut his knee when he tripped on a piece of wood. In another, a crane operator suffered a cracked rib, although this was not a result of his dangerous job, but occurred when he bumped into a pile of reinforcing steel while walking across the ground. Most accidents, in fact, are related to dangerous material left around the site, which poses obstacles as the men go about their work. One of Dupuis's biggest jobs is to make sure the place is cleaned and tidied frequently, a daunting task as there is more and more space to take care of.

The complex team effort required for construction projects is particularly evident in the matter of safety. A minimal hazard or obstruction left by one worker can be compounded by the actions of others who follow. Many large holes, for instance, are left in the horizontal decks where concrete is about to be poured, as space for the columns to follow later. A plywood patch is nailed over each of the holes so that no one falls down them. But if a worker comes along and pulls up the plywood to do something to the hole and then doesn't tack the cover down again, it becomes an accident waiting to happen. The next worker might be a carpenter greedily eyeing the piece of plywood for use elsewhere, or a labourer ordered to clean up the deck before the reinforcing steel is laid down. If either worker picks up the loose plywood and then takes a step forward, he might plunge right through the hole, directly onto sharp lengths of reinforcing steel protruding from the top of the column below. It has happened on countless construction sites, causing death and severe injury and leading to heavy fines and even charges for contractors. Eastern policy now requires such holes to be surrounded by guard-rails and warning signs.

Dupuis checks on such installations frequently. He also deals with provincial labour officials, who make unannounced inspections every three to four weeks. Stop-work orders can be issued for any serious problems they come across. For milder infractions, a contractor, an employer, a foreman or even a worker can be warned or fined. The flagman, for example, risks a penalty of $138.50 if he forgets to wear his orange safety vest while ushering in concrete trucks at the site's gate. Dupuis inspects the site throughout the day, alert to areas of the growing structure that need extra lighting, handrails, guard-rails or fire extinguishers. Sometimes he carries along electronic instruments to measure for undue noise or noxious fumes. Where warranted, he posts red metal warning signs that begin Danger Due To . . . , with a space left blank to write in the particular hazard with a marker, such as Missing Guard-Rails or Ice and Snow on Steps.

His office in Eastern's trailer near the Safety First sign is stuffed with volumes of manuals, safety paraphernalia, first-aid equipment and an eye-wash station. Here he administers bandages, splints, aspirin and cold packs from a well-stocked cabinet on the wall. He also issues Eastern employees with safety equipment from gloves to body harnesses. There is a stash of spare metal warning signs behind his desk and a cardboard box of dark blue Eastern hard hats for lending to visitors to the site. The books that fill his shelves include alphabetized plastic-coated binders that describe every hazardous material used on the project, government safety guidelines and periodic bulletins from numerous safety organizations. If he has a bit of time on his hands, he can reach for a stack of cards issued by the Construction Safety Association that suggest topics for five-minute safety sermons and first-aid quizzes to be delivered when workers are gathered for coffee breaks. "You can never prevent every accident from happening, but you can try," he says. "And you can learn from the ones you do have so they don't happen again."

To that end, Dupuis is one of three parties investigating Corrado's accident, reviewing how Eastern employees handled the event and trying to find out, along with Corrado's company, Avenue Structures, and the Ministry of Labour, if any violations of regulations took place. The early results of the inquiry seem to suggest no one is to blame. Even concerns that the plywood platform may have been icy or wet are dismissed; the site was sheltered here. The only conclusion is that Corrado alone was responsible for his fall. Dupuis says. "It's as clean as an accident can be." The final determination agreed.

Opinions among the Patullos themselves vary widely. In family counsels held around kitchen tables in their seven adjoining houses, or impromptu get-togethers around the foot of Corrado's hospital bed, they explore the possibilities. Brother Tony thinks that Corrado was probably checking a beam at the edge of the tall plywood platform when he fell. The beam was not yet bolted in place and could have given way, sending him pitching head-first to the ground. But there are other theories. Corrado might have simply tripped, experienced a dizzy spell or suffered from low sugar levels. There is some concern that the fall itself might have been caused by a minor stroke, although there is no history of such illness in the family. The confusion and disorientation that Corrado has displayed since the accident would seem to be consistent with a stroke, but just as likely could have come from the severe blow to the head that he suffered. The fall left him with a concussion, a broken right cheekbone that had to be repaired by surgery, a swollen ear and a blood clot on the side of his skull that was cleared up with blood thinners.

In the days following the accident, he regains his memory for names and faces bit by bit, but has no recollection of standing on the fly-form, falling to the ground or even going to the hospital. "It is a total blank," Tony says. The brain is a remarkably mysterious organ. Shortly after the accident, Corrado could perfectly recite the eleven-digit overseas telephone number of his best friend, a doctor in his home town of Boiano, Italy, so the family could call him and let him know about the situation. But when a physiotherapist—one of a tag-team of women who will work on the recovery of his memory over the next several months—comes to visit him in hospital, he is unable to identify something as simple as an orange that she presents to him.

Corrado will be kept in intensive care for three days and hopes to be released from hospital within a week. Meanwhile, preparations for his sixtieth birthday party with the family and a night of cards and conversation with about twenty workers from the site have had to be put on hold. Within a day of the accident, he was asking to call Simcoe Place, where brother Carmine is filling in for him, overseeing the construction of the last four fly-forms. Most of Avenue's regular labourers and cement finishers have visited him in the hospital, which is just east of the job. Across the site, workers brighten each time a report of his improved condition spreads. There is word that he may be back within a month, but in fact it will be twice that long before he makes a visit to Simcoe Place, and three or four months before he can fully return to work.

A few days after the accident, Bob McClellan, a spokesman for Ontario's Ministry of Labour, reports that health and safety conditions at the site are not to blame for the fall. Provincial regulations passed as part of the 1991 *Occupational Health and Safety Act* require workers to wear safety harnesses when they are more than three metres off the ground. According to ministry measurements, Corrado was not up that high.

Tony Patullo, as it happens, is a member of a provincial committee studying ways to protect people working at lower heights or in awkward places where they cannot be adequately harnessed. Known in construction as the leading edge, the phenomenon is common to roofing, steelworking and this sort of prefabricated fly-forming. "We're struggling with it day in and day out," he says. "Everyone faces that exposure at some point. It's hard to figure out what to do." In the case of fly-forms, it is impossible to install guard-rails and fall-restraints at all four outer edges of each of the structures, because they are needed to make a continuous, flat platform. Construction workers say that in situations where they are not safely secured, they count on a "skyhook" for protection. "It's the hand of God coming down," says Tony, "and you hang onto that. It's saved all of us a lot of times."

ELEVEN

HOW TO SKIN A BUILDING

The language of construction is a rich mix of metaphor, jargon and antiquated terms that can seem out of place on a modern construction site. There's the bull-float, for levelling and smoothing the surface of fresh concrete. Soldier piles stand guard around the edge of the site. Salamanders is the name of the heaters that keep freshly placed concrete from freezing. To ensure that everything happens on time, contractors talk about schedules following a critical path. Then there's the building's curtain wall, the most prominent feature of modern cities but a term that can stump even the most ardent followers of construction.

Slowly the lowest levels of Simcoe Place are adorned with this exterior covering of glass, aluminum and granite, even as the concrete work is continuing on the floors above and in the underground parking garage far to the west. The curtain wall finally puts a face on the building, establishing its identity on the skyline and giving the rough concrete structure its final look. But the term is little understood. What does the velvet and brocade drape that covers a theatre stage have to do with a typical metal, glass or brick façade? The answer dates to medieval times. The knights of yore, when they designed fortified castles for feudal barons, made massive stone towers the focal points. Between the towers they draped exterior walls, which did not bear the load of the structure but still protected the inhabitants with a generous topping of iron spikes and slivers of glass to deter advancing armies.

The execution has changed since the Crusades—glass slivers are hardly needed to protect a building thirty storeys above ground—but the principle of a simple exterior wall that does not hold up a modern building remains the same. It has not always been so. Castles were the exception, because the outer wall of a building was once a necessary part of its whole structure. Called a load-bearing wall, the building would have fallen down without it. The taller and heavier the building, the stronger and thicker the wall needed to be, with dense masonry in particular occupying prime space at ground level, where the load was the greatest. Before the introduction of electric lighting in the 1880s, getting enough sunlight into a building was also a concern. Windows weakened the structure and glass was hard to come by, so windows were slits more suitable for aiming arrows than for illumination.

As the 1900s progressed, the challenge was to build higher, more profitable structures while at the same time providing enough light within them. The curtain wall, resurrected in buildings as early as London's Crystal Palace in 1851, was one way to skin a building. And it became the most popular, judging from the look-alike skyscrapers that have sprouted since the technique became widely used fifty years ago. Daring modernist architects such as Ludwig Mies van der Rohe, a refugee to the U.S. from the Nazis, began designing buildings with cores or frames that were fortified by steel and concrete beams and columns. They could then cover them with sheets of glass and decorative stone framed in metal. Like many technologies introduced after the Second World War, the curtain wall got its start in munitions manufacturing. Mies van der Rohe's proposed technique would have been heavy and cumbersome to apply and might have deteriorated after being exposed to the elements for a few years. But the extruded or moulded aluminum that was crafted into ever-more lightweight and streamlined aircraft parts during the war made for ideal wall panels. These walls did not support the weight of the building, and could even be applied after the fact. They were almost inconsequential to the basic structure itself, except in terms of its appearance.

"You could cover the outside with almost anything you wish— even plastic and plywood—just to keep the weather out," says Len Lovely, a manager at Antamex, the company making and installing the curtain wall at Simcoe Place. Antamex first got a look at what the architects at NORR had in mind for Simcoe Place when it bid for the contract. The company's designers created a curtain wall that would cover the entire 37,000-square-metre exterior of the building at a cost of $10 million. The wall will be made out of six thousand separate panels that combine the architect's vision with practical considerations such as the effects of strong winds. The main ingredient is 450,000 kilograms of aluminum, made from bauxite ore mined in tropical countries such as Jamaica and Ghana. The ore is refined and smelted in plants in Quebec, where it is turned into logs, known in the industry as billets. These billets are brought to a second Alcan plant north of Toronto, where they are heated to become pliable and then pushed through metal dies that produce extrusions, long, made-to-measure strips of aluminum. Metal workers, machinists and welders at Antamex cut these extrusions with saws and assemble them into discrete underlying frames for the wall panels. These are fitted with seals and gaskets, and faced with appropriate glass, granite or sheets of more aluminum.

What most observers notice as the building goes up, however, are not the aluminum frames but the mirrored walls of glass. It is easy to be fooled by the number of windows on high-rise buildings. Not all the glass is clear—what glaziers call vision glass. At least a third of it is actually part of the spandrel, the place where the floors and beams meet the outside wall. The deception ends when the lights come on at night and those areas of the building become totally opaque, the glass backed by insulation and galvanized steel.

This backing helps keep the elements out and hides the ventilation and plumbing equipment inside. The building's mechanical contractors must make sure this working part of the wall has enough space to tuck away their pipes and ducts. Long ago, these contractors, along with the building's owners, tenants, architects and engineers, got a sneak preview of the wall's inside dimensions and exterior look. Antamex assembled a giant replica of the glass-and-metal wall on a stand in the factory parking lot, and invited all of the relevant parties to come for an inspection. It was the first time the people involved in Simcoe Place got a glimpse of the finished product. Mock-ups—of course, on a smaller scale—are common in construction. Getting feedback early in the process is practical; mistakes can be costly and cause delays. It was important for Antamex to hear any objections about tints and materials, for the contractors to measure and prod the wall's inner workings and for the designers to give their seal of approval.

The inspection was brief and the wall sample passed with flying colours, but there were more trials to come. Another massive section put together in the plant was trucked to an outdoor test centre on the outskirts of Miami. There it was erected on a frame and mistreated to make sure it could stand up to the lashing rains, wind, heat and intense cold it will face in downtown Toronto. After all, the curtain wall's purpose is more than aesthetic. It must fortify the building's occupants, stand up to strong winds, freezing temperatures and the searing sun, and reduce noise from the surrounding neighbourhood.

As the most prominent feature of a building, it also reflects the architect's vision through its materials and finishes. The early curtain walls for the United Nations Building, Lever House and the Seagram Building, all built in New York City following the Second World War, were striking glass, steel and even bronze symbols of progress and prosperity. However, although these early glass boxes appealed to people with modern tastes, they proved impractical. Their huge single-paned windows sometimes shattered, and they leaked energy to the outside while trapping unwanted heat from the sun's rays inside. Inadequate seals between glass and metal allowed water to seep through. The wall, assembled in a cumbersome process called the stick method, in which individual pieces of framing and pieces of cladding were fixed one at a time to the building, had a rigid look. It was also all done from a swing-stage, similar to the platform used by window-washers, which meant the wall was installed vertically up the building a side at a time. Most of the building had to be built before the process began and the technique exposed follow-on trades inside the building to the weather for longer.

New techniques, many of them developed in Canada, have repaired the curtain wall's tarnished image. Today, windows are double-glazed panels, made of glass that has been treated for strength and then coated to keep unwanted sun out and desired heat in. Stronger aluminum alloys and better ways of shaping them mean that not as much metal shows through. Modern rubber sealants stand up to the extreme conditions that a building encounters, and the glass can be made to adhere to the frames with a thin strip of glue called silicone glazing.

Most important, large sections of the wall can now be assembled far away, shipped to the construction site and then fixed to the building by a small crew working inside, covering one floor at a time. This is known as the panelized method and, by using it, most of a floor can be closed off, heated and occupied by workers installing pipes, ventilation, wiring and window blinds as the building is still rising above.

At Simcoe Place, the components are stacked in wooden frames and loaded onto flatbed trucks for the thirty-kilometre journey downtown to the construction site. Once the panels arrive, the efforts of Mike Daoust and his team of four ironworkers offer more clues as to how the curtain wall got its name. Each of the panels is attached to the building in only a few places, secured to the concrete floors with metal anchors. The wall fits together in a continuous sheet of glass, stone and aluminum. To add flexibility and make up for the fact that the edges of the concrete slabs are never made perfectly even—described as construction tolerance in the trade lexicon—the wall actually hangs about five centimetres away from the structure.

The formula for turning the panels into a continuous curtain is set out in stacks of drawings in Daoust's on-site trailer. Tacked to a wall above is a murky photocopy of a drawing of the building, the only representation of what Simcoe Place is eventually supposed to look like. "It doesn't mean much to us," shrugs Daoust, a short man with a round face, his cheeks and nose reddened by working outdoors all day. The visual flourishes devised by the architect will have to find appreciation elsewhere. Daoust is busy timing the arrival of the panels so they can be unloaded immediately by one of the site's big tower cranes and hoisted up to the level where they are needed. Under pressure to make up for the delays caused by bad winter weather, the cranes are tied up working on the main structure. As a result, most lifting jobs like this are done when the cranes are idle, usually on Saturdays, so at least one of Daoust's crews works then.

Cranes are also used to lift the heaviest panels—the granite ones weighs one and a half tonnes that cover the columns around the building's first three stories—into place. To fit the panels that make up the rest of the wall, each of which weighs a more modest 350 kilograms, the curtain-wall workers have their own miniature version of a crane, an electronic winch called a lifting rig. Putting each piece in place takes three men, two on the level where it is about to be installed and the third to operate the rig from the floor above. Ironworkers are familiar with scaling beams that are high off the ground, but working at the edge of the building can be risky. Everyone wears canvas safety harnesses clipped to a steel cable strung above.

After the panels have been hoisted up by the tower crane to the level where they are to be placed, they are laid out around the edge of the building in order of installation. The two men below take a panel and lay it on two dollies. The man working above then drops the winch's chain down the outside of the building. It is hooked to the top of the panel so that when the winch is turned on, the panel is dragged on the dollies to the edge of the building and swings up into the air outside.

The panel comes ready to go, with holes that are lined up with bolts, called inserts, that were embedded in the concrete floor back when it was made. A few tense moments pass before it is manoeuvred and fitted into place; commands are barked into radios and shouted to the man operating the winch above until the panel finally sits in position. Then metal plates, washers and nuts are secured over the bolts. Most of the connections will be welded for strength after a few floors have been completed. Some, called slip connections, will be left unwelded so they can move a bit, giving the wall room to expand and contract in extreme heat and cold.

The curtain-wall team will grow to fifteen when work on the main tower begins. Antamex hopes eventually to cover a floor a week, although the side of the building where the two construction-hoist elevators run will remain covered in plywood until the elevators are removed. Then the final panels of curtain wall will be installed. When Simcoe Place has been completely covered with its curtain wall, Daoust's ironworkers will move to the outside, installing bits of trim and adding caulking where extra sealing is needed.

For now the process of assembling all of the wall's components is still under way. To Glen Pestrin, nothing beats real rock. The young man serenely slides a hand across a slab of cool, shiny black granite, fingering the rich flecks of grey that run through it. All around him, in the noisy Gem Campbell Terrazzo and Tile plant near Toronto's airport, is rock quarried and shipped from around the world. Pestrin's father, Mario, is one of the owners and founders of the company. Glen likes to say he was born into the business, brought to the fabricating plant right after his birth because his father had to stop in to do some work at the office while bringing his wife and newborn son home from the hospital.

Italians dominate much of the granite industry. Mario Pestrin was born in the Friuli region of northern Italy, and apprenticed as a mason before coming to Canada with a friend to start Gem Inc. in 1959. Business was so slow that the two men shared a coat, working on alternate days until they made enough money to buy another. Eventually they joined with a granitic Scot named Campbell to form Gem Campbell, which today is one of the largest marble and granite companies in Canada.

Stone is one of civilization's oldest and most enduring building materials. But it is expensive and difficult to use, and builders long ago found cheaper and easier materials and techniques. The Romans were the first to realize they could carve rock into slivers and cover their buildings and monuments with just a little of it, for effect. Historian Daniel Boorstin says the well-known boast of Emperor Augustus that he "found Rome a city of bricks and left it marble" was actually wrong. The Romans, he says in *The Creators*, "found architecture a realm of marble and would remake it in concrete." Real rock was "a material more cosmetic than structural," he says, cut into thin slabs or decorative fragments that covered a core of concrete to make the grand and distinctive Roman buildings. The marble and mosaic on the marvellous coffered dome of Hadrian's Parthenon in the centre of Rome were just an illusion, a veneer laid on top of the concrete and brick that gave the structure its strength.

Two types of rock, Atlantic black and regal grey granite, were chosen to furnish the corporate image for the columns at the base of Simcoe Place, to darken the recesses at the outside corners of the tower, to make an authoritative reception desk in the lobby and to carve out sleek basins in the building's washrooms. Pestrin, a project manager at Gem Campbell, is responsible for the eleven thousand square metres of granite that will adorn the building, as well as the marble in its lobby and the stone tile flooring in the underground concourse.

The granite colours were designated by the architects when they first conceived of the building. The final selection was made by a roving team that included the architects, the owners and representatives from Gem Campbell. The regal grey, which has a salt-and-pepper look, comes from a quarry in Barre, Vermont, and the Atlantic black from St-Nazaire, Quebec. The material is cut out of the ground in large blocks and shipped to the Lecroix Brothers plant in St-Sebastien, Quebec. There it is turned into thin slabs, by machines called gang-saws that look like huge bread-slicers, before being polished and cut to the sizes specified in the building plans.

The pieces are brought in large wooden crates by transport truck to Gem Campbell, where they are assembled into the required shapes to be fixed to the curtain-wall panel and onto the building's concrete skeleton. To make the panels that wrap around the concrete columns at the base of the podium, workers glue together seven different pieces of regal-grey granite with a strong epoxy to form a box. The panels are then fitted with bolts in the back that will secure them to the building.

This demanding operation is watched closely by a scrawny, nameless cat, her short white fur heavy with dust, that thins the mouse population in the plant. On an unused steel frame nearby, the workers have made a cat toy in their spare time, a wadded ball of masking tape hung from a shoelace. The cat skitters around the open factory floor, taking swipes at imaginary adversaries, to the delight of her hard-working audience.

Granite is a difficult material to work with, and not just because it is heavy. It is also one of the earth's hardest natural materials and can be cut only with the hardest material—diamonds—embedded in a saw. Granite is formed by the slow cooling of molten magma and is the most abundant rock in the earth's crust, its colours resulting from the varying physical and chemical properties of its two essential minerals, quartz and feldspar. It comes in many varieties: fantasy blue from Sri Lanka, nero assoluto or absolute black from Zimbabwe and grigio sardo, a black-and-white granite from Sardinia.

With the recessionary lull in construction, Gem Campbell has expanded into new areas like specialty granite fixtures. The company was already making the occasional obelisk and monument, but lately it has begun producing custom-made items, including granite barbecues and bathtubs made of hollowed-out blocks of the rock. A wealthy man in Chicago even hired Gem Campbell to fashion a massage table out of granite, with an underlying layer of heating coils so the frigid stone would not chill the skin.

Glass, of course, is the most critical element of the curtain wall. Its ingredients are as old as the earth, and the idea of turning it into windows dates back to the time of Pompeii. But residents of the ancient city—who, archeologists tell us, let the light shine through tiny glazed windows set in bronze frames—would hardly recognize the vast sheets that cover a modern high-rise. The tinted, mirrored windows in the curtain wall here are the product of two companies in suburban Toronto. AFG Industries makes the glass itself, shapes it into sheets, cuts it and treats it for strength and colour. Then Trulite Industries makes it into a double panel to give office workers extra protection from the wind, rain, cold, glare and heat outside.

The process starts on Badgeley Island, a small speck of sandstone in Lake Huron, the Great Lake once reached by a canoe trail from Toronto. Stone mined here is crushed in a factory to make silica sand. This is mixed with other elements, including soda ash, dolomite and limestone, and then heated to a searing sixteen hundred degrees to turn it into molten glass. The glass that this mixture produces actually has a green hue, owing to a trace amount of iron in the sand, although the iron can be extracted if clear glass is desired. Metals can also be deliberately added to colour the glass in other ways: cobalt turns it blue, selenium turns it bronze and a combination of cobalt and selenium produces grey glass—which is being used for the stepped-in corners of Simcoe Place.

Windows are made by cooling the molten mixture in a specific way. This was once accomplished by inserting a wide piece of wire into the hot mixture and lifting it, which left a sheet of cooling glass hanging below. The problem was that this method produced a pane of glass distorted with waves and ripples, commonly seen on windows in older homes. Finer "plate" glass was made by grinding and polishing the two sides of glass to remove such imperfections.

To make seamless windows today, the ingredients for the glass are heated in a large tank. A thin layer of the molten mixture is allowed to flow out of the top of the tank and onto a layer of soft tin. When subjected to the extreme heat, the tin melts and the liquid glass finds a true level. This makes the cooling product, called float glass, perfectly flat on the bottom as well as the top.

Most windows destined for commercial buildings are strengthened and transformed with heat to help them resist warm weather, high winds and the unfortunate birds that sometimes smack into them. AFG puts the glass into ovens, where it is heated to 600°C and then cooled in a couple of different ways to build stress into its surface. "Tempered" glass is cooled rapidly to make it four times as strong as regular glass. When shattered, it breaks into harmless little granules, a good quality for the glass used in doors. "Heat-treated" glass is rendered twice as strong as regular glass by slow cooling. It is used in tall buildings like Simcoe Place because, although the glass fractures into large shards when hit, it holds together and remains in the frame rather than raining onto the streets below.

To receive the familiar reflective coating known to most people as mirrored glass, the window is passed through a vacuum chamber containing an electrically charged strip of metal. Fine bits of the metal fly onto the surface of the glass. The amount depends on how shiny the building should appear from the outside and how much the designer wants to dim the sunlight getting in. Its colour is determined by the type of metal in the chamber: stainless steel produces a silver or pewter look (the colour chosen for Simcoe Place), titanium turns the glass sky-blue, an alloy of copper and aluminum makes it appear gold, and copper, of course, gives it a copper look. Finally, the glass can be treated with what is called low-emissivity coating, a microscopic layer of silver oxide and other materials. Like an invisible piece of insulating foil, this helps to hold heat inside in the winter and keep it out in the summer.

The glass is shipped from AFG to Trulite, where computerized machines assemble it into some eight thousand well-insulated windows for Simcoe Place. These are essentially double-glazed panels, two pieces of glass separated by a perimeter strip of aluminum, called a spacer. The technique leaves a 1.3-centimetre layer of air between the two pieces of glass, which acts as an insulating barrier. It is critical that moisture does not come into this space, so it is treated with a powdered drying agent called a desiccant, similar to the bags of silica gel left in new appliances to keep out dampness.

The layering effect of the glass gives Simcoe Place its distinctive look. Four-fifths of the windows—those running up the main part of the building—are panels made of stainless-steel coated glass on the outside and low-emissivity clear glass on the inside. For the darker panels at the corners of the building, the architect requested grey-tinted glass outside and low-emissivity clear glass inside.

Glass walls may give the building its outer personality but, under the glare of bare lightbulbs, a team of masons is responsible for its soul. To construct the walls of a long underground corridor running behind the food court, one of them energetically scoops mortar onto a trowel, slaps the material on top of a heavy grey block, fits another block into place and swiftly scrapes off the excess mortar. "We do it one block at a time—just like the Egyptians," he says. He's not far wrong. The operation deep beneath the high-rise traces its origins back ten thousand years, when people first moved out of caves and made dwellings out of stacked stones. The Egyptians made their pyramids by fitting together blocks cut precisely with iron tools. The Romans designed kilns to shape soft clay into bricks and invented cement mortar to glue these bricks into structures. In fact, the quiet history of masonry did not change much until the end of last century, when the discovery of better cements meant that blocks could be made out of concrete with two voids or holes in the centre—the familiar figure-eight cross-section used today. The blocks are as sturdy as solid concrete but much lighter and easier to work with.

While the core of most large buildings is either steel or reinforced concrete, blocks are still the material choice of contractors looking for durable, fireproof and inexpensive interior walls. It will take ten masons and 154,000 concrete blocks in assorted sizes to give shape to Simcoe Place's out-of-the-way electrical and gas rooms, stairwells, storage rooms and hallways. Known as in-fill walls, they are made long after the main structure has been built. They will not take the weight of the building, although some concrete blocks are used to build load-bearing walls that must hold up a roof, as in low-rise warehouses and schools. In these instances, the block can be reinforced by putting steel rods through the holes in a succession of blocks and filling them with liquid mortar. A more refined type of concrete block, called architectural block because of its decorative finish, will add finesse to the exterior of the rear loading dock at Simcoe Place.

The blocks, made by TCG Materials, use the same formula as concrete—cement, sand, limestone and water—but the limestone is finely crushed to produce a smooth finish, and less water is used so the mix will set quickly. After being blended together and poured into moulds, the concrete is vibrated to shake out air pockets and help it settle. The blocks are removed after a minute and placed for several hours in a kiln, where heat, steam and high pressure encourage setting. After twenty-eight days, the blocks are ready to be used at Simcoe Place.

Masons on the site use tools and techniques developed and refined through generations. The most common (and strongest) way of arranging blocks is a technique called the running-bond, where each new block is placed halfway over the one below it. In the stack-bond wall, the blocks are laid one directly on top of the other. When starting a new row on top of an existing one, the mason first lays a block in mortar at each end. To ensure that the two blocks are plumb, or straight, a spirit-level is put on top and then a piece of white string, known as the mason's line, is strung between them. The string helps the masons keep the row straight as they add each new block. When a row is finished, a jointing tool is run along the space between the blocks to scoop out excess mortar and give it a uniform, concave finish. A contemporary innovation, a piece of shag carpet, is rubbed over the finished section of wall from time to time to smooth off any rough bits of protruding mortar.

Concrete blocks may all look the same, but in fact they differ in width, composition and complexion. The standard size of the face shell—the surface of the block—is always forty centimetres long by twenty centimetres high, but the blocks come in widths of ten, fifteen, twenty, twenty-five and thirty centimetres. The mainstay of the block industry is the twenty-centimetre block, which weighs 16.5 kilograms and is known as a Type-A. The Type-C, a lighter block, is made with more porous material such as slag, a by-product of the steel industry. At 13.8 kilograms, these blocks are not only easier for the masons to lift but are also valued for being more fireproof, since the air trapped inside the concrete acts as insulation.

There will be little appreciation for the various types of blocks once the walls are complete and the building gets its chrome, glass, granite and marble coverings. But the meticulous masons, like the medieval knights, will know this building's secrets.

TWELVE

GOING UP

Spring comes to the city with little warning. The heavy rains, colourless days and lingering mists that have shrouded the skyline and dampened sidewalks and spirits are quickly forgotten. The May sun that powers through is so hot that pedestrians find they are desperately overdressed. Finally venturing out of offices and meeting rooms for lunchtime strolls, they cannot help noticing that one year into construction, the building has grown. It suddenly looks more like a high-rise and less like an oversized concrete parking garage. A keen eye can make out the tapered shape of the main tower, with its distinctive stepped-in corners, several floors of which rise out of the podium at its base.

There is no ringing of bells to mark the first year of work, only the ever-present hiss of welding torches, whine of drills and rumble of concrete trucks. Brian Gardner likens this stage in the construction process to the middle of a long sea voyage: "You look at the horizon and see oceans of concrete. Below you, concrete. Above you, concrete." People in the construction business are not given to gushing about anniversaries. They prefer to focus on the hurdles ahead rather than on what has been accomplished. While waiting for a stubborn Toronto spring to warm up, anxious minds already cast ahead to next winter's deep freeze, by which time the concrete structure must be finished and wrapped in the curtain wall. This means sixteen-hour days for the concrete and steel crews, who work in two shifts, stretching from 6 a.m. to 10 p.m., to construct one floor of the building each week. With 225 workers, the site is nearing its full complement of hands. Most of them are involved in bringing the basic structure up to its full thirty storeys, although gradually the balance will shift as more and more finishing trades—carpenters, painters and tile-layers—come on board. Subcontractors responsible for the building's elevators, drywall, curtain wall and mechanical and electrical systems have put extra workers on the job. Officials from these companies and from Eastern spend most of their days in meetings, poring over schedules to figure out when work will be done and material delivered. The sense of urgency is noticeable; everyone is aware that the weeks spent idle during the frosty winter have set the project back. To allow for the delays, Eastern and Cadillac have added four weeks to the contract, setting a target of June 2 next year, thirteen months away, for the building to be "substantially complete." All but 1 per cent of the contract must be finished at this point; all but a thousand dollars worth of work must be done by July 20, the project's "total completion" date.

Out of sight on the top level of the main tower, work is in full swing. The builders, looking forward to better weather and grateful to have reached these carbon-copy floors, are speeding up the pace. The strict schedule drawn up by Eastern calls for one floor to be built each calendar week for twenty-four weeks to ensure the utmost productivity. The fly-forms that make up the new floor are to be lifted up on Monday and part of Tuesday, the reinforcing steel is to be in place by early Thursday and the concrete work finished by late Friday. This allows the concrete to cure sufficiently over the weekend so that the forms can be collapsed and removed once again. The cycle is also meant to match the week's natural rhythm and foster as much momentum as possible. The plan is ambitious, considering the set-backs that have plagued the job. It will depend on weather conditions, the goodwill of the concrete crews and the cooperation of the equipment.

No one element is as critical to the schedule as the site's tower cranes. They do the work of moving the forms, fitting them into place and, of course, hoisting every bit of steel and concrete that arrives on-site up to where it is needed. Which brings about a question that stumps the most seasoned watchers of modern construction: How do these machines get taller as the building does? Some think that new sections are continually added to the tower crane as the structure grows, leaving the base of the crane firmly rooted in the ground far below. Or perhaps the crane's tower is eventually incorporated into the finished product, becoming one of the building's elevator shafts. Others are aware that the crane somehow rises along with the burgeoning building. A peek through the completed lower floors of a structure under construction will show that the tower no longer extends all the way to the ground. But the realization that it is somehow lifted up raises more puzzling possibilities. Perhaps a helicopter flies in to do the job. Maybe the cranes working together on the site haul each other up. Despite constant vigilance, most observers are foiled in attempts to watch the process happen. Look away and suddenly the huge towers sprout from the building's top level again.

For an explanation, the most important thing to know about tower cranes is that they never get any taller than when they are first assembled and bolted to concrete foundations in the ground at the start of a project. That means a crane the same height as those being used at Simcoe Place also built the 550-metre-high CN Tower. So somehow the crane has to go up and be anchored within the building. After all, a crane must have enough clearance below its long boom to hoist material. Yet each new level of construction constricts its movement, so it has to be continually raised to a point a few floors above the top level.

The tower crane climbs within the structure. Hence its common name, the climbing crane. How it accomplishes this remarkable feat is a matter of planning, physics, some help from Mother Nature—and a lot of elbow grease on the part of Frank Goldstein, who has been brought in to do the job. Catching a climbing crane in the act is almost impossible. The manoeuvre often happens in the middle of the night or on the weekend, when there are no hoisting duties. Even if the crane rises in broad daylight, all of the work done on it is out of sight at the crane's base, known as its hydraulic climbing section, several floors below the uppermost level of construction.

Goldstein and his crew of four men work down there, far out of view of the sidewalk superintendents and even most of the construction workers. Each crane has its own peculiar method of climbing and comes with a thick instruction booklet, but Goldstein is pretty familiar with the technology. Since he immigrated to Canada from Hungary in 1961, he figures he has built, repaired, maintained and raised several thousand cranes. His trips to the Simcoe Place site are frequent. Cranes typically move up about two floors at a time, which can mean a climb every couple of weeks if the construction schedule is followed.

The crew starts preparing for the event several days in advance. With the base of the crane currently sitting on the sixth floor of the building, it's the team's task to move the whole machine up two storeys, so the base is even with the eighth floor. This will give the crane another eight metres of clearance above the building's uppermost tenth level.

A hefty 120 tonnes of steel, the crane must be supported with heavy steel scaffolding, called re-shoring, which surrounds the crane hole between the top floor and the bedrock to make sure it doesn't crash through to the ground. Equally important is horizontal support, wedges that prevent the crane tower from pressing against the sides of the holes in each of the floors or, even worse, falling right over. Care is taken to support the crane's massive weight during the climbing procedure and afterwards, to ensure that it does not damage the newly formed concrete floors, which after all have been designed to hold office workers and their furniture, not a giant column of steel.

On the eighth and tenth floors, the workers have lifted into place two sets of climbing beams, each made up of four thick steel bars shaped into a square, to act as a collar around the crane holes. These will bear the weight of the crane while it is climbing and secure the tower when it comes to rest at its new level. Two heavy, narrow steel bars with slots in them are hung vertically from these climbing beams. They are known as climbing ladders because the crane uses hydraulic power to literally pull itself up on them, like climbing the rungs of a conventional ladder.

If all goes smoothly, the climbing operation takes a couple of hours. During this time the crane is shut down. It also must stand in the hole without swaying, so this is a job only for calm weather. To make sure the crane is perfectly balanced, a seven-thousand-pound concrete weight is hung from the hook at the end of its boom to offset the effect of its massive counterweight. Goldstein's men use giant hammers and wrenches to knock out steel wedges, often seized with cold and rust, that have positioned the crane squarely in the middle of the hole. Once these have been removed, the crane stands freely in the hole, held up only by a climbing beam they installed for the crane's previous lift.

At the base of the crane in the hydraulic climbing section are two large steel bars with hooks at either end, known as dogs. Brackets that secure the dogs in place are removed, and one set of dogs at a time is released out into one of the slots on each of the climbing ladders to move the crane up. When Goldstein presses a button, a hydraulic piston pushes against the steel bar that connects the dogs. The crane is thus pushed up until the second set of dogs sticks into the next slot up the ladder. The piston contracts, this time pulling up the lower set of dogs, which then sticks out into new, higher slots, and so on.

The crane groans and creaks, and small bits of concrete and dirt that have accumulated around the edge of the hole break off and shower down. The men look away or cover their faces with their hands to avoid getting any fine grit in their eyes. The operation is slow and methodical, one rung at a time, continuing until the base of the crane comes even with the climbing beam on the eighth floor. Here the crew reverses the process used to free the crane two floors and two hours before. They replace the brackets that secure the tower to the beam and then hammer the wedges around the tower to secure it on the eighth and tenth levels of the building.

This may be a mammoth piece of equipment, but the final act is a delicate one. Goldstein puts a carpenter's level on the side of the steel tower and squints at the small bubble of air that shows whether the crane is standing perfectly straight in the hole. If it is even slightly crooked, it will have to work harder to hoist and swing its loads. With the climbing operation finished, Goldstein leaves and the crane can get on with the work of hoisting concrete and steel, newly freed from encumbrances beneath it.

The moment can never come soon enough for D'Arcy Gorman. As the field engineer in charge of the construction of the building's main tower, Gorman closely keeps track of the crane's movements. His office may be at the edge of a building high above downtown Toronto, but it isn't about to be mistaken for the executive suite. There are no mirrored windows or carpeted floors, not even a roof to protect him from showers and splashes of concrete from a bucket that the crane occasionally swings overhead. In fact, there aren't many comforts at the top of a building under construction. A slight breeze stirs the sultry air, saws and drills buzz and the bare wood beneath Gorman's feet jiggles with the movement of the vibrator as it helps settle concrete between the steel bars of a new floor.

He picks up the dust-covered receiver from a cellular telephone slung around a nearby wooden post. "This is D'Arcy at Simcoe Place," he shouts into the mouthpiece above the clamour. "We're going to need another seven metres of forty today," he says, ordering two truckloads of concrete that is forty megapascals in strength. As he talks, he carefully peers over a rail at the side of the building to see how many concrete trucks idle below. Gorman is Eastern's field engineer assigned to the tower, which means ordering dozens of concrete trucks and shipments of steel to come to the site each week, as well as booking the cranes and hoists to bring all of the materials to where they are needed.

At twenty-nine, he is one of the youngest workers at Simcoe Place. He grew up in Vancouver, studied civil engineering at the University of British Columbia and moved to Ontario in 1988 to work his way up through Eastern. Until now he has worked on shopping malls and small office buildings; Simcoe Place is the largest project he has been involved in. With his rise in the company has come an increase in responsibility. He arrives at the site between 5:30 and 7:00 in the morning, depending on the day's tasks. He and fellow field engineers Dean Sabean and Eugene Bristow take turns coming in early to survey formwork or new floors and staying late to oversee after-hours concrete operations.

Gorman starts the day by making a pot of coffee in the spartan trailer. Although he keeps a desk there for doing the obligatory paperwork, he's soon ready to head out. He carries his office with him on various holsters: one walkie-talkie to contact other Eastern employees, a second one to keep in touch with the crane operators and their foremen at Avenue, and a large steel tape measure and other devices to periodically survey the building with his colleagues to make sure it is rising straight and level or the concrete is settling on schedule. A sharpened pencil is at the ready in a yellow plastic bracket glued to the side of his hard hat for noting down measurements and concrete shipments.

On days when a lot of concrete is expected, Gorman stations himself right where the new slab, columns and walls are being made. That way, besides making sure a steady supply gets up to the floor, he can also ensure that the higher-strength mixes go where they are needed. He aims eventually to do his managing from a real office, but has learned a lot from his hands-on position. "It's nice to be out in the field and to work outside," he says. "But it's got its disadvantages, especially in the wintertime."

Orders and queries come thick and fast over the phone and walkie-talkies. A twisted cable on one of the cranes must be unravelled; time has to be found to hoist up two truckloads of wall panels that have arrived early; Gorman and his fellow field engineers banter over who will stay late to supervise the concrete work, which often continues until at least 6:30 in the evening. Much of the chatter on the radio is in Portuguese or Italian, which Gorman doesn't understand; "Only the swear words." Throughout the day, all of Gorman's colleagues at Eastern use their radios to respond to his invitation to an impromptu weekend barbeque at his high-rise condominium on the shore of Lake Ontario, which he has hastily entitled "Steak by the Lake." Much of his day is spent debating the finer details of Simcoe Place's concrete work with Robert Appio, the general foreman for Avenue, but all of the other trades also look to him when they need clearance to bring their equipment and materials into the tower. Pipes, wiring and the first panels of drywall, for example, need to hitch a lift from the cranes and construction elevators, but they must wait for a break in the key work on the structure.

During a lull, Gorman munches on his alfresco lunch—cold coffee and a Crunchy bar. He watches office workers taking it easy on sunny lawns down below and studies a line forming for the matinée performance of *Crazy for You* at the Royal Alexandra Theatre. Far to the east, he can see his condo building shrouded in the afternoon haze.

When the workload permits, Gorman heads down to a completed level of the tower to check the grade of a new floor to see whether it has set sufficiently for the supporting scaffolding below it to be removed. The test, known as shooting the level, is one of the continuing surveying responsibilities of the field engineers. Each floor is initially made with a hump, or camber, of a couple of centimetres in the middle. That way, when the concrete subsides under its own weight and that of the load it will eventually carry, the floor becomes level. Gorman checks to see how much it has already fallen. Later in the day, he will file all of the measurements he's made, as well as documentation about crane scheduling and concrete deliveries, in binders back in the trailer.

By 4:30 in the afternoon, Gorman has worked out how much concrete will be needed the next day, and at precisely what time. Finally sitting at his desk, he calls Dufferin Custom Concrete to place the order. He wipes the dust off the walkie-talkies and cellular phone and puts them into electrical chargers so they will be ready to be taken up to his high-rise station tomorrow.

Gorman is not the only one watching over the concrete movements. Developers themselves do a lot of studying to make sure materials and workmanship live up to expectations, and much of this concerns concrete. It must be strong enough, after all, to withstand the wind and external forces and the weight of office furniture, parked cars, restaurant equipment, elevators, electrical transformers and thousands of people that will fill the completed building. However, concrete is not necessarily a predictable, mass-produced material. It is made up batch by batch, hour by hour, the product of a chemical reaction that continues on a construction site open to the elements.

Builders are determined, with good reason, to achieve consistent quality in their concrete. To do this, the project's structural engineers specify the strength of the concrete for each part of the building. It is then mixed according to these instructions and rushed to the site in its freshest state. And even as it is being used to make floors and columns, it must pass the critical eye of John Salmon. His company, Trow Consulting Engineers, has been hired by Cadillac to maintain standards for the thousands of cubic metres of the material that make up the skeleton of the building.

The early-morning sky is bright and the air is moist, a promise of temperatures that will rise above freezing for the first time in weeks. While many construction workers are still in bed, Salmon is on the site, staking out an area near the gate where about seventy concrete trucks will arrive and unload their cargo through the day. A concrete crew joins him, the men grinning in appreciation of the ideal conditions for practising their craft. Then the first of the trucks arrives, and work begins on making one of the vast, half-metre-thick slabs that will cover the extended underground parking garage next to the main tower.

Salmon can be found at his post near the trucks, dressed in a green duffel coat, a toque pulled down over his red hair, whenever concrete comes to the site. The man has an eye for concrete. At forty-three, he has spent most of his life in the construction business, the last fifteen years inspecting concrete on sites from the Riyadh airport in Saudi Arabia to a nuclear generating station in eastern Ontario. He prepares for his work by laying out a set of tools and filling several buckets with water. He watches the concrete as it leaves a truck so he can judge its consistency, how it is handled by the crew and where it is going in the building. He performs a full formal test with every fifty cubic metres, or eight truckloads, of concrete. That means today's concrete will be tested once an hour for nine hours.

Salmon stands at the ready, his breath steaming warmly. He diverts a bit of concrete flowing down the chute at the back of a truck into a wide steel wheelbarrow and pushes it over to the area where he is working. He consults the ticket carried by the truck driver for the concrete's particulars. On a scrap of paper he notes the time the material was batched, or made up, at Dufferin. He also writes down the truck number, the concrete's strength and the exact place in the building where it is to be put.

Then he takes a thermometer with a disc dial on top—much like the instrument used to check the readiness of the Sunday roast—and plunges it into the concrete. Dufferin has already done its part to deal with chilly mornings by preheating two components of the concrete, the sand and the water. When they are added to cool gravel and cement, the mixture should stay at about twenty degrees, perfect for curing. Satisfied with the reading, Salmon removes the thermometer from the concrete, unceremoniously wipes it on the leg of his beige trousers and sticks it in his jacket pocket for the next test.

With a look of intense concentration in his cool blue eyes, he runs the back of a large aluminum scoop through the concrete in the wheelbarrow to see what kind of desirable air bubbles he might find. He next shakes a bit of it around in the scoop to see that it is well mixed, with no pockets of water or sand. He then determines these two factors more scientifically. Several scoopfuls of concrete are carefully poured into a metal cone. Salmon tamps down the concrete as if he were building a sand castle and then inverts it over a wooden board. What emerges when he lifts the cone is not a rigid castle rampart but a settling, or slump, of the material, showing it is holding together but is still moist. He then scoops more concrete into a large iron pot on which he clamps a lid, like a pressure cooker. This device compresses the concrete to determine what percentage is air. It should represent about 5 per cent of the concrete, enabling the finished product to expand and contract with the changing temperature.

By the time the sun has risen high above the surrounding buildings to warm the site, Salmon has looked at or tested twenty-three loads of concrete. His fair skin, reddened by the outdoors and the heavy work, is dotted with splashes of concrete. Though he wears a set of thick black rubber gloves—a gift from a friend who works in an auto-assembly plant—his hands are coated with a fine dusting of concrete. Periodically, Salmon wheels the concrete remaining in the wheelbarrow through the busy construction site and over to his 1972 Plymouth Volare, a beat-up boat of a car that acts as his mobile office, laboratory, closet and lunchroom. He pulls three large plastic cylinders out of the car and scoops the concrete into them, using the same careful tamping procedure as with the cone.

These cylinders will be used for long-range tests to make sure the concrete lives up to its potential. The number of containers he fills depends on the strength of the concrete being poured; more samples of high-strength concrete are required because they will be tested several times in the coming weeks to see that they set properly. The cylinders are covered with plastic bags to keep them from drying out and left in a wooden box at the edge of the site. The box is lined with Styrofoam and warmed with a lightbulb to keep the concrete from freezing, an ideal incubator for raising chickens.

After a day, the cylinders are picked up and taken to Trow's own laboratory, a large blue warehouse in an industrial park northwest of Toronto. While on-site testing gives a quick indication of the concrete's quality, here a more rigorous analysis can be done. Technicians test the concrete for up to ninety-one days to see whether it indeed meets the desired strength. Trow issues thousands of progress reports to keep the building's owners, as well as its team of designers and contractors, informed of the concrete's quality—and to alert them to any problems. Time is of the essence. The material they are testing is already part of the growing building. "Contractors can't pour concrete and worry about it for ninety-one days," says John Ryell, the technical director of concrete technology at Trow. "They have to sleep at night."

The testing procedure is set out by the Canadian Standards Association, the same organization that makes sure bicycle helmets stand up to tumbles, toaster plugs stay cool and gas barbecues don't blow up. The association's rules on concrete state how frequently the material must be tested and establish a process so that every laboratory does it the same way.

As soon as the cylinders of concrete arrive at Trow, the technicians look for early signs of trouble. How does the concrete look? Does it feel right? Do the samples meet a standard weight? The cylinders are then taken to the curing room, which is equipped with heaters and spray nozzles so the concrete can harden in ideal conditions of 23°C and 100-per-cent humidity. This is a considerable change from the frigid conditions lately on the site, but it ensures that all of the specimens get the same treatment.

Each sample is marked with the date on which it should be taken out of the curing room and crushed in a device called a compression-testing machine. The desired strength of the concrete ranges from thirty to eighty-five megapascals. The tests at Trow show that it usually ends up even stronger than that, allowing for a wide margin of safety.

The samples are handled in different ways according to their strength. Concrete that is intended to be thirty, thirty-five or forty megapascals is tested after seven and then twenty-eight days, at which time it should have reached its full strength. Stronger mixes are tested after seven, twenty-eight, fifty-six and ninety-one days. To measure strength, a sample cylinder is put between two metal plates in the compression testing machine; the bottom plate moves up and squeezes the cylinder until it shatters. The technician, wearing earmuffs to protect against the piercing sound, records the amount of force that was needed to break a cylinder. The shards of concrete are tossed into a bin to be recycled as landfill.

The testing goes on for weeks and even months, but the critical time is at the seven-day mark. At this point, the concrete should have reached 75 to 85 per cent of its potential, a good indication of whether it will harden completely. If the compression machine gives a poor result at this point, the technicians immediately call Grant Milligan to raise the alarm. If the concrete is not in a critical part of the building or is only slightly below the desired strength, the consultant may decide to take no action at all, but if a serious problem is acknowledged, the concrete may have to be removed with jackhammers or the structure reinforced by placing an extra column or beam nearby. Such a measure is expensive and time-consuming, but it could save costly maintenance and even lives in the future.

Working with concrete, stone, iron and wood makes most builders pretty down-to-earth people. No superstitions, rituals, voodoo or tales of the unexplained for this lot. Except in the practice of skipping the thirteenth floor. Consultants and contractors constantly have to remind themselves to avoid the unlucky floor when it comes to practicalities such as drawings and elevator controls. Not all designers or developers go along with this rule. Most of the no-nonsense government buildings in Ottawa, for instance, include a thirteenth floor, while most buildings in Toronto, including Simcoe Place, don't.

The discussion over a thirteenth floor can go on for weeks. It is usually decided by the building's owner or major tenant, who sometimes decides to drop the floor long after the plans to include it have been put in motion. "It all seems kind of ludicrous," says Brian Gardner. "Because don't the people on the fourteenth floor know that they're on the thirteenth floor?"

This kind of practicality usually prevails at the Simcoe Place site, but the strange behaviour of one of the giant tower cranes has left a few members of the structural crew spooked and the contractors worried. Without warning—and with no obvious electrical or mechanical fault—the crane would shut itself off, sometimes while hoisting a bucket filled with concrete. Two transmissions blew, their gears suffering when the emergency braking system suddenly jammed the bucket in mid-air. The crane had sputtered, only able to lift loads slowly, just a few metres off the top of the building.

Avenue, thrown off its plan to complete a floor a week, was perplexed. Had some kind of winch witchcraft or hoisting hex hit one of the most crucial pieces of equipment? The answer finally emerged when Emilio Patullo, the expert in the inner workings of the company's dozen cranes, huddled over the controls high atop the device. The crane was suffering not from black magic but from what could be called a twentieth-century disease: its electrical system was being attacked by an invisible shower of radio waves and microwaves, most likely from transmitters on the neighbouring CN Tower but perhaps from another nearby building. After weeks of head-scratching and endless discussions with electrical specialists, the cause was finally diagnosed: it was electromagnetic waves interfering with wiring on the crane's direct-current motors.

It's a new twist on an increasingly common and troubling problem. As wireless technologies that generate electromagnetic radiation flourish, the jumble of devices that transmit and collect the rogue waves they give off is causing concern for computer experts, airline pilots, robotics engineers—and now crane operators. "You learn a new one every day," says Tony Patullo, who admits to losing a few nights' sleep over the crane phenomenon. "Never in a million years did we think microwaves could be affecting us."

The answer came from a couple of workers on the site, who recalled similar interruptions in the running of two cranes involved in the recent construction of Scotia Plaza, a sixty-storey office tower

A building goes up:
the beginning of a foundation that will become Simcoe Place.

To go up you go down: hundreds of dumptrucks of soil and rock are removed from the site each day.

Concrete labours: Leo De Jesus opens the door at the base of the bucket to send concrete gushing downwards into a wall form.

The sidewalk superintendant: from peepholes in the hoarding a steady stream of people watch construction with a critical eye.

Al fresco:
lunch on the site.

Warming up: construction in winter means closing off areas below new
concrete with plastic sheets and firing up gas heaters.

The best laid plans: the site may look like happy chaos,
but nothing happens without forethought.

Hands-on management: Corrado Patullo (second from left) checks on the concrete operation.

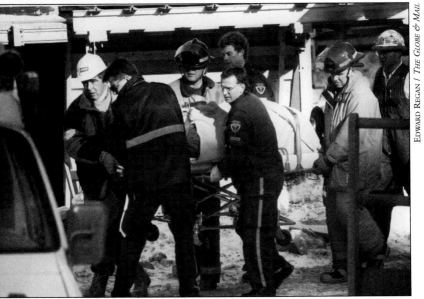

One false step: Corrado is loaded into an ambulance.

Half way up:
one year into construction, the building is on its way.

Corner offices: the design calls for sixteen corner offices on each floor, accomplished by the structural engineer by cantilevering the structure.

On the backs of labourers: formwork is continually set up and removed.

Close to the edge: curtain wall workers wear safety harnesses.

The model of a modern project: a scaled down version of Simcoe Place's corner entrance.

The real thing: the completed corner entrance.

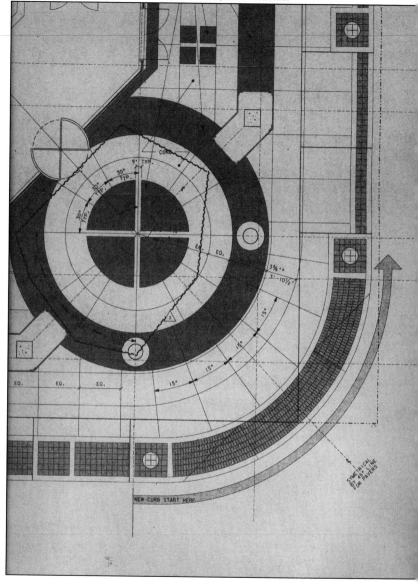

A section of the architectural drawings for the corner entrance.

The swamper:
Carvalho waits on the ground
for the concrete bucket.

In the trenches:
The shoring is removed and
the space surrounding the
building wall gets its fill.

Sky high: at its full height the crane takes five minutes to hoist
each load of concrete from the ground.

Zip it up: the last section of curtain wall goes up.

Topping off: The last buckets of concrete spring into place to complete the last floor of the structure

Oldsmobile styling:
chrome fins on the curtain wall, light fixtures and lobby
windows give the building an art deco look.

The building is up:
Simcoe Place claims its place on the skyline.

to the west. Those problems began, said a contractor who worked on that project, when the Scotia cranes climbed above a certain level. The symptoms and slow-downs were intermittent, apparently depending on whether the radio or microwaves were being transmitted or the cranes were in the right position to act as antennae. "You can imagine that when something like this happens, you don't immediately think of radio waves," Tony says. He thinks the Simcoe Place crane is similarly susceptible because it was recently fitted with a new direct-current motor and a low-power circuit board that runs at a frequency close to that of radio and microwaves. The other main tower crane, which has an alternating-current motor, is not affected.

The discovery called for a quick trip to a hardware store to buy a few metres of foam material coated with metal, the kind traditionally used to insulate ductwork. When this was wrapped around the case that houses the crane's controls, the problems disappeared. A more permanent shield was fashioned out of sheets of lead, which are used by drywall contractors to stop electromagnetic waves from penetrating the walls of computer rooms.

Protecting devices from electrical and magnetic fields has become an urgent quest in the age of wireless communications, says Emilie van Deventer, an assistant professor of electrical and computer engineering at the University of Toronto. There are lots of "intentional" transmitters and recipients of electrical waves, she says, such as radio and TV stations and police and fire emergency broadcasters, but there is also a growing list of "unintentional" sources and receivers of stray waves, including automobile ignitions, telephone lines, home stereo sets, computers and now cranes. Van Deventer says the goal of researchers—and of a new course she will soon offer—is to design such technologies so that they are compatible with each other. "Otherwise the problems are going to get worse and worse."

So add another item to the list of hazards associated with building tall buildings. Indeed, other trades at Simcoe Place have been troubled by electromagnetic interference as the structure has grown. Mike Daoust, the foreman for Antamex, the company making and installing the curtain wall, says the laser level device his crew uses to take precise measurements at the edge of the building has also been acting funny recently. The receiver that picks up the laser signal started beeping even when the laser was far off target or when the machine wasn't even switched on. Wrapping all but its tiny electronic eye with the aluminum foil that usually keeps sandwiches fresh in the workers' lunch-boxes seemed to solve the problem. Looking in the direction of his crew, high up the building, Daoust adds: "It kind of makes you wonder what the microwaves are doing to us up there."

THIRTEEN

THE INSIDE STORY

Anyone passing through the second storey of Simcoe Place could be excused for thinking that a small railway is being built there. Piles of rails, heavy steel wheels, cables, beams, sheet metal and motors that look like the carcasses of giant prehistoric animals cover most of the floor. The scene recalls a time when tracks covered much of the site. While it does owe a lot to the early days of rail, the technology here is considerably different. This is just part of the equipment that Dover Corporation will use to install twenty-two elevators throughout the building. Any thought that the elevator shaft would make an ideal opening for the tower crane is finally dispelled with an examination of the paraphernalia and process involved in installing elevators. Constructing, testing and inspecting them will take the better part of two years at a price of $6 million—6 per cent of the total cost of the building.

At last this sort of inside work can proceed, now that enough of the main structure has been built. Everywhere around the building, members of the all-important follow-on trades are on the job. On the lower floors that have yet to get their veil of curtain wall, the men can be spotted installing water pipes and air ducts, cascades of sparks pouring from their impatient welding torches. Small hoists, spools of cable and racks of tools locked at night in wooden boxes litter each level. An elevator crew from Dover arrived at the site at the beginning of last winter's deep freeze, when only a couple of underground floors had been built, to begin assembling the elevator materials. Now enough of the structure exists to allow for the first of the elevator shafts, and the machine rooms that will power them, to be put together.

The process is overseen by Dover's John Wordtmann and Pat Marley, who between them have spent sixty-three years sending people and goods up in the world. The elevators they will install were worked out by consultants for Cadillac Fairview and the Workers' Compensation Board. The group considered the flow of human traffic in the building, and weighed the speed and efficiency required of the elevators against their cost and the valuable space they will occupy. The task of hoisting people up the tower was divided into three banks of elevators, with greater speeds for those serving higher floors. Three low-rise cars travel between the ground floor and the building's podium, six mid-rise cars serve the ground to the fifteenth floor and eight high-rise cars will pick up at the ground and stop between the fifteenth and thirtieth floors. As well, separate elevators will serve the parking garage and the concourse, and a freight elevator will shuttle material between the third underground parking level and the highest penthouses.

Nothing characterizes modern architecture better than these banks of wood-and-mirror-panelled elevators whisking passengers to lofty corporate offices and suites. Once again, however, ancient Roman technology is at the heart of the modern-day lift. Vitruvius first described the practice of lifting loads by mechanical means in the first century B.C. Back then, platforms were hoisted by a system of pulleys and ropes using human, animal or water energy. By 1800, steam powered such vertical transportation, and later the hydraulic lift—a cylinder below the platform filled with high-pressure water—was introduced, sending the elevator car upward on a sturdy cushion of liquid.

Early elevators moved with the help of a heavy counterweight suspended from a hemp rope that extended from the top of the elevator car and over a pulley above, so power was needed only to raise whatever was inside. However, hemp could not be trusted for loads other than freight, so people opted for the stairs. Elisha Graves Otis, an American mechanic whose name is now forged on elevators around the world, made passenger lifts possible with his invention in 1853 of a safety clamp that would grip the rails on which the car was moving if the hoist rope failed.

His safety elevator, albeit improved over the past 140 years with electric motors, push-button service, power doors, automatic controls and solid-state computers, is still the standard in the industry. We rise and fall in either hydraulic or traction elevators, both of which are among Dover's inventory of lifts being installed at Simcoe Place. A visit to the company's headquarters and sixteen-storey test tower in Mississauga, just west of Toronto, is a quick lesson in the improvements on the Roman design.

Today's hydraulic lift is a descendant of water hydraulics, except that this version, dubbed the Oildraulic by Dover, rises and falls when high-pressure oil is pumped into or released from a cylinder below the elevator. The plunger that pushes the elevator up is almost identical to the hoist used by garage mechanics to lift cars and work on their undersides. Hydraulic elevators can only be installed in buildings that are about seven storeys or less, because room is needed below them for their long hydraulic cylinders. These are also the slowest elevators, reaching speeds of only sixty metres a minute, but they are considered simple and are much cheaper.

Traction elevators require a machine room to be built and outfitted two floors above their highest point, which can only be done once the main structure is finished. While costlier and more time-consuming to install, they climb much higher and faster. As their name implies, they perform much like the traction used to elevate broken limbs in hospitals, balancing a load with a counterweight. In most traction elevators, a cable runs between the car, up and over a pulley, called a drive-sheave, and down to a heavy weight. Both the car and the counterweight run up and down the elevator shaft, or hoistway, on guide rails. An electric motor controlled by a computer mounted in the machine room above operates the sheave to move the car, and slows down the elevator at the desired floor, which has been registered in the computer. Two types of motors run traction elevators. Geared machines use an alternating-current motor, which slowly turns the sheave through a series of gears, reaching a top speed of 120 metres a minute. Gearless machines run on direct current, a smoother and faster system affording a speed of 425 metres a minute or more.

Safety concerns have been raised about elevators since the early days of hemp, but special features stipulated in provincial codes help to allay such fears. The governor, a cable that runs alongside the car, applies a strong clamp or "safety" to the rails if the car picks up too much speed. No car can start unless the outer and inner doors are closed, and sensors stop the doors from closing on people or other obstacles. A counterweight equal to the weight of the car plus 40 per cent assists the motor. In the pit deep below the elevator, heavy spring and hydraulic buffers are installed to absorb the force of a car if it does fall, a common fear of elevator riders everywhere. Hemp is still used for flexibility, but it makes up only a fraction of the core of elevator cables, which are still known as ropes but get their strength from heavy bundles of twisted steel. Most elevators are suspended by six of these ropes, although with a capacity of ten tonnes, just one would do.

As the general contractor, Eastern is responsible for making the concrete shafts in which the elevators will run. Each is divided by steel beams, called trimmers, that support the vertical rails on which each elevator rises and falls. Then the Dover technicians take over. The first step in making a traction elevator is to install the steel bars and safety buffers in the pit at the base of the shaft. Next, the first two guide rails on which the elevator will travel are attached, and the technicians build a sling for the car itself in the middle of the shaft: steel beams made into a square (reminiscent of a picture frame) that will eventually hold the elevator car. A large steel platform bolted to the sling becomes the elevator floor, and the elevator is wired into the new machine room above. Hoist ropes are bolted to the sling and threaded up and over the drive-sheave in the machine room and then down to the counterweight, a series of steel plates stacked together on another set of rails at the side or back of the shaft.

The elevator is now ready to move, although in this condition it hoists only the Dover technicians until more rails are added to the space above and the sling is fitted with its finished car. Soon those for the parking garage and low-rise elevators are scheduled to arrive, brought to the site in sections and assembled in the shaft, along with the push-button controls and the lanterns, the lights that hang on the walls over the elevator doors to indicate which direction the car is travelling.

Wordtmann says the most time-consuming part of the process is adjusting the elevator to make sure it runs smoothly, "so your stomach doesn't stay down there," he says, pointing knowingly at the ground. There are also lengthy tests and approvals required from the province's Ministry of Consumer and Commercial Relations. The timing is especially critical when it comes to finishing the service elevator that runs from the parking garage to the highest penthouse. At the current rate of construction, the top of the structure won't be finished for months and months, and the machine room and equipment that control the elevator will take a while to put together after that.

Eastern, facing pressure to begin turning over some lower floors to the Workers' Compensation Board in the near future, would love to get the service elevator working as early as possible in order to transport materials. This is an important piece of the giant puzzle that must be solved to make the building. Once it is finished, the construction hoists running up the side of the structure can be dismantled and the curtain wall that has been left off the side of the building can be installed, closing off the floors so they can be finished and handed over to the WCB.

Only the service elevator will stop at the building's imposing but well-hidden podium mechanical floor. Almost twice the height of an average office level, this space has been slipped, incognito, between the building's fourth and fifth floors to house much of the equipment necessary for such a building to function. None of the elevators that eventually carry the public to the top of Simcoe Place will stop at the level or even mark its passing.

The mechanical floor might be well-nigh invisible, but anyone who looks carefully at the outside of most high-rise buildings will see tell-tale signs of such floors: louvres, for instance, that allow fresh air to come in and stale air to move out of the air units. Simcoe Place's mechanical consultants, Smith and Andersen Consulting Engineering, decided to put two such levels in this building, one in the podium to serve its first fifteen floors and the other in the three penthouse floors to provide air and other services up to the top. The engineers also designed an air-circulation system that mixes the air from the outside with that in the building. The Ontario Building Code requires that 15 per cent of the air in a building be fresh; in Simcoe Place, twice that much air will come from the outside, and it will be delivered separately floor by floor to ensure a proper distribution of invigorating oxygen. Many older buildings draw in the right proportion of fresh air but are not able to circulate it well.

Of course, not all outside air is desirable in a big city. The louvres are designed to admit air only on the north side of the building, where the atmosphere is less sullied by diesel fumes coming from the trains at Union Station and traffic exhaust from the Gardiner Expressway to the south. A giant fan that looks like an airplane propeller feeds the air-handling units, hulking machines like oversized heat-pumps that use copper coils cooled by three chillers high in the penthouse to reduce the temperature. The air is sent through galvanized-steel ducts to two air-handling units on each floor, which blend it with cooled, recirculating air.

Vince Robbins is the project manager for Sayers and Associates, the subcontractor responsible for installing all the mechanical systems, like so many nerves, veins and vital organs within the building's growing skeleton and skin. Right now, Robbins is busy overseeing a large mobile crane inflating the lungs—bringing a network of fans, pipes, electrical switches and air-conditioning units to the site.

With military planning, Robbins makes this system come together. Before he even connects fans to ducts, he has to get the material from the plant to the site and then up into the building. This is done in giant shipments—thirty-five fans, thirty-five air-handling units, three tractor-trailer loads of piping and five motor-control centres are delivered to the loading area in a single day. At such times, a mobile crane is brought in from B. W. Haggart Crane Service to hoist the cargo, leaving the tower cranes to work on the main structure.

Such intrusive activities are also scheduled for Mondays, the day in the building's tight five-day cycle set aside for moving flying-forms high above, so that the loading area on the ground is not crowded with shipments of reinforcing steel and concrete. Robbins's company is the largest subcontractor at Simcoe Place; its work on the air-conditioning, heating, plumbing, ventilation and fire-protection systems accounts for 15 to 20 per cent of the project's total cost. Most of the pipes and ducts are made by Sayers in a plant west of the city, but the mechanical bits and pieces come from more than a hundred suppliers.

Robbins not only coordinates when each of these components comes to the site but also schedules dozens of workers from five different trades—plumbers, steam-fitters, sprinkler-fitters, sheet-metal workers and people called controls who work with sensors and thermostats—to install them. Sayers was one of the first subcontractors on the site, installing drains in the bedrock when the excavation reached that point. The company will also be one of the most critical in finishing the building and conducting safety tests to show that Simcoe Place is ready to open.

Much of the work will go completely unnoticed by the building's tenants. Glance up at the ceiling of any modern building, for instance. There, in all likelihood, are metal posts like teardrops hanging down. Most people pay little attention to these automatic-sprinkler heads, but Gil Cadeau, who is in charge of installing the devices throughout Simcoe Place for Sayers, is devoted to them. "Each one of these is a little fireman," Cadeau says, looking up reverently at the sprinklers, which hang like Christmas ornaments over the future fast-food area in the underground concourse. "He doesn't take coffee breaks, and he'll sit there and guard your property and your life, too."

By the time the building is finished, more than ten thousand of Cadeau's sentinels will watch over the food court, as well as the offices, stores, corridors, storage lockers, mechanical rooms and parking areas in the complex. They are being installed by a crew of ten sprinkler-fitters who work for Life Safety Systems, a subsidiary of Sayers that specializes in fire equipment.

Although they are not universally admired fixtures of modern architecture, automatic sprinklers date back to 1874, when they were invented by an American, Henry Parmalee, to protect his piano factory. Fires in plants, warehouses and cotton mills were common and costly, and owners of such buildings quickly saw the value of installing Parmalee's new devices. They were rare in residential and commercial buildings until the 1940s and 1950s, when a series of spectacular blazes in nightclubs and hotels in U.S. cities claimed hundreds of lives. Noticing that sprinklers were doing a good job of looking after property, fire officials and insurance companies promoted them as a way of protecting human life. Sprinklers have since become a $300-million-a-year business in Canada.

Even though they are common, most people have no idea how they work, says Cadeau. His real-life explanations are undermined by action-film heroes (or comedians) who set off banks of the devices with a mere puff of cigarette smoke. In fact, automatic fire sprinklers react to heat, not smoke. Although tied into a vast network of high-pressure water pipes suspended from the concrete slab above, each sprinkler works independently. The water is held back by a cap, which is secured in place by either a small spot of metal solder or a glass tube filled with heat-sensitive liquid. When the temperature rises to what is known as the sprinkler's designated operating point, the solder melts or the liquid expands and breaks the glass, opening up the pipe. In most commercial and residential buildings, this operating point is 74°C, but sprinklers installed in hotter mechanical rooms, furnaces and kilns are designed to react to much higher temperatures.

Once the solder melts or the glass breaks, the cap pops off and a steady stream of water is released from the pipe at the rate of about twenty-five gallons a minute, becoming a spray as it hits the distinctive round piece of metal on the sprinkler known as the deflector. Meanwhile, a sensor installed in the sprinkler system, called a flow-detector, sounds an alarm and sends a message to a panel in the lobby, directing building security staff and fire-fighters to the particular area of the floor where the water is flowing.

The most common sprinkler head is the pendant type seen in many offices. In response to complaints from architectural aesthetes, they are now often recessed or covered over by a flat, colour-coordinated metal plate that pops off when the temperature rises, just short of the sprinkler's operating point. Two types of sprinkler systems are used at Simcoe Place. One is called wet, because water stands at the ready in the pipes leading up to the heads. This kind is ideal for warm offices, lobbies and retail areas. Dry sprinklers are used in cold areas, such as underground garages and unheated service corridors, where the water standing in the pipe might freeze and cause it to split.

Instead, the pipes here are filled with pressurized air, holding back the flow of water until excessive heat causes a sprinkler head to open.

The layout of the sprinklers at Simcoe Place was designed by the consultants at Smith and Andersen, who followed the guidelines of the National Fire Protection Association, found in the Ontario Building Code. Rules for the devices vary widely from province to province. Ontario does not require sprinklers in most residential buildings, but contractors in British Columbia must even install them in every new single-family home. Cadeau has installed a sprinkler system in his own basement and thinks they should be mandatory in houses, which are where the vast majority of fire deaths occur. "Everyone could use a few extra firemen," he says. When not proselytizing for the sprinkler, Cadeau divides his time between Simcoe Place's fifth floor, where the sprinkler-fitters are roughing in pipes, and the building's three underground parking levels, where the system is further ahead. Cadillac Fairview hopes to begin raising some revenue from the building soon by opening the garage for business, so the sprinklers on those levels must be ready first.

Sprinklers aren't the only fire deterrent. The other is the standpipe, the fire-hose that will eventually hang beside the office bulletin board or outside the building's washrooms. Many people, if they were honest, would admit to eyeing those hoses with the idea of aiming their tantalizing, white canvas coils at a wall of fire. Legs braced and arms steady, they would battle the blaze with a stream of water while their co-workers fled the licking flames and thick clouds of smoke. But unless they have the strength of several people, are trained as firefighters and come to work in fireproof coats and pants, boots, self-contained breathing apparatuses, helmets and visors, such hero daydreams should be kept on hold. The ubiquitous fire-hose cabinets in today's buildings are for professional use only. In fact, the 187 hoses being installed throughout Simcoe Place's offices, stores, lobbies, machine rooms and garages are much the same as the fire hydrants lining the sidewalks outside, waiting to bring water to the hands of fire-fighters. "The fire department doesn't want any heroes," says Bill Jamieson, the plumbing foreman on the site for Sayers.

Jamieson is installing the pipes that supply the building's washrooms and kitchens—known as its domestic supply—as well as its fire-fighting equipment. The two systems are distinct, separated when two twenty-centimetre steel pipes branch off from the municipal water main that runs along Front Street. The pipes come through an underground wall of the building into a corner of the concourse called the fire-pump room. There, the fire-fighting system is again divided: some of the water goes to the overhead sprinklers while the rest flows to the hose cabinets, known in the business as standpipes. Unlike the sprinkler system, which needs to be ready only when the building or part of it is formally occupied, the standpipes must be operational in case of a fire during construction. The plumbers' work lags just two floors behind the new structure.

Putting out a fire in a high-rise means delivering a steady supply of water with adequate volume and pressure to all floors. Water is provided to most levels of Simcoe Place by a large fire pump (with a second used as back-up) fixed to the floor in a room on the concourse level. It feeds water to four fifteen-centimetre steel pipes, called risers because they rise up the core of the building. The water constantly stands in the risers at a prescribed pressure, ranging from 270 pounds per square inch on the concourse, because it is much closer to the source, to sixty-seven pounds per square inch in the upper penthouse. When the pressure on any floor drops five pounds below the level it should be—indicating that a hose has been turned on—the pump automatically comes alive to feed the system.

In the parking levels, once again because of freezing, the pipes are filled with pressurized air. When a hose here is turned on, the drop in air pressure triggers the flow of water. On each of the huge parking levels there are ten fire-hose cabinets. The large podium floors at the base of the building have seven cabinets each, and the smaller tower floors have four. The design of the cabinets, their locations and the way the system functions were devised by Smith and Andersen with one eye on the rules of the Ontario Building Code and another on the requirements of Cadillac's insurance company. During Jamieson's thirty-four years in the business—thirty-two of them with Sayers—the fifty-three-year-old plumber has seen designs change considerably in the fire-safety field. When buildings grow above ninety metres, for instance, they require back-ups for fire pumps because city water pressure can't be counted on to send water higher than that. If both pumps at Simcoe Place fail, water can even drop down from the two 45,000-litre storage tanks in the penthouse. The fire department can also add water to the building through its Siamese connection, a two-headed pipe mounted on the wall outside the lobby, although the pressure will send the water up only as far as the twentieth floor.

Kim Dobson, a fire-prevention officer for the Toronto Fire Department's central district, says standpipes rarely fail unless there's a massive explosion, such as the bombing of New York's World Trade Center, which ruptured the skyscraper's main water supply. Dobson, whose office inspects fire systems and will eventually test the one at Simcoe Place, says the major problem with standpipes in older buildings is that they are hidden in the back of photocopy and coffee rooms. Having the hoses positioned prominently in hallways, especially close to stairwells, is critical for fire crews, he says. If there is a fire, the crews set up a command post near the stairwell on the floor below, where they pull the hose out of the cabinet, lay it out and turn it on—a routine known as charging. They carry it up the stairs to begin fighting the blaze and to help them reach the cabinets above.

Dobson doesn't recommend this for civilians, who can easily be knocked unconscious by a slapping high-pressure hose or overcome by the toxic brew from burning furniture, computers, paint and fabric. Amateurs can also make the fire worse by scattering burning debris with the high-pressure jet of water. "The best place to be in a fire," he says, "is across the street, watching it from a coffee shop."

On most nights it would appear that the entire city is burning, judging by the murky amber colour of the sky. It is lit by rows of street lamps, clusters of car headlights and towering buildings, where fully lit windows cast a fluorescent shimmer long past quitting time. For twenty-seven years, since he came to Canada from the town of Frosinone, just south of Rome, Domenico Petrilli has done his part to make the night sky brighter. He has installed lighting that ran for twenty-four hours a day on large, open-concept floors without a light switch in sight. Keeping the lights on permanently and paying for the use of hydro was cheaper for building owners than installing equipment to turn them off.

With electricity rates soaring and technology improving, today Petrilli, the electrical-system superintendent on the construction site, is trying to dim the contribution of newer office towers to the urban glow. In this wise high-rise, motion sensors, energy-saving light fixtures and a computerized low-voltage control system installed by his company, Plan Electric, will monitor the use of electricity. These cost-cutting controls form a part of the building's $11-million power-distribution system, designed by the electrical-engineering consultants at Mulvey and Banani International. Plan and its suppliers have devised a way to translate Mulvey's vision into a network that includes 160 kilometres of electrical conduits, 765 kilometres of wire and cable, 17,000 lighting fixtures and 35,000 light bulbs.

Plan Electric first arrived to install the temporary electrical system to power the site's first machinery. The company will stay to look after blown fuses, burnt-out bulbs and other problems covered by warranties that last for a year after the building opens. Currently the team of thirty electricians is scattered throughout the site, pulling wires through conduits that run through the finished concrete floors, replacing lightbulbs in the underground parking lot and planning the installation of outdoor light fixtures in the park still to be created next to the building.

Petrilli is a popular figure here. Every few minutes, his name crackles across the two-way radio in his side pocket. A walk through the site is constantly interrupted by contractors bringing up problems and project coordinators furiously waving schedules. Besides looking after day-to-day and moment-to-moment interventions concerned with the electricals, Petrilli must also schedule deliveries of equipment, such as a twelve-tonne emergency diesel generator that will soon be on its way by truck from Vancouver. It will come in three pieces so it can be more easily hoisted by the crane to the mechanical penthouse.

"There's a lot of headaches," Petrilli says gamely. He gets little respite when he retreats to Plan's tiny trailer, perched at the edge of the loading dock on the ground behind the building. It is full of material, instructions and equipment, from the nuts and bolts used to install electrical switches and panels to the building's large architectural drawings, hung sideways on a rack to conserve space. The drawings show every piece of electrical equipment, wire and conduit in the building, each numbered to correspond to a detailed diagram prepared by the manufacturer.

On the job, a colour code helps the electricians differentiate between the various components of the complex electrical network. Bright spray paint marks pipes, boxes and receptacles so the electricians know which part of the system they belong to. The colours are dictated by technical specifications for the building drawn up by Mulvey and Banani. Beyond the requisite red, used for all fire alarms and emergency back-ups, the colour scheme is largely at the consultant's whim. Black marks anything having to do with the public-address system, green is for the 120-volt service, the telephone system is coded in purple, the 600-volt service comes in blue and orange draws attention to security alarms.

The larger pieces of electrical equipment, such as transformers, switchboards and bus ducts, the copper-lined boxes that distribute electricity through the building, also have their own hues. In most buildings, such heavy equipment is usually painted battleship grey, but here the transformers are white, the 600-volt equipment is light blue, the 120-volt equipment is green, the emergency equipment is red and the telephone equipment comes in canary yellow. The colour coding has become Mulvey and Banani's trademark, invented in the sixties by company president Gerry Mulvey when he decided it was too depressing and stolid for electricians to work in a sea of grey. Mulvey and Banani's reputation among contractors for using unusual colours such as purple and yellow has earned it the nickname Mulberry and Banana.

Equipment painted in vivid colours costs more, Petrilli says, and has to be handled more carefully so the paint does not get marked. With grey, scratches don't show because the metal below is usually the same colour as the paint. Nonetheless, Petrilli believes the colours make the job more pleasant and help the people who work on the electrical system differentiate the devices more easily. No members of the public will ever see these splashes of colour in Simcoe Place's out-of-the-way electrical rooms, but at least they enhance the building's inner workings. "Don't let anyone tell you," Petrilli says in a wry tone, "that an electrician's life is dull."

With all of these mechanical and electrical components being delivered and installed, cloud watching continues to be a preoccupation for the builders. But the clouds that Robert Leonardelli sees are not stratus or cumulonimbus, they're drawn on blueprints stacked in the Eastern trailer and they indicate a change in building plans. Change matters to Leonardelli. As Eastern's project coordinator, he handles the subcontractors' billing for all the work laid out in the technical drawings and specifications that were prepared three years ago by Simcoe Place's consultants and the architects at NORR. Each of the subcontractors studied the documents, met with the consultants and then calculated how much every intricate detail would cost and how long it would take to do. This calculation eventually formed the final contract between Eastern and Cadillac Fairview.

But even the best-laid plans are altered, as every home renovator knows. You rethink the position of a microwave or the choice of floor tiles, and then the builder tells you how the adjustment affects the bottom line and the schedule. When the project is a thirty-storey tower involving hundreds of subcontractors and suppliers over two and a half years, changes can be disruptive. So when there are revisions, from adding an architectural flourish or reconfiguring a set of offices to changing the wattage of a lightbulb, Leonardelli has to establish the new order.

Often the process starts with an informal discussion with NORR, which is the developer's representative on the site, about how a change may affect the project's price and timing. A change that is not expected to cost more or take extra time, such as altering the colour of an exit door before it's been painted, is noted on a pink form called a supplementary instruction. Known as an SI, this clarifies points for the contractor or simply fine-tunes the plans. So far, one hundred SIs have been received by Eastern, and they're not always minor. For instance, SI 27 and SI 50, issued early in the project to deal with previous oversights in the construction plans, resulted in almost all the drawings being updated and reissued to incorporate new information. To make it easier for subcontractors to spot the desired refinements, NORR notes changes to the plans inside hand-drawn clouds, which look like the scallop-edged bubbles that show the thoughts of cartoon characters. Beside the cloud, a triangle with a number in it indicates where to look in the documentation for information about the change. When a plan is later updated, the changes are drawn in and the triangle is all that's left.

With all these revisions flying about, keeping track of the paperwork can be tricky. Eastern secretary Rosy Pereira wears another hat as an expediter, dispatching the forms to each trade involved in the work and collecting the responses. George Kotanidis helps by filing the information.

When an alteration involves a change in price—"though we don't want to nickel and dime over one hundred dollars on a $100-million job," Leonardelli says—NORR issues a yellow form called a contemplated change order, or CCO. This asks Eastern to price the change by consulting its subcontractors and indicate how the work may affect the schedule. Sometimes there is a request from NORR to "price and proceed," meaning the job should go ahead whatever the cost. But more often, the architect pauses to consider Eastern's estimate, challenging the price or revising wish-lists to reduce the cost. So far Eastern has received 160 CCOs. Fifty of them still need to be acted on by either Eastern or NORR, while the others have been formally processed. Such changes usually end up increasing the price of an entire contract by 5 to 10 per cent. Some change orders cost just a few thousand dollars, like installing wiring for pay telephones on the ground floor (CCO 135) or floor tiles with ventilation holes in computer rooms (CCO 114). The decision to go ahead with the work is easy. Others, such as CCO 20—redesigning the tunnel that runs under the road behind the building—have proved sticky. The original contract called for a relatively straightforward tunnel. But it became clear that a sewer that runs under the road had to be rerouted and the tunnel lengthened, a costly change that has led to thirteen months of delays. The inside story here has been one of haggling and negotiations between the builders and the owners.

FOURTEEN

THE FINISH LINE

Far below the steel and concrete workers who are making the building one floor taller each week, other crews are giving Simcoe Place its personality. These are the finishing subcontractors, hired to beautify the basic structure and the maze of mechanical and electrical intestines. Concrete, steel, pipes and wire may be at the heart of every modern building, but few of us want to be reminded of it.

It is hard to imagine anyone thinking about the finishes that will make the space habitable on a site that is still a jumble of construction workers and heavy machinery. The structure is half-way finished and has assumed its place on the skyline. Even so, the process of actually building it seems impossibly slow, despite summer weather that brings ideal conditions for curing concrete and erecting the curtain wall. However, once again, the ability to layer the different parts of the building process is critical, and already the mix of workers each day includes more of the finishing trades.

Stonemasons and marble-setters are turning the rough concrete walls of the lobby into a showpiece of marble and granite. They evoke a tradition that dates from the Industrial Revolution, when the vaulted entranceways of banking halls, public edifices and railway stations were built of sumptuous materials and richly decorated, projecting prosperity, grandeur, power and stability. Late twentieth-century austerity has intervened, though, making Simcoe Place's entrance less grand than intended. The three-storey-high ceiling originally called for in the plans, for instance, was scaled back when the Workers' Compensation Board said it would rather use some of the space as an extra floor of offices.

"That's the way it is with economics these days. Clients see lobbies as a waste of space," laments Alex Weick, site foreman for Gem Campbell Terrazzo and Tile, which is supplying and installing the lobby finishes. The company is already providing granite for the building's curtain wall, but here its role is more direct. In the lobby and on columns and decorative facings, the stone is applied one piece at a time in the old-fashioned way by stonemasons and marble-setters. Their palette includes Crema Marfil, the beige marble picked by the fortunate architects and consultants who went to Spain, as well as the black-and-grey granite from Vermont and Quebec used on the outside of the building.

The stone is applied to the concrete block walls that divide the lobby and separate it from the rest of the ground floor. Gem Campbell estimated the amount of material required to cover the walls and then calculated more precise field dimensions after the block walls were made. The stone panels each weigh fifty to eighty pounds and fit tightly together like a jigsaw puzzle to form a smooth, flat surface. There's nary a nail or screw in sight. One stonemason, assisted by a labourer, can install fifteen to twenty panels a day. He inserts several stainless-steel wires into holes drilled in the back of a panel, lifts it into place, then embeds the other end of the wire in a hole in the wall. Each panel is held in place by the wires, resting on the one below and hanging about ten centimetres away from the wall. The stonemason globs plaster of paris around the wire and on the middle of the panel; when it hardens, the plaster will stop the stone from falling off or being accidentally pushed towards the wall.

"It's a physical job, but you have to have a delicate touch," says Weick, who is thirty-two and, like many stonemasons, inherited the technique of lifting and securing the large pieces of stone from his father, Rolf. He worked summers at his father's side from the age of fifteen. Now sixty-four, Rolf still does the same work, overseeing the installation of stone facing at a new museum two kilometres up the road. The job is demanding, but there are advantages, such as work-ing inside a shaded and breezy lobby with the cool, smooth material as the weather heats up. However, Weick laments that he often has the misfortune of working inside in the summer and outside in the winter. He's hoping the curtain wall he will eventually install around the outside of Simcoe Place's lobby—known as the storefront because it consists mostly of glass and encloses the retail areas on the ground floor—arrives before the winds turn cold in the fall.

The lobby will occupy roughly a quarter of the ground floor, which also houses the building's day-care centre, retail shops, loading docks and two escalators that transport office workers and shoppers between the ground floor and the food court in the concourse below. Finishing the stonework in the area will take about nine months, the same amount of time it takes to build the concrete structure from the ground to the thirtieth floor.

A few levels up, the Pavic family is swiftly rendering more of the building's rough edges a distant memory. Vlado Pavic and his sons Tony and Nick are boardmen, three members of a team of carpenters who spend their days installing drywall in the building's core, machine rooms, bathrooms, hallways and stairwells. They work for Cesaroni Contracting, one of the project's largest finishing contractors, which is responsible for the interior walls, ceilings and window shades. Cesaroni's thirty carpenters and labourers will grow to fifty as their work spreads to more and more completed levels of the building.

The Pavics' job is not purely cosmetic. Their walls not only divide up each floor and cover up the concrete, but also muffle the sound that comes from machinery and can help stop fire from spreading between the floors of the high-rise. The miracle material that makes all this possible is gypsum, a mineral formed about 300 million years ago when the salt-water oceans that covered the earth began to recede. Technically known as hydrous calcium sulphate, gypsum is 50 per cent water by weight, which remains in crystal form but is released as water when the rock is heated to 100°C, making it naturally fire-resistant. The ancient Assyrians discovered that heating gypsum reduced it to powder. They added water to turn it back into its rock-like state and used it for sculptures, calling it alabaster. The Egyptians made it into plaster to line the walls of palaces and pyramids; the ancient Greeks named the mineral *gypsos*, hence its modern name. Today, gypsum is used widely for making moulds, is added as a filler to products that include Aspirin, toothpaste and white bread (labelled as the more appealing ingredient "calcium sulphate") and is used in surgical casts, blackboard chalk and, of course, on walls.

Gypsum used to be applied by hand as a plaster slurry—known as wetwall—but the pressure to construct barracks quickly during the Second World War led to the process of preforming the gypsum and water into drywall boards that could quickly be applied at a building site. The drywall here comes from CGC Inc., a building-products company that mines its gypsum at Hagersville, Ontario, a small town east of the city. The gypsum, a flat deposit just over a metre thick and thirty metres below the surface, is blasted out of the rock and then crushed and heated to remove its water. The resulting powder is combined with water and other additives, such as glass fibre for greater fire-resistance. This mixture is turned into boards several centimetres thick by squeezing it on a roller between two sheets of recycled paper. The final product is hardened in a kiln, then stacked and trucked to construction sites or home-fix-it stores. About 93,000 square metres of drywall will be used by Cesaroni here. Even more will be used by Simcoe Place's tenants to divide floors into offices, meeting rooms, coffee stations and libraries.

Putting drywall on top of concrete means first installing the galvanized steel tracks and studs that form the skeleton of walls, screwing the drywall boards to them, then smoothing and strengthening the joints between each of the boards to create a continuous surface that will last for many years. There is a price for aesthetics: the work is physical, noisy and dirty. First, the studs are held in place with power-actuated fasteners, otherwise known as guns because they use .22-calibre shells to shoot fastening pins through the steel and into the concrete. Tony Pavic's weapon of choice is a screw gun, a large drill that then drives a three-centimetre screw through each board and into the stud to a proper depth. The head of the screw must end up just below the surface of the drywall without ripping the paper. On a good day, Tony alone will drive in six thousand screws, fastening 370 square metres of drywall. Needless to say the work is repetitive. He sticks hockey tape on his left index finger to avoid paper cuts when he picks up the boards, which each weigh between twenty-seven and ninety kilograms, depending on their size and composition.

Vlado, fifty-two, was born in Croatia, moved to Germany, where he worked as a concrete former, and finally immigrated to Canada twenty-eight years ago. He got a job working with concrete, but a foreman suggested that with his tall, strong frame, he was ideal for handling large sheets of drywall, which was still a relatively new building material and was scorned by traditional plasterers. He does not necessarily want the trade to be picked up by his sons, but he realizes there is little else for them in the current economy. The youngest, Tony, twenty-three, dropped out of a college architectural program to work full time as a drywaller five years ago, although he still takes a night course in architecture. Nick, twenty-six, has three university degrees in arts and history, but joined his father and brother as a boardman last year because he couldn't find other work. The three drive to the site each morning at 7:30 from their home in the west end of Toronto, and spend much of the time until they leave at 3:45 working together and speaking in Croatian. Family harmony is maintained despite such proximity, Tony says, although "once every two or three weeks, there's going to be a blow-up."

One point of agreement among the Pavics—and most boardmen—is their respect for the workers who follow them, the tapers. They have one of the most delicate and messy jobs on the site, putting the finishing touches on the Pavics' walls in three steps using different types of drywall compound—a plaster-like material made of fillers and latex that is known in the trade as mud. First, it is spread with a trowel on the joints between the boards and a strip of drywall tape is pressed into it. After it has dried, another coat is added, which dries and then is sanded before a third and final coat is applied. The process ends with a light sanding, and the wall is left for the painters to beautify.

Richard Belanger and Jean-Guy Aube are carpenters who also work for Cesaroni on other finishing jobs in the building. Right now, they are looking up at the ceiling. It may not be the Sistine Chapel, but it evokes a sparkle of artistic pride in their eyes. "Not a bad job, eh?" Belanger asks his partner, squinting up at a seemingly endless grid of aluminum bars hanging above the third storey to make up a suspended ceiling. While associated with modern structures, these false ceilings were first put in Victorian offices for their acoustical qualities, necessitated by the increasing clatter of urban life and the newly introduced telephones and typewriters that intruded on the resonating spaces of a gentler era. Felt, cotton sheeting, oil cloth or the fibres of wood and sugar cane were found to be suitable ceiling materials. Tiles became more widely used in the 1930s and 1940s, as the International style of architecture turned away from ornamented finishes to simple, sleek materials.

These days, the ceilings in most buildings, from commercial complexes to basement rec-rooms, are mineral-board, a combination of mineral wool and starch baked dry in kilns. They make up what is known in the construction industry as a T-bar ceiling, for the inverted T shape of the aluminum rods that hold the tiles. They are hung from wires in the ceiling in a rectangular grid, with the wings of the Ts supporting the edges of the lightweight tiles.

A standard T-bar system and more permanent ceilings made of drywall (which will be found throughout most of the building's ground floor and its underground concourse) cost about the same, says David Hyde, Cesaroni's superintendent at Simcoe Place, but each has its own uses. Drywall appears more smooth and professional, but it takes more effort to install, reflects sound and blocks access to the services above. T-bar has a more broken look, but saves labour, absorbs noise and allows maintenance crews to get at sprinkler pipes and over-head wiring or to move ceiling features more readily.

"This is lighter material and it's easier work," says Belanger, who is from St-Georges, Quebec, and has spent twelve of his twenty years as a carpenter installing ceilings. He and Aube, from Bathurst, New Brunswick, happily discussing the day's news in their native French, can finish an entire level between them in just two weeks. They begin by drilling a series of holes in the concrete slab four metres above, using a drill mounted on a tall tripod. A small post with a ring on the bottom is hammered into each hole. Then a 1.5-metre-long wire is hung from each ring. The wires, or hangers, are spaced 1.5 metres apart; sixteen hundred of them are installed on each of the building's larger podium floors. The wires are bent, and the aluminum mould-ing is fixed to each of the walls at the level where the ceiling should be. Measurements must be precise; Belanger and Aube work with a laser level mounted on a tripod that looks like a large flashing light on top of a police car but sends out a fine, perfectly positioned beam of light as it turns. It is lined up with the top of the window, where the ceiling will meet the edge of the building. That level is then continually flashed on the walls and wires hanging in a large area, acting as the carpenters' guide.

Next comes the T-bar, which has been made to measure by a company in Winnipeg and shipped to Toronto by truck. Made of aluminum painted white and cut in lengths of one and a half and three metres, the bars snap together to form a rectangular pattern. Belanger and Aube put together a small section on the floor, then lift it up and tie it in place with the wires, adding more and more bars as they go along. The tiles, a CGC product like the drywall, are added next, the material cut to fit around any sprinkler heads, speakers and exit lights that hang below. The office lighting, made to fit into the T-bar grid, will come last.

The ceiling makes the third floor look more like an office, although it also reduces the overall height of the room by a third. Hyde, who has worked on ceilings in countless offices, public buildings and even cathedrals, says few people will be aware of Cesaroni's handiwork hanging overhead. He is not about to suggest that modern ceilings deserve the attention lavished on Michelangelo's artistry, but, he says, "I'm amazed at how much work gets done up there that no one notices." To compensate, he has become his trade's best popularizer. When he accompanies his wife to a public building where Cesaroni has installed the ceilings, he gives her a nudge and tells her to look up.

Looking down, there is more finishing being done in the building, this time not false ceilings but false floors. In most offices, the revolution in computing and telecommunications is obvious. The space under desks once left for feet is usually a tangle of wires and cables, or the wires travel discreetly to posts or walls where they climb to the ceiling and become intertwined with a nest of others. Just the thought of such confusion makes Glen Foden cringe. And with good reason: Foden works in cable management, making subfloors that conceal the wires while allowing movers and technicians easy access to them.

The technique for constructing this roadbed for the information highway paralleled the progress of computer technology, as huge mainframes gave way to the powerful personal computer. Computers first came to offices and manufacturing plants in the 1950s. Whole rooms were set aside to house these massive beasts, and only highly trained, white-coated technicians were admitted. It was difficult, though, for these experts to manoeuvre around the thick cables and wires that ran between the huge computers and connected them to the rest of the building. To keep the mess underfoot to a minimum, technicians took the rough wooden skids or pallets on which the computer equipment had been delivered and lined them up side by side, making a platform. Laid strategically on top of the cables and wires and then covered by rubber mats to render them more navigable, the pallets formed a continuous floor with a generous cavity underneath. When the equipment was moved or the wires needed to be worked on, the pallets could easily be lifted out of the way.

By the 1970s, companies such as Bell Canada developed in-house computer systems requiring less expertise. They issued more and more employees with increasingly powerful machines and accommodated the wiring with office-wide raised floors made of sturdy plywood and steel and covered in carpet. Seizing an opportunity, flooring manufacturers moved in, renamed the raised floors access floor systems and began offering them in a wide range of styles. With computing power shifting from mainframes to PCs, the floors were lowered to reflect the smaller cables.

Simcoe Place will be one of the largest office towers to have this kind of flooring throughout. The product was specially ordered by the Workers' Compensation Board to cope with the extensive databases used to keep doctors' letters, prescriptions and voluminous correspondence from lawyers and employers on its two hundred thousand injured clients. A team of twenty workers from Foden's company, Camino Systems, is installing $4 million worth of the flooring throughout the building's offices as well as in its computer rooms.

The floors are made up of large, square-shaped panels of concrete that are completely encased in steel. They rest on top of steel pedestals, which are fifteen centimetres high in office areas and forty-five centimetres high in computer rooms, where they must house extra cables as well as subfloor air-conditioners to cool the equipment. The pedestals are glued to the existing concrete floors and the panels are screwed to the pedestals. While the resulting floor can be taken apart easily, it has the feel of a continuous surface once carpet tiles are added.

Here the panels added to the controversy surrounding the Workers' Compensation Board headquarters. These are made by C-TEC Inc. in Grand Rapids, Michigan, which prompted a complaint from a member of Ontario's opposition Liberal Party, who favoured cheaper wooden-cored panels made locally. Foden says the U.S.-made panels were chosen because the concrete core makes them feel more stable. To satisfy demands for more Canadian content, sheets of steel and bags of cement are being trucked from Ontario to the plant in Grand Rapids to be turned into the panels.

For a flooring company like Camino, though, this controversy is minor compared with the troubling possibility that office computers and telephones will one day be connected by radio signals, eliminating the need to manage wires altogether. Foden remains optimistic about his business's future. Banks and stockbrokers, he says, will be nervous about sending information through the air, and wires will still be needed to plug in the fax machines, photocopiers and lamps that proliferate in offices.

Simcoe Place's finishes are under a lot of scrutiny these days. While work on the structure continues above, tests set up on lower floors give the project's architects, developers, subcontractors and future tenants a chance to imagine and study the final product. One group begins gathering at 6:00 in the evening, an unusual hour for a formal meeting on-site but a good time for a little shady business. Cranes sit idle, tools have been tucked away for the night and construction workers have repaired to watering holes or family supper tables. Talk of schedules and deadlines among the ten contractors, developers and designers is the only sound reverberating through the empty structure as the group makes its way to the twelfth floor. They pause in what will eventually be an office in the northwest corner of the building, now a wide expanse of concrete where a flood of evening summer sunlight pours in through newly installed windows. It is time for the test.

Watching as one shade at a time is pulled down to cover the glass, the group ponders the amount of light that each allows in and considers how well they can see through its material to the surrounding landscape. Within an hour, densely woven, medium-grey roller-shades are chosen, nipping out a grey-beige combination in the final tally.

The demonstration of the window shades—strategically timed and positioned to catch the sun at its most severe angle—was arranged by Solarfective Products, the company working for Cesaroni to supply about $500,000 worth of roller-shades and related hardware to the building. Covering the windows of a tower made almost entirely of glass and filled with light-sensitive computer screens is no small matter, but curtains, blinds and shades were once an afterthought. Now they are as much a part of basic construction as installing heating and air-conditioning.

Donald Patry, the sales and marketing agent for Solarfective, claims shade technology goes back to cave dwellers who first put animal skins over south-facing openings in simple homes. But most people associate roller-shades with the spring-loaded, white-vinyl variety that covered the windows at Grandmother's house. That material was slowly pulled from a roll at the top of the window by tugging on a bar across the bottom of the shade. Ratchets at the edge anchored the roll at a desired level. The shade was sent skyward—sometimes at a startling pace and with a loud noise—by a sharp tug that released the ratchets and activated the spring.

"Grandma wouldn't recognize the products we make," Patry says. Gently pulling a chain between his thumb and forefinger, he quickly veils a floor-to-ceiling window with a huge rectangle of material previously hidden in the ceiling. The shade is made of polyester thread coated in vinyl, woven into fabric and heated to bind it together. Different amounts of heat and light pass through according to its colour and the open space in its weave; even the tightest and darkest material recommended for offices admits enough light for people inside to work comfortably and see the surrounding world. "You haven't got the feeling that someone has put you in a dark room and thrown away the key," Patry says. Shades are more expensive than venetian blinds, but are easier on the eye, require little cleaning and allow office workers to make fine adjustments up or down, depending on how much glare and heat there is. A vent between the shade and the window ensures that cold, heat and condensation do not build up when the shade is down.

Since it started operating fourteen years ago, Solarfective has covered 150,000 windows in North America, Asia and the Middle East. Its products range from shades that black out the windows of computerized trading floors to the massive motorized window coverings at the all-glass National Gallery in Ottawa, which Patry says is the largest shading job in the world. The work at Simcoe Place is much less challenging, but still requires custom design: Solarfective developed a special aluminum bracket to fit the oversized windows in the building. Installation of the brackets will start soon; the winning grey roller-shades and their chains will come just before the building opens.

Mention of interior design brings to mind the image of an overexcited consultant laden with fabric swatches leaping about a room gesturing madly at drab walls and insisting on "splashes of colour." It's an image the people at the interior-design firm of Rice Brydone try hard to dispel. Claire Lavoie, a project manager for the company, says only one-tenth of interior-design work actually involves finishing flourishes and furniture-arranging. The other 90 per cent is the project's master plan, known in the bureaucratic design business as facilities management and project management. This means drawing up schedules, budgets and strategies to make the best use of space, getting the work done and moving three thousand people into the new headquarters of the Workers' Compensation Board at Simcoe Place.

It's a huge job, but that does not deter Lavoie, an architect by training with a taste for long, tailored suits, her dark brown hair dramatically sculpted into points that end below her ears. The project has occupied the better part of Lavoie's time for the last four years. Interior-design lingo reduces the completed thirty-storey structure Eastern is now creating to the base building, a mere shell equipped with ceilings, lights, sprinklers, mechanical systems and basic finishes that requires "tenant improvement work" before anyone can move in. At Simcoe Place, this started when the WCB eyed the first twenty-one floors of the building as a possible new home but noticed a few nips and tucks it could make in the original plans. Rice Brydone was hired to incorporate the WCB's needs into the vision of the building's architects at NORR Partnership.

Lavoie says such build-to-suit work is becoming more popular as developers look for tenants before they put up structures costing hundreds of millions of dollars. As plans for Simcoe Place evolved, Rice Brydone put its stamp on everything from the number of elevators and washrooms in the podium to the exact places where holes will be left in the concrete floors for the coffee machines. The major demands included shrinking the lobby and adding a third large podium floor at the base of the building to house the units that deal directly with the injured workers who will come to the building. An extra bank of low-rise elevators and other services such as washrooms will accommodate the visitors. A large revolving front door will provide access for handicapped people, and there will be an information desk and public-service centre to hand out information in a separate WCB portion of the lobby. Each floor will have service centres for mail, supplies and photocopying, and "hub-rooms" for computer equipment. The WCB changes also included the special flooring to hide the cables for its extensive computer systems and telephone equipment.

Rice Brydone's contract with the WCB stretches to four and a half years, almost two of them conducting studies, defining needs and sketching out a master plan, another year deciding fine details, nine months drafting specifications and working drawings, and a final year supervising construction and moving people in. To mark the third anniversary of the job, Lavoie brought a box of muffins to the regular tenant-coordination meeting. The celebration lasted five minutes, then attention quickly turned to white boards and drawings that spell out how to turn Simcoe Place into a home for WCB workers.

The consultation has been endless. Rice Brydone has studied the best type of ceilings, floors, lighting, window shades, partition walls, sprinkler systems and elevators for the offices. Issues range from how the workers will heat their lunches, distribute mail and walk the corridors to the management of traffic in the freight elevator. "Everything's a strategy," says Lavoie, who attends at least one and as many as four meetings a day. One of her company's biggest tasks directly involving the WCB is to evaluate, count and move most of the organization's furniture to the new offices. Four of her people are currently in the middle of the four-month process of sticking bar-code tags on each chair, desk, bulletin board and bookshelf, and recording the corresponding numbers and descriptions in hand-held computers. Lavoie expects that once the bits and pieces are counted, there will be somewhere between 60,000 and 100,000 items in a master coding system; 80 per cent will make the trip to the new head-quarters, while furniture that is tattered or ergonomically incorrect will be disposed of.

The main preoccupation for the designers at the moment is laying out each of the building's floors on paper. Your mother may have told you not to fill your plate, but Rice Brydone has followed no such advice when it comes to fitting workers, computers, telephones, files, meeting rooms, potted plants and coat closets onto Simcoe Place's floorplates, the term that designers and architects use for the surface area of the building's floors. Working with a blank slate of 48,825 square metres on nineteen levels, Rice Brydone is spending long hours trying to match needs with space.

The floors come in two sizes—the larger ones in the podium of the building and the narrower ones in the tower, from the fifth floor up. Figuring out their area is not as simple as taking out a measuring tape and multiplying width by length; in fact, it depends a lot on who's doing the figuring. The architect measures from the outside of the windows through the building core. In Simcoe Place's tower floors, this "gross" floor space amounts to 2,500 square metres. The developer, meanwhile, is concerned about "rentable" space, measuring from the inside of the windows and subtracting features such as the columns and the elevator and stairwell shafts, known as penetrations. This shaves off 7 to 10 per cent of the gross area. Interior designers then calculate "usable" space, eliminating mechanical and electrical rooms, toilets and the lobbies in front of the elevators, finally reducing each of Simcoe Place's tower floors to just 2,120 square metres.

The challenge is to allocate the space on each floor for three different uses. Offices will occupy 70 per cent of it, but 20 per cent will be common areas for conferences, computer rooms, photocopy nooks, reception areas and coat closets, which are shared by the entire organization and duplicated on each floor. Another 10 per cent will be special areas dotted throughout the building, including libraries, staff lounges and computer centres.

Rice Brydone had to plan these special and common areas in advance so the contractors could make the necessary structural, mechanical and electrical adjustments to the building: adding reinforcing steel to hold up weighty library books, for example, or bringing pipes to the sinks in lunch rooms. The rest of the space—the office area—does not affect the structure of the building, but is strongly influenced by the structure of the company. Determining where three thousand employees will sit requires foresight, diplomacy and design principles known as stacking and blocking.

In stacking the building—slotting the entire organization floor by floor—designers figure out how close departments need to be to each other and to these lowest levels where the public will come. As a result of the designer's calculations, 140 employees on average will work on the tower floors and three hundred will work on the larger podium floors. The WCB's upper levels, from the tenth to the twenty-first floors, with their sweeping views of Lake Ontario and the Toronto Islands, are not reserved, as you might think, solely for those with clout, but instead are meant for employees who don't have to meet with members of the public, for instance, those in the information-services and human-resources departments. The WCB's staff has been strictly divided into five categories to determine their so-called space standards, the furniture they will get and whether they need a closed office made with what are called relocatable walls or a simple open workstation. Most managers, directors and senior executives will work in offices that range from 9.3 to 21 square metres according to their rank, while clerks and administrators will get workstations that are 5 to 7.5 metres square.

Once the vertical distribution has been sorted out, each floorplate is blocked horizontally, a process overseen by directors or administrative assistants in each department. They make sure that workers with similar functions sit together and that room is left for filing cabinets, shared computer terminals and the like. In deciding who goes where, the designers keep in mind building-code requirements (the distance to fire stairs, for example) and the needs of people with disabilities—especially important for an organization that caters to injured workers. To let in as much light as possible, the WCB has decided to put many of the managers' walled offices in the centre of the floor, giving clerks and administrators, in their open-concept areas, more of the enviable window space. This nod to the board's egalitarian principles is ironic, given that the building was originally designed to maximize the number of exclusive corner offices.

The blocking of Simcoe Place is just about finished. Next, Rice Brydone turns to finalizing the details and producing the working drawings of the floorplates. A team of twelve people from Lavoie's office is now at work, as final decisions on design are made and a team of drafters begins to draw up the project's detailed plans and specifications. These will be given to a contractor, Jackson-Lewis Co., which will soon begin overseeing the construction work inside the building, as Eastern completes its own finishing work and hands over the building bit by bit.

FIFTEEN

GOING DOWN

Parks and plazas put the greenery in our concrete jungle and attempt to give the rows of skyscrapers that dominate cities a more natural look. But Joe Porciello knows the secret of their inner workings: these outposts of nature are really miracles of modern technology. Porciello has the job of protecting Simcoe Place's underground shopping concourse and garage from the park that will take shape above. The concrete structure is finally finished, long after the same levels were completed underneath the main building. A crew has dismantled the orange luffing-boom crane at the park end, its job of marshalling the concrete and steel for the giant space finally over. Part of the roof of the garage has been turned into a driveway and loading dock to bring materials to the construction hoists fixed to the west flank of the structure. The builders can now turn their attention to creating the park itself.

Work on the 4,700-square-metre area—which bears the name Simcoe Place Park on construction drawings, pending a more creative title—is split several ways. The entire space is designed by Moorhead Associates, a firm of landscape architects. The greenery, statuary, lighting and park benches above are a job for landscaping contractor Bruce S. Evans. And Porciello's company, C. A. Tedesco Waterproofing, looks after the sealing and drainage below.

Long before the topsoil, grass, trees, fountains and benches are delivered to the site, Porciello must ensure that moisture will not migrate from the tree roots in the park to a doughnut shop or souvlaki stand in the food court down below. To achieve this, he and his fellow waterproofers must tie the park into the city's storm sewers and seal the half-metre-thick concrete slab above the concourse, making it act as a huge drainage basin. "The water is not going to go through the slab, I can guarantee that," says Porciello, whose confidence is based on thirty years of sealing underground garages, concourses and tunnels.

Porciello helps create the seal by layering nine different materials on top of the uppermost concrete slab. Each component plays an important role on its own; combined, they form a flexible membrane that should keep the area down below dry for fifty years or more. The first, sprayed directly on the concrete, is a thin coating of sticky asphalt that acts as a primer. Then comes a product commercially known as Hydrotech 6125, a gooey black mixture of rubber, asphalt, oil and plastic that stays soft after it dries. It comes in what are called cakes, oversized hockey pucks that are turned into liquid in a portable steel kettle heated by oil burning at three hundred degrees. The steaming, pungent Hydrotech is poured from a tap at the base of the kettle into plastic buckets and spread with long-handled squeegees on the site by four men sweating profusely under the late-summer sun. For extra strength, two layers of the material are applied, separated by a sheet of fabric.

Next comes another sheet of plastic, followed by a layer of drainage mat, which looks something like the Miracle Car Mat advertised on late-night TV, with bumps and grooves that channel slush away from a driver's trouser cuffs. The construction variety fulfils much the same function, except that it has a layer of fine mesh on top to keep silt from plugging up the grooves and to help channel the water to drains around the site. The next layer is a sheet of blue styrofoam insulation, known as a thermal barrier because it not only keeps the lunchtime crowd warm in the concourse below but also stops the heat from migrating up to the greenery that will be planted above. If the tree roots were subject to constant heat, they would dry out in the summer and forget to shut down in the winter. The waterproofers top off their seal with a fine filter cloth to keep out silt, and then fifteen centimetres of gravel, which provides drainage for the landscaping above and protects the membrane below.

Before pliable materials such as Hydrotech were invented, waterproofers used tar and asphalt to form membranes, but they tended to harden and crack over time. The earliest underground concourses, those built in the 1960s, failed and have had to be dug up and resealed. Porciello practises a hidden art. The people who bask in the park or browse in the shops below will be oblivious to his handiwork. "To be honest, I don't care," he says. "If it starts leaking, then people are going to notice it. I don't want that."

Margaret Rankin has an idyllic picture in mind of the park that will take shape on top of Porciello's work. It looks something like this: Lunch hour has not yet begun, but people are already perched on the wall, a low outcropping of polished granite backed with a mound of lush grass and warmed by the late-morning sun. They smoke, sip cappuccino, talk over last night's ballgame and pore over newspapers, oblivious to the bustle of the city around them. All of this, though, is still fantasy. The granite reposes in a quarry in Finland, the lawn is but grass seeds waiting to sprout at a sod farm and the wall is only a squiggle on the large sheet of paper laid out on her drafting table. Yet the landscape architect at Moorhead Associates is confident the park will become a refuge for office workers, theatre-goers and passers-by.

The park is one of Cadillac Fairview's obligations to the city under the Planning Act, demanded in exchange for the development rights to the prime downtown block. Two years after it is finished, the $1.6-million landscape project will be turned over to the city's Parks and Recreation Department for the token price of two dollars (not one dollar; even nominal fees have been hit by inflation). As the future owner, the city, as well as the developer and the site's neighbours, had a hand in the park concept drawn up five years ago by Steven Moorhead, the company's chief. Rankin is responsible for choosing the materials and methods that will give life to Moorhead's vision.

The word landscape conjures up images of lush, ordered greenery, but plants, trees and soil—known in the business as softscape—cover only a third of most urban parks. The rest is called hardscape—pavement, lighting, planters, walls, fountains and furniture, as well as services buried deep beneath the ground. Green spaces in the downtown core are scarce, and this one must play a dual role, giving idlers a place to sit, eat, lie in the sun and listen to live music on occasion, while also serving as a passageway for people making their way among the surrounding corporate towers and public buildings. Such heavy traffic can reduce grass to an ugly maze of dirt paths. To steer the flow away from the greenery, Simcoe Place Park features a central mound of grass, edged in trees, shrubs and perennials and circled by the low wall of Finnish granite. Curved in a stylized semicircle, it looks from above and on architectural drawings like the outline of a human ear, and in fact has been nicknamed "the ear" by the construction workers on the site who are watching it take shape.

So far, this urban retreat is more grey than green. All you can see is the vast roof of the parking garage, getting its topping of waterproofing, and huge boxes of concrete, referred to by the workers as dog-houses, that will act as foundations for heavy items such as the granite walls. Designing a park means thinking of more than just perennials and pedestrian flow. The plan, for instance, calls for a planter in one corner of the park to disguise a vent that will supply air to the parking garage below. In another corner rises a fountain in the shape of a pyramid, part of a memorial to John Graves Simcoe, entitled *Campsite Founding*, meant to represent the first lieutenant-governor's encampment. Concrete paving stones edged with granite, which cover most of the park, are interrupted at one point by a stage for outdoor performances.

Trees and shrubs will decorate the park, including tried-and-true city varieties such as maples and ash, as well as the more exotic cork, katsura and hackberry. In the next few weeks, Rankin will slather No. 30 sunblock on her fair, freckled skin, pull a sun hat over her red hair and head out to local nurseries with representatives of the landscaping contractor, the developer and the city to inspect and select the trees.

Supervising the landscaping contractor at Simcoe Place keeps her busy, but Rankin is also applying her talents to planning and planting at three suburban malls in southern Ontario, a minor-league baseball stadium in Erie, Pennsylvania, and a retirement community near Ocala, Florida. But it is the chance to work on an empty plot of land in the middle of Canada's largest city that she says is the culmination of her career so far. At thirty-seven, she has had a wide variety of work, including a three-year job (with a $2-million budget) installing flags and banners at the Expo 86 site in Vancouver. There, her pride was short-lived: her work was torn down when the fair ended.

The landscaper who will turn her plans at Simcoe Place into reality is Bruce Evans. Evans once worked summers in the family landscape-gardening business, a task that would be pure drudgery for most thirteen-year-old boys. But now he looks back on the experience fondly—and with good reason. He's parlayed the planting and mulching techniques he learned fifty years ago at his father's side into an international business that has constructed golf courses, resorts, zoos, theme parks and family-entertainment centres, along with Simcoe Place Park.

Evans learned about soil, sod and stonework as a teenager, then earned a degree in physical and health education from the University of Toronto. In 1954, while in his last year of university, he started a landscaping company specializing in recreational facilities with his two brothers, Bob and Gordon, who have since branched off into their own contracting firms. The company's first big venture was at Expo 67 in Montreal, where it developed Île la Ronde, the fair's giant amusement park, to wide acclaim. Since then, Bruce S. Evans Ltd. has blossomed into a group of companies with more than 750 employees involved in large-scale urban landscaping, golf courses and amusement areas from Universal Studios in Florida to the MGM Grand Theme Park in Las Vegas.

Working on a one-acre refuge of green and granite in downtown Toronto is a return to the company's roots—"shaping the earth," Evans says. No longer restricted to gardening, landscapers today act as general contractors, hiring subcontractors to install concrete foundations, lights, fixtures, irrigation pipes and fountains. On most projects, Evans's company is responsible for everything but the buildings—what he dismisses as "the vertical stuff."

The landscaping these days at Simcoe Place is emphatically horizontal, and it is very heavy work. Taking over from the waterproofers in adding layers of material in preparation for the greenery, eight men from Evans's firm have begun filling in the area below the street level with a mixture of sand and stone, known in the industry as Granular B, and topping it with pure stone, a firmer mixture called Granular

A. The material, which will eventually be one and a half metres deep, is spread in layers and then tamped down with a compactor, a machine equipped with either a vibrating drum or pad. Compacting will prevent it from settling later on and causing concrete paving stones to crack or lawns and gardens to sink. The landscaper's keen interest in keeping the park and plaza stable is not just a point of pride; the company is responsible for any problems for two years after the park is created, until it officially becomes the property of Toronto's parks department. Keeping the trees, shrubs and grass healthy during this period is a cause for concern amid the drought, pollution and human traffic of the concrete city.

To keep the plantings healthy, Evans will create beds for shrubs and flowers with about half a metre of planting mix and topsoil, and will lay down fifteen centimetres of topsoil for the grass. Trees (the large ones have root balls of just under a metre in diameter) are treated to topsoil mixed in with the Granular B for drainage below and a diet of potting mix around their roots. Tree roots have been known to disturb underground city services or delicate fixtures, such as the careful layers of waterproofing on the concrete below, so landscapers and designers stay away from those with large tap roots, such as poplars and some varieties of oak. Even roots a few centimetres below the surface can become tangled in wires and pipes. Sensitive underground services are protected by root-guards, thick sheets of plastic that deflect the roots.

The seventy trees at Simcoe Place make the project small in comparison with the extravagant theme parks Evans's company has created in Las Vegas and Orlando, where budgets rise to $15 million or $16 million, but he enjoys the return to his landscaping background. Now sixty-two, he's hard at work managing the business, but he spends some of his summer days at the lakeside resort and golf course that he built near Bracebridge, a town in the heart of Ontario's cottage country where he moved the company's head office several years ago. When he's on the lake, he knows his company is in good hands: those of his own five children.

Meanwhile, deep in Toronto's underground, next to a food stand that serves juice from a giant plastic orange, the talk has turned to golf.

Dark clouds have deposited dismal autumn rain on the city for the better part of two days, but the patrons don't seem to care. "Have you heard that Bob Hope has a twelve handicap?" one man asks another as he scans his datebook to check the tee-off time for a weekend game, weather permitting. Oblivious to the wind and showers playing havoc with hair and umbrellas on the street above, the two sip juice and relax in a space that's always dry and warm. Around them, a stream of people dressed in office finery, their heels clicking on granite and marble tiles, stroll past food outlets that smell of pizza, buttered popcorn and roasting espresso beans.

This is one block in Toronto's sub-ground neighbourhood, the commercial catacombs stretching ten kilometres below the downtown streets. Next year, Simcoe Place will officially join the network, but it is already incorporated into the maps and signs that help pedestrians negotiate this winding underground refuge. The origins of the climate-controlled route date back more than four decades, when the city's first subway was built and the skyscrapers that today cover much of the downtown core were still grand schemes in architects' imaginations. Municipal planners, concerned about crowded streets and sidewalks and all too familiar with the bitterness of Toronto winters, proposed walkways linking the basements of each future development with train and subway stations. Developers, meanwhile, envisioned underground shopping malls that offered a whole new level of retail space to lease. The idea took root, and now twenty-seven tunnels and three overhead bridges link forty-eight office towers as well as hotels, theatres, cultural centres, transit stations and shops, one of the largest underground shopping areas in the world.

This week, work began on a new tunnel between the Simcoe Place site and the rest of the network to the north. For Cadillac Fairview, the tunnel connection to a food court in neighbouring Metro Hall is important: it makes Simcoe Place more valuable to retailers, because of the increased pedestrian flow, and more attractive to prospective office tenants, who want easy access to the subway and nearby buildings. Unfortunately, the staggered development of Simcoe Place—one phase now, a second building if and when the real-estate market improves—has caused a glitch. The concourse of the second building, completion date unknown, has been designed as the link to the under-ground network. So for now, the junction point is the edge of a park-ing lot abutting Wellington Street behind Simcoe Place.

This interim compromise extends the underground system south towards Simcoe Place only as far as an elevator and a flight of stairs that emerge at the edge of the parking lot behind the building. From there, pedestrians will enter an enclosed, heated walkway for the rest of the trip to Simcoe Place. Constructing the $2-million tunnel under the road is expected to take seven to nine months and requires a hole to be dug seven metres deep, five metres wide and twenty-seven metres long. Work is beginning late; Eastern spent more time than it would have liked settling the designs and costs with the developer, securing approvals from the city and coming up with plans to accom-modate the road and the services that run above the tunnel.

The two companies that long ago shored up the ground around the construction site with steel and wood and dug the huge hole for the building are making a return visit to open space for the tunnel. To be sure that their drills and pile-drivers avoid the tangle of pipes and conduits carrying vital services under the road, engineers and repre-sentatives of the utility companies spent the last few months making rough maps of the underground. This week, workers from Alsi Contracting, which specializes in locating and protecting services during such construction, made a series of holes in the road and side-walk to expose the pipes and conduits so site engineers could make note of the precise locations.

The intelligence will be passed along to consultants for Anchor Shoring and Caissons, which plans to drill holes for structural steel soldier piles in the next couple of weeks. As they did around the larger construction site, the piles, combined with planks of wood, will act as temporary walls for the excavation team from Rumble Contracting, which will start by digging the deep shaft for the eleva-tor and stairs. When it is time to take the tunnel across to Metro Hall, Alsi will open up the road and lay down a steel deck that supports the cars driving over it while it holds the services below on slings. That way, the area around and beneath the pipes and wires can be safely dug out and work can proceed on just one half of the street at a time, complying with the strict terms of the street-occupancy permit granted by the city.

The scene is considerably different about one hundred metres to the south. Simcoe Place's garage is nearing completion. Powerful lights shine on bright surfaces. Huge fans are in place to circulate fresh air. Large signs are being prepared to help lost souls find their way about. Above ground, the final touches are being applied to the equipment that will efficiently move 750 cars and their drivers in and out of the three-storey structure.

Cadillac is in the last stages of selecting a company to take over the running of the garage and plans to open it early, about the time the last bit of concrete is placed on the building's roof high above. In the mean-time, Eastern has to make sure the garage's electrical system, fire alarm, sprinklers and fire-fighting equipment are up and operating—and have been inspected by the proper authorities. They also have to ensure the garage's concrete floors are secure from the salt water that will inevitably drip off cars once winter sets in. Already the steel is coated with the protective epoxy, but for extra insurance a crew from Vulcan Asphalt and Supply has spent ten weeks coating the concrete slab with layers of asphalt, rubber, glass fibre and a rock-hard mixture of asphalt, lime-stone and concrete sand known in the business as mastic. Next week, Vulcan will put the last coat on the garage's entrance ramp, which runs off Front Street to the south of the building.

For the parking garage to open, it will also be necessary to switch on Simcoe Place's permanent electrical supply, the large transform-ers and other gear in the main electrical room on the building's concourse level. Until now, electricity has come from the site's tempo-rary supply, which was hooked up to power the construction equip-ment more than a year ago. Back then, there wasn't a great need for much power; bare lightbulbs caged in strong plastic guards and strung along the garage ceiling were good enough for contractors to do their work. But the permanent power must be running before the building can be occupied, since Toronto's by-laws stipulate that park-ing garages have an intensity of light—five candles per square foot, in lighting's technical terms—that is about twice as strong as the temporary lights could provide.

The electrical service will power not only the new fluorescent lights that have been installed throughout the garage but also the fire alarms, emergency speakers, ticket-spitters, gates, and cash registers and booths to collect money when the cars leave. Power has also been connected to fifteen giant fans that will automatically draw fresh air through the garage when electronic sensors mounted on support columns detect high levels of carbon monoxide. Electricians are also working on the garage's new crisis-alert management system. This is the fancy name for a series of panic buttons spread throughout the parking area that set off alarms and allow people to communicate through microphones with the building's security office. It will not be functional until the office tower opens and Cadillac's security people are in place.

To minimize the confusion that seems to be a part of underground parking, 109 extra-large, extra-clear lighted signs are being made by Provincial Sign Service in Ajax, east of Toronto. The signs, with aluminum bases that hold fluorescent bulbs and are covered in coloured Plexiglas, will be installed by a crew of six men. They will be almost the only show of colour in the sea of white paint covering the walls and ceilings. Such startling whiteness, a requirement of Toronto's parking-lot by-law, not only makes the dingy space look clean and lively but also intensifies the brilliance of the lights.

The painting of the parking lines on the asphalt will be left until the last minute, to ensure it looks as clean as possible when Eastern turns the garage over to Cadillac. Eastern's last job involving the garage will be to make sure the people who park below can walk in and out safely while the construction project is still active above. Temporary corridors fashioned out of steel scaffolding, topped with wooden planks and sided with orange plastic snow fencing, will lead underground pedestrians from the tops of the six exit stairwells scattered around the busy site to its hoarding boundaries, giving them a sneak preview of the construction site when they emerge into the daylight.

SIXTEEN

TOWER OF BABEL

It is a long way from the peaceful pastures of the Azores, but the construction site reminds Artur Teixeira of home. Sitting amidst the hurly-burly of the loading dock eating his mid-morning snack of cheese sandwiches, he can pick out three men from his birthplace on São Miguel, the largest island in the Azores. Teixeira and his compatriots are labourers who haul steel buggies of concrete to fill in crane holes and build kerbs on the increasing number of finished levels of the building, as well as remove wooden formwork, clean up debris and tote endless materials.

For twenty years, the forty-five-year-old Teixeira has tested his back with this work. The squat concrete buggies, their long steel handles worn smooth by many pairs of hands, look like toy chariots, but each holds seven cubic feet of concrete; a full load weighs 475 kilograms. It's hard work, pushing almost half a tonne of concrete, but his efforts are well compensated: the basic wage before benefits is $24.39 an hour, quite close to the crane operators' rate of $26.90 an hour. Teixeira is the shop steward and health and safety representative for the forty members of the Labourers' International Union who work on the site. The pay might be good, but the job takes its toll. Three years ago, Teixeira hurt his back when he tried to lift what he thought was a box full of garbage. It turned out to be loaded with steel, and he spent eight months off work, easing the constant pain with pills and physiotherapy.

Just as he recovered his health, the economy faltered. He was laid off for five months before getting the job here at the site with Avenue Structures. His wife Helena's support kept him going when he was off work, and now that he is back at it, she helps him by getting up at 5:00 to make a breakfast of eggs and crusty bread and to fill his small cooler with lunch and assorted snacks. Around 6:00, he drives off to work from his home in Brampton, a bedroom community northwest of the city. By 9:30, he's already eaten the two cheese sandwiches Helena prepared. Lunch, taken at noon, consists of another two sandwiches filled with tuna and a spread of hot peppers that Teixeira makes in a big vat each fall. Rounding out the day's menu are a pear, a banana, a bunch of fat red grapes, an orange and two cans of President's Choice Cola. Teixeira lays off coffee when the weather is warm—it makes him too hot—and he quit smoking more than two years ago because it made him feel sick every morning. While the other men light up during long waits for the construction hoist, he chews one of the mints he keeps in a pocket of the dark green work pants that Helena buys in quantity at Zellers for $15.99 a pair.

He was born in Ribeira Grande, a town of twelve thousand in a farming area known for dairy products in the Azorean archipelago, one thousand kilometres from the Portuguese mainland. In his homeland, school was compulsory only to Grade 4, the level at which most of his fellow Portuguese workers quit. But on the urging of his father, the town barber, Artur stayed in class until he was fifteen. Then he found work in a factory making cheese, butter and powdered milk. After six years, he was conscripted into the Portuguese army and served for a year until Helena, his seventeen-year-old sweetheart who had immigrated to Canada with the help of relatives, encouraged him to join her in Toronto. The two filed documents of marriage at their respective city halls—allowing Helena to sponsor Artur's immigration to Canada in 1973—then held a formal ceremony at a Portuguese Roman Catholic church in Toronto's west end.

In Canada, Teixeira took a job placing interlocking paving stones in driveways, then became a labourer on large construction sites. "I couldn't go to work in an office," he says matter-of-factly, "because I couldn't speak English." Like many Portuguese immigrants who worked in construction, the first language he picked up was Italian, because it allowed him to communicate with the foremen and the vast majority of workers on the site. Indeed, around this construction site he is called Arturo, the Italian version of his name, even though these days most of his colleagues here, and indeed hands-on workers throughout the construction industry, are Portuguese. Many of them also came from the Azores in the 1960s and 1970s, in a mass exodus that spread a million Azoreans around the world and left the nine islands with a population of only about 250,000. But once an Azorean, always an Azorean. Talk on the site is of village soccer teams, local cafés and deaths in the family back home. Camaraderie and chatter soften the hard labour as the men haul their concrete and materials through the day.

It's a picture that well illustrates the fortunes and fate of immigrant arrivals to the city. They join vast communities of fellow countrymen in neighbourhoods occupied previously by migrants from a succession of other places. They buy homes as quickly as they reasonably can. They perform difficult but financially rewarding work, often unrelated to the employment they had previously and the sometimes extensive education acquired in their homelands. They are often looked down upon by other Canadians, and see their relationships with their own children challenged by a gap in language, education, culture and employment. Eventually they better themselves to the point that they move to new suburbs far away from their former ethnic neighbourhoods, but they continue to perform difficult work and keep up their ties with compatriots.

The Italians and Portuguese typically came to Canada alone under work contracts, leaving their wives and children behind in order to earn enough money to sponsor their passage and provide them with decent shelter when they arrived. They settled in what sociologists call the city's reception area, just west of downtown, close to unskilled factory and construction jobs, social services, friends, eating places and shops, their display windows frothing with colourful goods. The predominant immigrant group in the area shifted as new waves of people came to the country. First came the Jews, then the Hungarians and Ukranians and finally the Southern Europeans, each nationality overlapping the previous one as it moved on. Tony Patullo, who arrived in 1955, remembers his first meal in Canada, eaten in his older brother's Russian-Jewish rooming house: blintzes and potato latkes. By the late 1950s, the area was predominantly Italian and by the 1970s, it had become known as Little Portugal. Today it is predominantly Chinese.

For people who came to Canada with nothing but a pair of hands, the purchase of a home represented a shift from migrant to immigrant, from sojourner to settler. Property represented security, permanent roots and status in the community. The first home in Canada was usually bought together with a group of friends or relatives, each party buying a fraction of a house and settling his family into a couple of rooms when they joined him in Canada. Historian Franca Iacovetta, the daughter of postwar Italian immigrants, says her father, her uncle and several of their friends pooled their money and split their first house five ways. Each partner slowly moved on when his fortunes improved or the space got too tight. Just before the Iacovettas moved out, the house was still divided between her parents and five siblings, her grandparents, her uncle's family and a basement tenant.

The jobs the immigrants came to fill in Canada were unlike any that most of them had known. Some had experience rebuilding Europe following the war, or were hired to do construction work for brief periods when agriculture waned. But for most, forming concrete was a far cry from farming cattle. However, in her book, *Such Hardworking People*, Iacovetta says the Italians naturally gravitated to construction. Unlike tedious factory jobs, the work offered a degree of autonomy and variety. Seasonal rhythms were similar to those previously experienced working the land. And there was always employment to be found through myriad contacts in the community.

Life was difficult. Iacovetta remembers the men in her home coming in from construction sites each night. Because they worked until dusk, the household ate supper much later than others. Before they came into the house, each man scrubbed at the dirt encrusting his body under a crude shower in the basement. On Sunday mornings before mass, her father, a labourer who became a bricklayer with his own small subcontracting company, tried in vain to scrape the shameful dirt from his gnarled knuckles.

Dark-skinned and smelling of garlic, the immigrants were outsiders who concentrated on making their own communities. Owning their own homes was the key; Italians have the highest rate of home owner-ship of any ethnic group in Toronto, including Anglo-Canadians. Real status, though, came from leaving the reception area altogether. When the Iacovetta family moved from Little Italy in the 1960s, its destina-tion was Willowdale, then a new suburb on the northern edge of Toronto. Their house was a two-storey brick affair with a two-car garage built on a corner lot by her father and his co-workers; it stood out in the collection of tidy postwar bungalows. The Iacovettas' move was a common one; many Italians relocated to the northern outskirts of the city. Proud and profoundly conservative, they live today in self-sustaining neighbourhoods of Italian businesses, churches and social clubs. They build elaborate villas decorated to reflect their new stations with faux arches and columns. Madonnas and Sacred Hearts grace ornamental gardens befitting the Italian aristocracy.

The attitude towards the immigrants whose hands shaped the skyline and urban development was double-edged. Some people felt they were little better than animals, toiling in the dirt and filth for long hours. "We were known as diggers: that was the only thing we could do," says Corrado Patullo. The more liberal-minded Canadians real-ized the difficulty of the unsafe and unhealthy working conditions, and marvelled at how they were transforming the city. In March 1960, the Hogg's Hollow tunnel disaster brought this aspect to light and drew sympathy for the plight of the construction worker. Fire swept through the main shaft that provided air and access to a crew of six "sandhogs" or underground-tunnel workers who were building a water main in Hogg's Hollow on the northern limits of the city. Without fire extinguishers, and facing a rising wall of mud and water when the air pumps stopped, five men died, all Italians. People in the city were stunned by reports of the poor conditions under which the men toiled and the inadequate safety equipment available to rescue workers. The tragedy brought new respect for the immigrants and the vital role they played in Toronto's booming postwar economy.

Culturally, the immigrant groups slowly brought colour and life to what was a bland, subdued city. Arts writer Robert Fulford, in his book *Accidental City: The Transformation of Toronto*, says that before the war, the city's most "obvious quality" was reticence. "Toronto was a city of silence, a private city, where all the best meals were eaten at home and no one noticed the absence of street life and public spaces. Sidewalk cafes were illegal, and there were no festivals. The idea of public art was still exotic and alien." Much has changed. Beginning in the 1950s, the city was transformed by the new people it absorbed, with their street fairs, religious parades, family restaurants and homes replete with brightly coloured paint, religious shrines, vegetable gardens and garlands of grape vines.

Portuguese immigrants to Canada followed the path of the Italians, although Portugal's reputation as a proud nation of explorers placed them here long before. Portuguese fishermen are considered the first Europeans to have visited the eastern shores of Canada, and there have been suggestions that they reached the New World at least seventy years before Columbus. But there was little immigration to the country from Portugal until the 1950s, when a trickle of people came from mainland Portugal as well as its overseas provinces in the Azores and Madeira. This became a steady stream by the 1960s and 1970s. Like the Italians, they came from rural societies, although the Portuguese were primarily fishermen rather than farmers. Many came as contract workers destined for farms but quickly headed for the large cities, especially Toronto.

These unskilled newcomers poured into industries such as construction that were hungry for hands in the buoyant economy. They quickly developed extensive chain-migration networks to sponsor family and friends. In Toronto, they settled into the area around Kensington Market, several square blocks of two- and three-storey row-houses with commercial streets that quickly filled with Portuguese bakeries, grocery stores, fishmongers, travel agencies and driving schools. It was also close to sources of unskilled employment. Men worked in construction and janitorial positions, women in the textile and clothing factories or as housekeepers. In the 1970s, the cost of living rose sharply, and housing became scarce. Some of the Portuguese immigrants slept in beds in rooming houses rented through the day in eight-hour shifts. They saved to afford a down payment on a house that they typically split with others or rented out to new arrivals and relatives they sponsored.

Abel deCarvalho has carried on this tradition. He still rents out the top floor of his two-storey brick house to a family of four that parks a massive van in the front driveway. He says the house, which he and his wife, Otilia, bought in the northwest part of the city ten years ago, has everything he needs. There is a garden for Otilia, equipped with a huge grill that he made with a friend to roast a whole pig one year on his birthday. In the basement is a cold room, or *taverna*, that smells of mould and fermented grapes; the family uses it for storing wine, preserves and the cured legs of *presunto* ham that Abel makes into sandwiches for work.

DeCarvalho was born in Barcelos, an area of northern Portugal known for its *vinho verde*, a spritzy white wine drunk when it has just finished fermenting. Money was tight, and after Grade 4 he quit school and worked in a bakery to supplement the family's meagre income earned from a small vineyard. He decided to immigrate to Canada—he rubs his thumb against his fingers to explain why—after making several trips to the country in the late 1960s to visit his cousin Manuel, who had come to join the ranks of construction workers in Toronto. DeCarvalho started as a house cleaner earning ninety cents an hour, and moved on to a job in a rubber factory, making bumpers for cars, until a colleague told him there was better money in construction. He started as a labourer and became known as Carvalho. He graduated to his present position as a swamper—the crane operator's right-hand man—at the suggestion of someone who noticed his expert work tying up a load. He took the step after completing a two-week course, the certificate for which is proudly displayed in the family living room.

On-site, Carvalho sprints across the newest floor of Simcoe Place, slowing down only to move an errant board and kick a chunk of concrete out of his path, scrambles up a wooden ladder and rotates his hand in the air to guide a five-tonne section of formwork hanging from the hook of the tower crane into place. On Mondays, when the forms are hoisted to start building the next level of the structure, Carvalho rises at 3:15 a.m. and heads to Simcoe Place after a coffee and a couple of pieces of toast prepared by Otilia, who leaves soon after for her own job in a factory that puts together the wiring for small appliances.

At the height of Toronto's construction boom in the 1980s, Carvalho made $90,000 a year, but the job has its price. His hands are stained dark with oil and crossed with seams of acrid concrete powder. All four pairs of workboots he bought on sale at Sears at Christmas are worn out by the middle of the summer, and his Levis, even with careful patching by Otilia, fall apart after a couple of months. Carvalho's tiny frame is an asset when it comes to moving beneath the five-foot-high trusses of the forms, which cause taller men to bang their heads and curse. Despite the dangers of the job, he has never been off work due to an accident.

He wishes he had a better command of English, especially to communicate with English-speaking crane operators, but his attempts to take classes after work always fail because he falls asleep instead of learning. Carvalho has an especially hard time remembering the distinction between "foot" and "feet" when asking on the radio for the crane's hook to be moved a certain distance. To make things more confusing, an unsympathetic construction-site wit has spray-painted orange labels on concrete buckets 1 and 2. The first reads "1 feet" and the other "2 foot."

Keeping loads steady is the chief source of pride for swampers. Until recently, Carvalho could boast that he had never broken a window in a building, but then a set of precast concrete stairs destined for the fire escape glanced off the curtain wall on the second floor and shattered a pane. He shrugs at the memory. He's more intent on his next trip back to Portugal to visit his seventy-one-year-old mother, and talks wistfully of a wish to open a bakery and café like the one where he worked in Barcelos long ago. Otilia is not so ready to return permanently to her homeland, nor is the couple's teenaged daughter, Amelia. She speaks Portuguese fluently and translates for her parents, works in a Portuguese bakery and attends Portuguese festivals, but has no desire to live in Portugal. Carvalho, like each wave of immigrants who has worked in construction, hopes that his children will not have to work in such a physical, demanding job. The attitude is, "We worked with our hands and our children should work with their brains," says Iacovetta. It's an important ethos.

The sentiment is shared by all the men but is troubling for the construction trades charged with bringing new blood into their fields. Wherever labourer Joe Gouveia is on the Simcoe Place site, chances are his son can be found close by. At nineteen, Joe Jr. shares his father's tall frame, curly black hair and easy smile. Since he was fourteen and earning money working on construction sites during school breaks, the younger Gouveia has laboured alongside his father, learning to lift hefty sacks of drywall compound, work shovels full of concrete into narrow trenches and drag carts piled high with boxes through crowded job sites.

Soon this shared experience will end. When the senior Gouveia heads to another project at the end of this one, his son will enter college to study for a business degree. "He'll look nice in a tie, with a briefcase," says Joe Sr., who is fifty-two and came to Canada from the Azores twenty-five years ago. With his dark, drooping eyes, he looks over his son's current uniform of a plaid flannel shirt and work pants, frayed in places and flecked with concrete and dirt, as the two haul wheelbarrows of concrete. "I want him to be something. I don't want him to be in construction like me. I'm nothing." It's a common refrain. Men like Gouveia and Carvalho are proud to have built the office tower and others around it with their bare hands, but when asked about their children's future, construction is rarely mentioned, unless it involves joining the professional ranks of engineers and managers on the site.

These sentiments worry Cosmo Mannella, who oversees the apprenticeship and training program for Local 27 of the Carpenters and Allied Workers Union, which represents thirty-four carpenters on the site. Most of the men in the union brought their individual skills and strong constitutions to Canada from Italy and Portugal after the Second World War. As immigration from places that share Canada's building traditions has slowed, and younger generations have opted for white-collar jobs, the average age of workers has crept up. Mannella's union expects 35 per cent of the carpenters now working to retire from the business in the next five years.

The realization that new blood would be needed, coupled with the development boom in the late 1980s, prompted unions and governments to create apprenticeship programs that combine construction theory with practice. Drawing on neglected labour reserves, the programs' organizers encouraged women and visible minorities to apply. The Canadian approach differs from apprenticeship programs in Europe, where construction companies themselves take responsibility for training workers on the job, moving them up through the ranks to finally become what are known as journeymen.

Given the negative tone the word *journeyman* can carry, it may seem an odd title for those who have reached the top of their craft. But the word has its origins in medieval Europe, when youths who completed their years of servitude as apprentices were expected to take their newly learned skills on the road for three years. Dressed in the distinctive corduroy suit of the *wandergeselle* and carrying just a backpack full of tools, they walked from town to town or even country to country, forbidden to marry, accept income outside of their trade, incur debts or own any form of transportation that would compromise their wandering. Some say the term extended to the practice of paying such workers by the day, from the French word *journée*.

Sensitive to the changing mores, Local 27 refers to its licensed carpenters as journeypeople. To qualify, apprentices work four years, or a total of 7,200 hours, and take three eight-week courses at a huge training centre in suburban Toronto, where they learn house framing, structural forming, cabinetry, stair building and blueprint reading. Working apprentices are paid on a scale that begins at 50 per cent of a carpenter's wage of thirty-three dollars an hour (including benefits) and rises to the full amount by the fourth year.

Two apprentice carpenters hired by Avenue Structures at Simcoe Place are currently working, with the guidance of full-fledged carpenters, to build the wooden and aluminum frames that will make the building's concrete roof. "The average age here is very old," says twenty-eight-year-old Tony Sciortino, who is in the fourth year of his apprenticeship, as he gestures exaggeratedly towards his nearby mentors. "But there's always something new to learn from them." Eusebio Coleiro, who at thirty hopes to soon write his exam to become a full carpenter, says he's been lucky to have seventeen months of continuous work here. Once licensed, he's prepared to take the title of journeyman literally, travelling "to wherever the job is."

Joe Gouveia plans to retire from the job in five years at the age of fifty-seven, the earliest age at which he can collect his full thirty-year pension from the labourers' union. He and most of his colleagues once believed there would be an endless supply of construction jobs in the ever-growing city. But they have been stung by the recent work shortages and are increasingly leery about the high-technology future. "Eventually they won't need construction workers like me any more," he shrugs. "Machines will do our work."

Mannella says the current shortage of construction work has hurt apprenticeship training. Many trainees can't work the hours needed to become journeypeople, so they leave the program. The 750 apprentices working their way through the system in 1989 have dwindled to 350, of whom 145 are currently unemployed. Many of those who joined the program most recently—the women and members of minorities—were the first casualties because they couldn't hope to accumulate the necessary hours.

Some formal apprenticeship programs, such as the operating-engineers training institute in eastern Ontario, which teaches people to manoeuvre cranes, won't accept apprentices who haven't already lined up some kind of work. The consequences for the industry could be disastrous, says Steve Sheridan, a long-time crane operator and instructor at the institute, whose three sons have also eschewed construction to take jobs as a truck driver, an assistant fire marshal and a chef. Sheridan believes a sudden building boom would bring "real panic" because there wouldn't be enough people trained to do the work for several years.

Standing on one of the building's top floors with his concrete buggy waiting for the construction hoist, Artur Teixeira is not worried. He dreams of the Azores as he watches the wind raise white-caps on Lake Ontario. His black Reebok T-shirt—a gift from one of his three teenaged daughters after she tired of it—flaps in the breeze. He squints at a tall ship cutting through the swell. "In the Azores, it smells nice, everything is green, there are flowers in the streets. Here at the lake," he says, holding his nose, "sometimes you cannot stand too close."

Then the memory fades, and he straightens up, adding, "I love Canada—it is my country now, and it will always be my home." He revisited the Azores only once, sixteen years ago, and has no plans to return there, since both of his parents are dead. By 3:45 in the afternoon, a hard day's labour finished, he is ready to head home for an early supper with his family and a night of World Cup soccer on television. There will be lots of talk about the game at the site in the morning—in many languages—but he knows he'll fall asleep long before it has ended.

SEVENTEEN

THE VIEW FROM THE CRANE

Bob Hughes's mind is already at work as he leaves his home at 5:00 a.m. for the thirty-minute drive to the site. Scanning the brightening sky for hints of the day's weather, he turns on the car radio in search of a forecast. For Hughes, who operates one of the two tower cranes high above the construction project, the news is bad: autumn winds will gust up to sixty kilometres an hour and there's a chance of thunderstorms later in the day.

He arrives at the site as the sun's rays begin to filter through the Toronto skyline, climbs a narrow steel ladder up the inside of the crane's tower and shimmies down another ladder to the door of the crane's cab. Once inside, he settles into the large vinyl chair where he will spend the next ten hours, switches on a walkie-talkie, tunes in an early-morning AM radio show and presses two green buttons on the panel in front of him that bring the giant machine to life.

Within a minute, the first words crackle across the walkie-talkie: "Hello Bobby, my boy. . . . Twelve o'clock. . . . All the way to the ground." The voice is that of Carvalho, serving as Hughes's eyes and hands down below, hooking up each load and anticipating every new task for the crane. Carvalho has divided the construction site into the hours on the face of a clock to let Hughes know where he must pick up and drop off material; twelve o'clock is the building's north side, where the day's first truckload of structural steel awaits pick-up.

Hughes removes the brake that has secured the hook in its resting position next to the cab overnight. His giant hands grasp two sticks covered in black rubber. When he pushes the left one forward, the hook is sent out along the boom, known as trolleying out. When he flicks the stick to the left, the boom swings around to face north. Pushing the right stick forward sends the hook quickly earthward. "Down ten feet. . . . Down three. . . . Down a touch. . . . Stop." The process is the same whether Hughes is hoisting scaffolding, buckets of concrete, stacks of plywood or dumpsters full of garbage. As usual, he can't see the bundle of steel he is about to lift this time but waits for the signal—"You're free, my boy. . . . All the way up."—and moves the joysticks to raise the load up to the men working on the building's seventeenth floor.

By the time most workers have arrived in the office buildings around him, Hughes has eaten his lunch and considerably lightened the day's pack of cigarettes. After twenty-three years of operating a crane, he has learned to forgo the sweetened coffee that his co-workers buy from the catering truck. He seldom takes a break in the day for a trip to the washroom, and anyway, there are few visitors to bring him such treats. The job has its consolations, though. Each week has brought a different view as the crane climbs above the city. Today, almost all the way to the top, he sees the retracting roof of SkyDome and the ferries crossing to the Toronto Islands. He can even see the Skylon Tower at Niagara Falls if he looks through the binoculars he uses to check the condition of the crane's cable. His cab is spartan: a wooden floor and a steel wall painted blue on which someone long ago tacked a water-stained sheet of styrofoam to keep out the frigid winter wind. It is not needed today. An air conditioner blasts at full throttle in the small space to counter the October sunlight streaming through giant windows freshly cleaned with Windex. On the radio, there's a call-in show about skin cancer.

As a young boy, Hughes decided to be either a pilot or a racing-car driver, but by his early twenties he settled for a menial job repairing large construction machinery. While dangling from the end of a boom fixing a crane 120 metres above the ground on a freezing winter day in 1971, he decided it would be safer and more lucrative to run the crane itself.

The transition from technician to crane operator was not as easy as he thought. The early days on the job were trying, made bearable only by downing tranquilizers to calm his frazzled nerves. The crane did not have a cab where the operator sat but a large remote-control panel that the operator hung from his neck and manipulated while standing below in the middle of the construction site. Hughes found it impossible to get a load to travel in the desired direction. At one stage, he knocked himself right off the top of a building under construction with a bucket of concrete that the crane was hoisting. Still gripping the controls and hanging on to the load at the end of the hook for dear life, he had to figure out how to reverse the process.

"When I trolleyed myself back onto the building," he says, "I was a nervous wreck. I just couldn't get the hang of it." He considered quitting, until he held his first sizeable pay cheque. "I said, 'I'm going to slow down, I'm going to take my pills and I'm going to master this.'" Now, long free of the tranquilizers, he lifts concrete for twelve hours or more a day, trolleying in, hoisting and swinging the mammoth machine at the same time. "A crane operator's either got it or he doesn't," he says. "You have to keep the load steady. You don't want to kill anybody or hit anything."

It is also painstaking work, and as the building approaches to its full height, it takes longer and longer to hoist each load. One trip up from the ground with the bucket or a load of steel takes five minutes. But Hughes' efforts are well-paid. At forty-nine, and already earning $65,000 to $80,000 a year, he wants to slow down. He isn't greedy about overtime, but for now he has to do extra work to speed this project along.

The storms have not materialized by mid-day, but a strong wind buffets the cab, muddying the walkie-talkie communications and turning the four-tonne bucket of concrete at the end of the cable into a swinging pendulum. Wind can be a real problem for the crane, especially as it gets higher and higher above the site. The column of steel below him sways and pitches like a small airplane in turbulence. Wind whistles in the rigging. Hughes is not worried as long as the gusts stay below sixty kilometres an hour, at which point he knows the brake that keeps the boom from turning may stop functioning, meaning he could lose control of the load at the end of the hook. "The crane's the safest place to be on the construction site," he says as he watches the breeze rip hard hats off the men below and blow debris around the top of the building. "At least nothing can fall on your head."

Wind not only affects the construction of a skyscraper but is also an important factor in the design and operation of the building. Both developers and city planners have long been preoccupied with the environment, especially wind patterns. Landlords want outdoor cafés, stores and plazas to be as inviting as possible. Meanwhile, the city needs to determine how the mass, shape and height of a new structure will affect the surrounding area. "We want people to be able to use the streets," says Ted Martin, Toronto's director of urban design and author of the provisions for wind, sunshine and shadow in the city's official plan. "We want to have a more tangible discussion about what effect a building will have."

There are several phenomena caused by skyscrapers that leave pedestrians feeling they have stepped into a wind tunnel. One is called downwash: fast-moving wind hits the side of a building and is channelled down a wall, straight to the ground. Another, called the venturi effect, occurs when air squeezes through any narrow slots between adjacent buildings, causing it to accelerate. Then there is the canyon factor, when rows of closely spaced tall buildings push a wall of air down a broad street. And finally, just to ensure that no one is left standing, strong winds that hit a building raised up on columns like stilts are sucked through to the building's downwind side, making it difficult to walk underneath.

As it grows to its full height of thirty storeys and is closed in with walls of aluminum, glass and granite, Simcoe Place will start having its own influence on the wind patterns in downtown Toronto. These will be watched with interest by Colin Williams and Mike Soligo, engineers at Rowan Williams Davies and Irwin in Guelph, Ontario, a consulting firm hired to conduct studies and devise an environmentally friendly plan for Simcoe Place. Builders began learning about the nasty tricks wind can play on buildings—and the areas surrounding them—in the 1960s, when the first high-rise projects flourished. Experts and the general public quickly realized that the vast plazas at the base of most skyscrapers, designed for picnicking office-workers, also invited gale-force winds.

In 1964, Alan Davenport, a young civil engineer at the University of Western Ontario in London, conducted the first study of how wind would affect a proposed skyscraper—New York's World Trade Center—and the land around it. Since then, Davenport's laboratory and other Canadian consultants, such as Rowan Williams Davies and Irwin, have run tests before a good number of the world's tall structures are built. Davenport says the most difficult part of calculating the effects of wind when he studied the World Trade Center was that the wind tunnels of the day, designed primarily to test aircraft for their aerodynamic properties, could recreate only strong, uniform wind. While typical in the upper atmosphere, such conditions bore little resemblance to the gusty, unpredictable winds close to earth. So a new type of test chamber, called a boundary-layer wind tunnel, was developed for assessing objects here.

The boundary layer is a term used to describe the flow of air near any surface, such as a car body or boat hull. The earth's boundary layer is the first three hundred metres above the ground. Here the air becomes turbulent as it encounters obstructions—known in the trade as roughness—including hills, trees and buildings. A boundary-layer wind tunnel is a wide corridor with a huge fan at one end that generates winds up to one hundred kilometres an hour. Rising from its floor are hundreds of adjustable obstacles, known as roughness factors. These resemble small building blocks, and can be used to reproduce the exact landscape—be it a forest or the Manhattan skyline—around a model of a building, a bridge or an oil-drilling platform installed in the tunnel for the test.

The findings from the wind tunnel are then applied to meteorological information about the wind climate that is likely to affect a structure when it is built. For Simcoe Place, the engineers looked at fifty years of data supplied by the nearby Toronto Island Airport and found the prevailing winds on the site will come especially from the west, as well as the southwest and northwest. The city's official plan requires developers to "protect pedestrians from negative effects of wind induced by buildings," but defining an acceptable level of wind isn't simple. It depends on the project's design, and whether people will be walking, standing or sitting in an outdoor café or a park. Williams suggests comfortable conditions for these activities should prevail at least 80 per cent of the time.

The final design for Simcoe Place has received good marks in the wind tunnel, where the wind speed was measured by sixty-seven different sensors positioned strategically around a model of the building. The fact that each corner of the building angles back in receding surfaces not only creates more prized corner offices, it also presents a smoother, more aerodynamic face to the prevailing west wind, helping it to flow more easily.

Based on their tests, the engineers called for additional landscaping to break up the wind that will flow through a long corridor in the park at the building's base. Here a little knowledge of forestry helps. Areas that are subject to fierce gusts in the winter, such as the park, are candidates for coniferous trees that don't lose their foliage in the winter. Leafy maples and poplars offer shelter in the summer months if the wind is the greatest then.

Simcoe Place got especially good marks from the wind consultants because of the large podium at the building's base. While making the streetscape friendlier, a podium also deflects downwash winds that hit the building's upper wall and roar earthward. That will take care of the worst of the wind, but Williams says no one expects or even wants the plazas and sidewalks to be totally windless. A certain amount of breeze is desirable to dissipate exhaust fumes from cars and to cool off pedestrians on hot summer days.

Air quality is among the many environmental issues the engineers at Williams's company studied. Others included how the building will affect snowfall, sunlight and even noise levels. Concern over how a new building will influence its surroundings goes back to the earliest modest skyscrapers of New York, which bothered neighbours by blocking out their sunlight and view of the sky. The protests prompted the inaugural zoning by-laws in the U.S. in 1916, limiting a building's total floor area to twelve times the size of the lot it sits on.

The science of studying future developments has been vastly refined since then. Williams and Soligo call their inquiries crystal-ball gazing. "You can find out what's going to happen long before something is put in place," Soligo says. The consultants first began thinking about Simcoe Place back when the original four architects were invited to submit competing designs for the high-rise development. All of the concepts and eventually models of each proposal were shipped to the engineers' company for a battery of tests at the request of Cadillac Fairview. Taking such precautions steers architects and developers away from unworkable plans. But discretion among the engineers at this stage of a high-stakes architectural competition is critical. Models of the competing buildings brought into the laboratory were draped in black cloth, and a separate partner of the company was assigned to each of the projects. All were sworn to secrecy.

Having dealt with the gusts of wind, the engineers' imaginations and tools turned to other ways the building will affect its surroundings. The models were submerged in a device called a water-flume to demonstrate how snow would accumulate around them. The resulting drifts—actually fine sand introduced into the flowing water to simulate a storm—on the winning model showed the area along the south face of the building will require some extra shovelling in the winter.

Noise studies looked at how Simcoe Place's mechanical rumblings would affect the neighbouring area, and whether passing traffic, whistling wind and activity from other nearby developments would disturb those inside the building. Internal noise, such as the clamour of crowds entering the marbled lobby and the clanging of air conditioners, had to be considered so appropriate buffers could be designed. In another study, the engineers examined how to vent noxious fumes from the building's underground parking garage. They suggested pumping fresh air into the garage and mixing it with the stale air, to make sure people standing near vents at ground level were not blanketed in carbon monoxide.

A large building by its very nature also affects the interplay of light and shadow around it. Rowan Williams Davies and Irwin used a computer program to show how much sun would reach areas around the building, such as the day-care centre's play area, and how the building's own shadow would fall on the hotel and condominium that may one day be built kitty-corner to it. City planners have recently grown concerned about how sunshine and shade influence the temperature on the street, as well as the psychological well-being of passers-by. Toronto's official plan even sets standards so specific that they stipulate whether streets should have three, five or seven hours of sunlight a day, as calculated on the autumnal equinox. However, Simcoe Place sits on the edge of Toronto's financial core, where buildings are so high and tightly spaced that the standards have been waived. While the city requires high-rise developers to study the shadows their buildings cast, says a planner, "The sun's a goner in much of that area."

The sun has long disappeared behind billowing black clouds, but Bob Hughes is still at work in the crane cab, two hours after his shift should have ended, when the wind howls menacingly. "Shut her down," Carvalho shouts. Hughes needs no convincing. He manoeuvres the trolley back to its resting position beside the cab and releases the brake that would normally stop the crane from swinging or slewing from side to side. This allows the giant device to weathervane, or turn in the wind, as it desires. The crane is normally left in this position at night, even without a storm threatening; that way, a strong wind or sudden gust will spin the boom around harmlessly. Most off-duty cranes thus continually indicate the direction of the wind. Hughes presses an orange button to cut the power, turns off the walkie-talkie and leaves the cab, locking the door behind him and climbing down the ladder, disappearing in the late afternoon.

EIGHTEEN

TOPPING-OFF:
THE BEGINNING OF THE END

The frosty November wind comes in gusts and the outsized form rests on uneven ground, but Corrado Patullo's footing is sure. He grips a heavy crowbar in one hand and a wrench in the other, wielding them in turn to loosen the bonds between the aluminum, wood and fibreglass that make up the platform under him. Corrado is once again in charge of the building's structural work, almost nine months after plunging head-first from a similar position. Now he is back on the job, present at one of the last stages of the tower's construction. This elevated piece of formwork, one of forty-five used to make most of the building's concrete floors, has finished its work. The last full bucket of concrete will be added to the roof today, known in the industry as topping-off.

The milestone will be celebrated with a small lunch of sandwiches. The festivities will be low-key, however, because of the building's low budget and tight schedule. Moreover, a large celebration seems inappropriate; many of the labourers, carpenters, concrete finishers and ironworkers who are beginning to leave the project know it will be hard to find new work.

Those building the concrete skeleton see signs that their jobs are coming to an end. Corrado's Avenue Structures has already begun shifting its efforts back to ground level, where the fly-forms must be dismantled into their component parts. Salvageable wood, aluminum beams, lengths of scaffolding and an assortment of rusted steel bolts and fasteners are piled and tied with rope so they can be shipped on flatbed trailers to the storage yard northwest of the city where Avenue keeps its equipment.

The sooner the materials are brought out of storage to construct a new building, the better. Avenue had no other project of this size on the horizon, (though it has since). In 1994, its only job is building a high school in nearby Newmarket and the foundation of a new wing of a hospital. Without another big building to create, there will be no use for some of the material on the site. The twenty-five large pieces of fibreglass shaped like open, shallow boxes, which made up the beams in some of the fly-forms, are destined for the landfill site. Their configuration is peculiar to Simcoe Place, and their smooth surface has roughened with handling and exposure to caustic concrete. Some contractors, reluctant to waste good fibreglass, use the boxes to make shallow wading pools or fish ponds in their gardens. Corrado encourages anyone with a truck to cart one away. "I offer to buy them lunch," he laughs.

As for himself, the middle Patullo brother is lunching light these days. His doctor suggests his fall from the fly-form might be a consequence of his passion for delicious but fatty salami and prosciutto. The accident left Corrado with not only a severe concussion, a broken cheekbone and a blood clot on the side of his brain, but also the need for a lot of therapy. He slowly regained his memory and the ability to recognize letters and colours, but after a few months he still couldn't make sense of some things, like the clock on the wall. "Not just what time it was," he says, pausing for effect. "*What* it was." Over the summer, especially during a two-week trip to visit his home town of Boiano, he gradually improved, though he still finds it difficult to turn letters into words when he reads. To stimulate his mind, he does crossword puzzles in Italian and he hopes to take a night class in English.

"Every week he's better," says Amadeo Pozzobon, Corrado's best friend and a superintendent who joined Avenue thirty years ago at the age of eighteen and is considered a tough taskmaster by the men on the site. He worries about his friend, and since the accident has made a point of seeing more of Corrado, whom he calls *Combare*— godfather in Italian—because Corrado is godfather to his son. This fall the two men rented equipment to turn Palomino and Carignan grapes into nine hundred litres of wine. It is stored in casks in their basements and will be bottled at Christmas.

Twenty-five pounds lighter after heeding the advice of his doctor, Corrado's already baggy clothes hang on his hunched frame and his cheeks are hollow. He no longer drinks (though he may make an exception when the wine is served at his daughter's wedding next summer). The accident has changed his lifestyle, but he has no plans to leave work. "If I feel fine, why retire?" he says, shrugging. His job at Simcoe is not over. Once most of the forming materials have been cleared out, he and a small crew from Avenue will stay at the site to make the concrete enclosure for the building's rear loading dock. Later they will come back to work on the concrete tunnel that will fill the hole being dug under Wellington Street behind the building.

Avenue's two large tower cranes are staying just long enough to hoist any final heavy loads and will turn to the job of erecting the steel framework for the remaining mechanical penthouse high on the roof once the last of the concrete is finished. Corrado squints up at the building, the creator admiring his creation, satisfied to see its position among its neighbours. It looms over the squat Broadcast Centre, the low-slung Metro Toronto Convention Centre, the sloping glass theatrics of Roy Thomson Hall and the high-rise Metro Hall. Much finishing work remains to be done over the coming months, but Corrado will be long gone. By then, he hopes to be supervising his formwork team at another job and assessing the progress of his wine to make sure it is good enough for the wedding guests.

First, though, he has the rest of his work to do and Christmas to look forward to. But right in the critical period leading up to the holidays, a persistent, freezing wind has plagued the contractors, making outdoor operations slow or impossible. Murphy's Law governs the thoughts of everyone around the site these days. After an autumn blessed with mild weather, cooperative machinery and brisk progress, the laws of nature and civil engineering have intervened. Equipment failures have slowed the pace of the critical work of lifting materials to the structure's upper penthouses. There is also the occasional mishap, such as when the crews shoring the tunnel behind the building hit a major water main and flooded the street during the morning rush hour.

"When things don't go right, they really don't go right," sighs Brian Gardner, shaking water from his work boots after fording the stream created by the break. His problems began three days earlier. In the first operation of the day for the white crane—lifting sections of the curtain wall up to clad the tower's penthouse—the block and hook froze in mid-air, refusing to go up or down. The hoist motor had blown, which meant bringing in a new part and lifting it onto the crane's rear section. Breakdowns like this happen often with well-used equipment exposed to the elements, but here the problem was compounded. The trouble was thirty-five storeys up, in the top of the taller of the two cranes on-site. That meant the red crane could not be used to lift the new motor into place.

To make matters worse, the wind was rising. The hook, which weighs 450 kilograms even when empty, had begun to gyrate just a few metres from the side of the building, threatening with each gust to crash into the mirrored windows, aluminum and granite trim of the shiny new wall. Throughout the morning the wind grew stronger. When it reached forty kilometres an hour—considered moderate by Environment Canada—the roofers' sheets of insulation turned into sails and small squares of plastic became menacing projectiles. At about fifty-five kilometres an hour—classified as strong—the red crane was shut down for fear of blowing into the side of the building or its long boom hitting the cable of its disabled counterpart. At noon, construction elevator operator Guy Boire held his small wind-speed indicator aloft, found that the wind was sixty-nine kilometres an hour—gale force—and shut down his two hoists.

Despite a peak of ninety-three kilometres an hour—storm force—recorded by the Toronto weather office, the wind did not cause the broken crane's hook to do any damage, but for the next two days the staff at Avenue wondered how to get the huge machine running again. One possibility was to lower the crane—reversing the climbing procedure—so the red one could lift the part into place, but the wind made the operation risky. As well, the dead crane could not manoeuvre its hook to pick up the three thousand kilogram weight that is necessary to balance its counterweight when climbing (or, in this case, descending). Lifting the part into place by helicopter could cost tens of thousands of dollars. The only option was to set up a chain winch on the back of the crane to lower the faulty motor down to the roof and raise up the replacement.

But with gale-force gusts for two days, nothing could be brought to the top of the building. When the wind finally dropped enough for the repair operation, there was another unwelcome surprise: the red crane, which was needed to hoist the heavy motor to the roof from a trailer on the ground, would not move, its brake frozen from two days of sitting idle. An hour later, the brake had thawed and the work proceeded, but there was more bad news: the construction elevator that runs up to the building's second penthouse was also broken. The pulley at the top of the elevator shaft, which guides the cable between the cab and the counterweight, had also seized, requiring a day of repairs.

Workers going to the roof, including the crane-repair team, had to walk up from the twentieth floor, the highest point the second elevator reaches, and all materials had to be carried from there. There wasn't much to do but take such adversities in stride. Meanwhile, on the ground around the building, those materials and equipment that required the cranes and elevators piled up.

By the time the cranes and elevators were all back in running order, the contractors were rushing to the burst water main, arranging for the city to shut off the water supply and repair the pipe so the work on the flooded tunnel could resume. Everything was expected to be back to normal quickly but a few fingers were crossed. The forecast again calls for high winds.

Indeed, winter has come early. Snow swirls through the huge beams resting on the cold ground, whipping the faces of three men as they slowly assemble lengths of steel into a metal puzzle. The conditions are bad for outdoor work, but the crew is grateful to be on terra firma behind the building and not 140 metres up on the roof, where steel covered with the decorative curtain wall will enclose the cooling towers, boiler vents, stairway and elevator-control room that stick out of the top of the building. There, the wind has made standing difficult and once again shut down the two tower cranes.

Long before it reaches the site, the steel structure is well on its way to being finished. Sheltered from the weather in the plant of Mariani Metal Fabricators in northwest Toronto, a dozen metal-fitters and welders first create large sections of the eight-metre-tall structure. These are trucked to the site, where the crew of Spark Steel Erectors assembles them into larger sections on the ground, to be hoisted by the crane and finally joined together into a one-storey frame on top of the building.

Being able to put together most of the new floor of the building in a factory or at street-level is a decided advantage of structural steel. The material is one of the most important innovations in modern building, although the use of iron in construction dates from the Industrial Revolution. Structural elements of iron were first incorporated into late eighteenth-century churches and textile mills. Soon, many buildings and bridges were constructed of cast iron, made by heating iron ore and coke in a blast furnace and then pouring it into moulds made of sand. The material could withstand heavy loads, but its high carbon content made it brittle, limiting size and scope. In 1856, Sir Henry Bessemer, son of a British engineer, developed a furnace that continuously introduced air to purify the iron and burn off its carbon, thereby producing steel. Stronger than iron and easier to produce in large volumes, steel revolutionized building. It led to structures both practical and fanciful, from the curved bridge in St. Louis, Missouri to the Eiffel Tower.

Structural steel, a mixture of iron, carbon and trace amounts of manganese, phosphorous, copper and aluminum, is known for its tensile strength—it won't stretch easily under tension—but it does not possess the compressive strength of sturdy concrete. A narrow length of it may buckle under pressure. To make the steel stiffer, pieces are rolled into a shape that in cross-section resembles a capital I, commonly known as an I-beam or girder. Exaggerating the flanges that run across the top and bottom makes the central beam even more rigid. Because fire might cause the exposed metal frame to buckle and collapse, the ironwork is clad with fireproof tile.

Chicago, which was largely destroyed in the great fire of 1871 and subsequently rebuilt, was a proving ground for the new steel technology and the development of the modern office building. So-called cage construction could offer more lucrative rental space without thick masonry-bearing walls at a building's base, and it allowed for large windows to brighten up the interior. It also gave architects' imaginations the chance to soar upward, says Daniel Boorstin in his book, *The Creators*. The sky became the limit. Cities, he says, came to be identified less by their street plans and more by their skylines. The tops of buildings were emblazoned with commercial messages for life insurance, sewing machines and five-and-ten stores.

The speed and ease with which a steel building could be erected were not the least of the material's attributes. Its potential was demonstrated in the fabled Empire State Building in New York City in 1931. Built in just one year and forty-five days, the steel parts for its 102 storeys were prefabricated at a depot across the bay in Bayonne, New Jersey, and assembled with military precision on-site. However, since the 1930s, advances in concrete construction, the rising price of steel, the cost of construction-site as opposed to factory labour, and the design needs and preferences of structural engineers have led to a debate on the merits of concrete versus steel design. Concrete reinforced with steel tends to be cheaper, but it is generally heavier, and can become expensive if a building is taller than about thirty-five storeys or has long, heavy beams that require massive columns to support them.

The equation is a familiar one to Vince Mariani, whose company is responsible for all of Simcoe Place's "miscellaneous metals." This covers everything from the railings in exit stairwells and the frames supporting 150 bathroom vanities to the canopies over the rear loading dock and the steel on the roof. Mariani's company, which he started five years after he moved to Canada from Cassino, Italy, with a degree in metalworking, employs thirty people. They put together everything from steel structural frames to stainless-steel architectural finishes on the outside of buildings.

Larger companies that make entire structures out of huge quantities of steel are directly supplied with I-beams, sheets of steel and assorted sections by mills, but for the modest three hundred tonnes of metal required at Simcoe Place, Mariani comparison-shopped at about a dozen local warehouses that get their steel from mills in Canada, the United States and even England and Belgium. Following the plans supplied by Quinn Dressel, metalworking machines at the Mariani plant cut the steel and the punch holes for bolts. The pieces are fitted and welded together to create larger sections, such as the fifty-six units that will make up much of the roof frame at Simcoe Place. Finally, the sections are coated with grey paint, which is rich in zinc to prevent rust, and then are trucked to the site to be assembled.

The most striking image of modern construction is of the daredevils who work with steel. Negotiating narrow beams high in the air, they wrestle outsized girders into place, fastening piece after piece into a mid-air lattice. In fact, their craft is two centuries old. The first construction of cast and wrought iron was in the late 1700s, and the artisans, called ironworkers or bridgemen, had tough, noisy and dangerous jobs. Some of the earliest ironworkers in North America were Native Indians. Tradition has it they came by "skywalking" naturally, from the methods the Iroquois used to build their extravagant palisades, catwalks and longhouses. In the 1850s, when the Grand Trunk Railway built a bridge across the St. Lawrence River through the Kahnawake reserve near Montreal, Mohawks hired as labourers were adept at climbing as well as connecting and riveting the lengths of iron. By the 1930s, teams of Natives had found work on steel buildings throughout North America. Thousands of them settled in tenements in Brooklyn and built New York City.

Today a good deal has changed. Safety restraints make the work less risky. High-strength bolts have replaced hot rivets. Concrete competes with high steel as the builder's material of choice. And as immigration transforms Canada, new faces join the ironworkers. Bahadur Bains, not a North American Indian but a thirty-seven-year-old from India, stands out among the crew of six erecting the steel frame on the building's roof. A farmer's son from Sikandarpur, a small village in the Punjab, he took a B.A. in political science and English and worked as a clerk in a sugar mill before immigrating to Canada in 1980. Once in Toronto, he did small jobs in factories, learned welding in a steel-fabrication shop, took a course on blueprint reading and finally moved outdoors as an ironworker in 1986. He now earns about thirty-three dollars an hour, including benefits, more than a week's wages at his old clerk's job in India.

His workmates find it hard to get their tongues around the name Bahadur, so they call him Bob. He doesn't mind the anglicized name, but he's not shy about exposing colleagues to Indian culture, especially at lunch. While the others munch on cold salami and cheese sandwiches, he sits down to pungent dal, a curried mixture of lentils, potatoes, garlic, ginger, onion and spices that he keeps hot in a stainless-steel Thermos and scoops up with roti, an Indian flatbread, torn into bite-sized pieces.

There is a different Indian dish every day, all cooked by his wife, Gulsheran, who comes from a village just fifteen kilometres away from his. The two met in Canada in 1990, when they were "introduced," as he puts it, by a friend of his and Gulsheran's uncle. His arranged marriage brings comments from his colleagues, Bains says, but "it works for our culture. We have fewer problems than Canadians." These days the two barely see each other. Bahadur rises at 6:00 a.m., heats up his lunch while he eats a breakfast of toast and gets to the site at 7:30. By the time he leaves work at 4:00, his wife has started her night-shift, packing medicines at a pharmaceutical plant. Bahadur makes dinner and looks after the couple's two children until he goes to bed at 10:00 p.m., long before his wife gets home.

Sleep is welcome. His job is demanding and still dangerous, despite—and sometimes because of—modern safety equipment and standards. The ropes intended to keep steelworkers from falling, for example, also restrict their freedom to move and can trip them. To cope with the cold—ironworkers necessarily spend their entire shift outside—Bains dresses in long johns, trousers, two sweatshirts and a padded coverall. The hood from one of the sweatshirts is tucked for extra warmth under his hard hat, which is permanently turned backwards so the brim does not interfere with his sight in the narrow spaces he negotiates. A thick leather belt slung around his waist supports ten kilograms of tools, including a hammer, a pouch for bolts, and a bracket holding two spud wrenches that between them weigh four kilograms.

These wrenches are the indispensable tool of the ironworker. They have a long tapered handle ending in a pointed spike, which is used to line up the holes in two pieces of steel before they are bolted together. Thus armed, the ironworkers cajole the steel into place. After it is certain the piece of steel is level, the bolts are inserted and tightened, first using the other end of the spud wrench and later a compressed-air torque wrench.

The work is exacting, but the pay is good. It has enabled Bains to taste the good life. He has bought a new house (where his parents will soon join him from India) and another property for a future home north of Toronto. The unemployment typical of construction work has spared him. When he leaves Simcoe Place, he'll spend four months working on a school, then take a break in July to attend a citizenship ceremony that will make him a Canadian.

Meanwhile, inside the building, interior designer Claire Lavoie is imagining the people who will be moving into their new offices at about the same time. The parallel lines of dark blue chalk on the third floor are barely noticeable, scuffed in places and lit only by the dim glow of temporary lights strung from the ceiling. But to Lavoie, the faint markings stand out as if they were etched in neon. On each of them will soon sprout a drywall partition to divide up the space into its offices, meeting rooms, coffee stations, waiting areas and corridors. "The reception desk will be right here," Lavoie says firmly as she moves along. Her eyes follow the lines and linger on points where they intersect or are marked with numbers, circles and slashes to indicate pipes and wires. "This will be a medical examining room with a sink in the corner."

Her certainty comes both from her architect's ability to decipher the drywall contractor's chalk hieroglyphics and from the years she has spent poring over the plans to turn nineteen empty floors of the high-rise into Workers' Compensation Board offices. Now her team's plans, schedules and budgets are becoming reality. Eastern has begun handing over floors to the WCB's contractor, Jackson-Lewis Co., which is doing the customizing or tenant-improvement work. While basic construction continues on the building above and below, the master plan drawn up by Rice Brydone and the staff at the WCB will be used to create the new headquarters.

With little ceremony, the building's large second, third and fourth floors have been handed over. Led by a representative of NORR Partnership, officials from the two contracting companies, Cadillac Fairview, the WCB and Rice Brydone inspected the building on a "walk-through." They took note of deficiencies—such as chipped ceiling panels—as well as work that has intentionally been left incomplete—the exterior curtain wall, for instance, which has yet to be finished. With photographs and reports from the project's electrical, mechanical and structural consultants, the group's findings will be presented in a "certificate of turnover," which lists all the work still to be done by Eastern and formally gives the floors to Jackson-Lewis. The new contractor assumes legal responsibility for the space and becomes the constructor of record registered with the provincial Ministry of Labour.

So much for the formalities. In fact, even before the walk-through, Jackson-Lewis's project manager, Jim Wheatley, had already summoned the main subcontractors to a suite of temporary offices on the building's third floor. It's a step up from the construction-site trailer, but the setting is still rough-hewn compared with the product the team will deliver to the WCB. Drywall boards adorned only with tape and plaster enclose the rooms, wiring hangs exposed from the unfinished ceiling and every footstep resounds on the bare steel floor. The sixteen contractors who will share these offices, chosen through a lengthy tendering process overseen by Jackson-Lewis, Rice Brydone and the WCB, do everything from electrical and mechanical installations to painting and carpet-laying. At the peak of work on the nineteen floors, Wheatley expects there will be as many as 150 tradespeople on the job. With so many people on-site working for different contractors, safety and security becomes a concern. Each of the workers will be given a black-and-white Jackson-Lewis hard-hat sticker to distinguish them from Eastern's team.

Now schedules are being prepared for the work to come. First, the lines are drawn on the walls and floors, indicating the precise locations for fixed components such as partitions, wiring, plumbing, cabinets and shelves. When Rice Brydone gives the go-ahead, these are installed, and then tiles, carpet and paint are applied. Movable components, such as the "demountable" walls that divide up offices, will be erected next and finally desks, chairs and potted plants are brought in. The job of transforming the floors is daunting, but Lavoie is enthusiastic about the task ahead. "This is the time I really like," she says. "Until now it's been paper and graphics. Now someone's taking tools and materials, and building."

For this improvement work to be done, massive amounts of tools, construction materials and office supplies must be brought to the site. Materials are brought up in the two construction elevators when they are not being used by Eastern. Jackson-Lewis must pay the general contractor for the use of the elevators and book them two days in advance.

The work of the hoists continues long into the night. The sound of Guy Boire's voice echoes through the crisp air of the loading dock. "Okay, Sandman, you're up!" he bellows in a heavy French accent, waving an arm in front of Al Grey. The sleepy workman steps forward, pushing a cart loaded with large plastic bags of sand onto Boire's construction elevator. The operator hops in quickly after him, latches the two latticed-steel doors and flicks a lever to send the small cage lurching upward to the building's seventh floor. There he opens the door to let Grey and his cargo out.

While the cab drops earthward, Grey adds the thirty-five-kilogram bags to a carefully arranged row he is leaving for a crew of tile-layers who will arrive in the morning to begin making the concrete base of a slate floor. Within a couple of minutes, Boire is back, accompanied in the elevator by four men with two long, empty trolleys from higher levels. They greet Grey with his new nickname: "Hello, Sandman!" He glares at the hoist operator and manoeuvres his own cart into the tightly packed cab.

There is no conversation on the trip down. Grey, a driver for Amber Tile and Terrazzo Inc., has just passed his twelfth straight hour of work. He started the day at 7:30 a.m. by gathering supplies around the city for the tile work. He arrived at the site at 4:00 p.m., as scheduled, to begin the process of bringing the materials into the building. It's now long past a typical construction work day, but he is joined on the loading dock by a crowd of men hauling boxes of pot lights and electrical conduits, long rafts of drywall, tall wooden cabinets for coffee rooms, panels of raised flooring and massive air-conditioning units. They mill around the concrete platform to pass the time and stay warm in the plummeting temperatures, listening for the telltale clangs and squeaks that herald the arrival of the cabs of the two elevators and waiting patiently for Boire or the other operator, Jim Torkos, to signal their turn to ride up.

There is a sense of urgency, not just because the hour is late but also because the way materials are moved to the floors above will soon change. It's time for the tower crane to be dismantled and lowered to the ground, and these two man-and-materials hoists that have been running up the west side of Simcoe Place for the past year are about to be taken apart and shipped away, turning the work of lifting materials and equipment over to the building's soon-to-be-completed permanent freight elevator.

Eastern is eager for the day when the hoists are removed. Then the curtain wall can be finished and the temporary loading dock beneath the hoists can be cleared and transformed into the park. For their part, subcontractors still hungry for materials and equipment in the floors above are not anxious to use the service elevator. These simpler construction hoists can carry larger and heavier loads and are exposed at ground level, so transport trucks can back right up to them. Materials brought to the permanent loading dock tucked away at the back of the building will have to go down a one-storey shuttle elevator and travel through a long corridor to get to the lone—and no doubt overtaxed—freight elevator.

The solution is to spend nights "loading" the floors—stockpiling as much material as possible in the building each day after four o'clock, when the hoists are no longer needed to move workers and tools. These are also the hours when deliveries are made to Jackson-Lewis Co. "It's a little crazy here sometimes," says Boire, who started work at 6:30 a.m. and will stay until after 8:00 p.m., operating the south hoist, which goes to the twentieth floor. Jim Torkos's elevator, which goes all the way up to the top, will be in demand until after midnight. These long hours aren't a problem for either man. Torkos just started the job two weeks ago, after six months of unemployment, and is happy to rack up as many as eighteen hours a day. Boire bought the hoists on credit and is trying to pay them off. There is little time tonight for him to eat the sandwiches and container of potato salad that his wife, Luce, has made for him. Breaks are few, and are usually taken by stopping the cab quickly at one of the floors that has a working bathroom. The job requires concentration, remembering the levels where he has deposited various workers and trolleys and keeping track of the timing of larger deliveries such as huge air-conditioners, which must be rolled onto the cab on a series of narrow steel pipes because they are too high for standard carts.

The mood around the dock is buoyant, free of the day's rules and demands. Boire and Torkos usually end up lending a hand to shove stubborn loads on or off the hoist. Strictly speaking, it's against union rules, but at this stage their assistance is never refused. When the hoisting is finished in the wee hours of the morning, there's a big pot of coffee in the Jackson-Lewis office on the third floor, where the men come to talk about the night's activities. The real sandman will come along in due time.

Meanwhile, across the city, the friends who had dropped into Ersilia and Dominic Alonzi's home for a cup of Christmas espresso finally left. While her husband went to bed to get some sleep before heading to his job as a labourer for Eastern, Ersilia went to work. She filled two large pots with water, added liberal amounts of salt and olive oil and set them to boil, adding the wide ribbons of lasagne that she had made earlier in the day. Then, with a precision that would make the crews at the site proud, the assembly began. In two large aluminum pans—the kind sold at supermarkets to roast oversized Christmas turkeys—she laid down a layer of the cooked noodles. On top she spread some sauce made from ground veal and her store of homemade tomato paste. Then she scattered mozzarella and Parmesan cheese from a mound grated earlier in the evening by her husband.

She added layer after layer of noodles, sauce and cheese until the pans were filled to the brim with lasagne. At 3:45 a.m., she heaved them into the oven to bake for an hour and a half. By the time the lasagne was ready, Dominic's workmates were idling in a car outside the couple's suburban house. The pans were carefully stacked in a large insulated container to stay warm and placed in the trunk. When the car had pulled off, Ersilia finally headed up to bed.

In another neighbourhood, Maria DiPetta, who works late as a cook at an Italian restaurant, was sending her husband, Mike, out the door with a heavy pan of tiramisù, a dessert she had made earlier with eggs, mascarpone cheese, Italian biscuits, espresso and Tia Maria liqueur.

Their culinary efforts were appreciated by the thirty-six people at the annual Christmas party for Eastern Construction's labourers, carpenters, staff and friends. The lunch is held on the Friday before Christmas, a good time for a party because Fridays tend to be half-days on the site since unions shortened the work week to thirty-seven hours. Instead of going out for a meal or ordering take-out chicken and ribs, as in past years, the workers were persuaded to bring their own food and drink, writing in their selections on a sheet that also asked them to "bring along necessary serving utensils." The list quickly filled as participants offered antipasto, potato salad, lasagne (one of them the traditional kind offered by Dominic Alonzi and one made with asparagus brought by Eastern project coordinator Robert Leonardelli), manicotti, pizza, capicollo, salami, bread, assorted desserts, fruit, soft drinks and—the workers' pride—assorted wines made with palomino, alicante and barbera grapes.

The guests brought their contributions to the office and went off to work. The ten labourers and four carpenters mostly cleaned ice and garbage from the roof. Meanwhile, the office staff prepared for the party, buying paper decorations, warming food in the ovens of a muffin shop across the street and lighting charcoal to grill lamb chops in a barbecue made out of an old steel drum found on the site. Tables and chairs were arranged in a large storeroom in the underground concourse behind the space that one day will house all of the building's fast-food outlets. A boom-box was set up on a stool to play Christmas carols. A large propane heater, once used for warming formwork and freshly laid concrete, was fired up to take the chill off the hard grey floor.

By noon the workers arrived, heaping paper plates with food from the buffet table and filling plastic glasses with wine. They sat at a long table, Italian immigrants like Alonzi and DiPetta, both with thirty years' experience at Eastern, encouraging young professional engineers and managers to try their wine, cured meats and home cooking. The Italians and Portuguese in the group refer to the native Canadians as "mangia-cakes," or cake-eaters, for their bland taste in food. "They don't eat like this," DiPetta explained, gesturing to the piles of garlicky pasta and creamy desserts.

By the time everyone had had their fill, the food on the tables seemed barely touched. Some have volunteered to take the leftovers to the soup kitchen at the nearby Scott Mission. Ersilia Alonzi and Maria DiPetta are happy their cooking reached such a wide and appreciative audience, and, for their labours, they received invitations to Eastern's annual dance and dinner of turkey and mince pie ("mangia-cake food," says Dominic Alonzi, shuddering), to be held in the ballroom of a suburban hotel.

As Christmas approaches, Maria and Ersilia are busy preparing festive family dinners Italian style. In the tradition of her region of Molise, Maria has already bought a whole lamb, parts of which she'll marinate and barbecue. Ersilia plans to serve a combination of cannelloni and fettuccine, which she'll also make fresh, starting in the wee hours of Christmas Day. Once again, sleep will take second place to the preparations for the feast.

Ersilia Alonzi's Lasagne

Noodles:	12 eggs, 1 cup water, about 1 kg flour.
Sauce:	A little olive oil, 2 kg ground veal, chopped onion, garlic, celery, parsley, 5 L tomato paste, water, salt and pepper.
Cheese:	4 balls mozzarella, 450 g Parmesan cheese, grated.

Thoroughly mix noodle ingredients in pasta machine and squeeze into wide lasagne noodles, dry them slightly and later boil them in salted water. Fry meat with olive oil, onion, garlic, celery and parsley in a large pot. Add tomato paste, salt, pepper and water and simmer at least 1-1/2 hours. Layer in pan, starting with noodles, then sauce, Parmesan and mozzarella; repeat layers five times. Cook for 1-1/2 hours at 300°F. Serves 36.

Maria DiPetta's Tiramisù

12 eggs, 500 g mascarpone cheese, 1 cup sugar, 2 packages Italian (Savoyarde) biscuits, 6 or 7 small cups espresso, 2 small glasses Tia Maria liqueur.

Separate eggs and beat whites until stiff. In another bowl, beat yolks, slowly adding sugar and cheese until thick. Carefully fold in whites and refrigerate. Prepare the base by quickly dipping each of the biscuits in a mixture of coffee and liqueur. Place them side by side on the bottom of a large cake pan. Pour on a layer of the mascarpone mixture, then more soaked biscuits, and more mascarpone; repeat, ending with a final layer of mascarpone. Sprinkle with cocoa and refrigerate for a least 12 hours, so the biscuits soak up the cheese and the tiramisù stays firm when cut. Serves 20.

NINETEEN

103 DAYS TO
SUBSTANTIAL PERFORMANCE

Christmas is traditionally a slow time at work, as bleary-eyed employees recovering from revelry and visits from in-laws struggle in. They set their minds to jobs that have been neglected in favour of office parties, long lunches and shopping excursions. Well into the New Year, some companies are forced to get by with skeleton staffs as workers use up holiday time, sunning themselves in warmer climes or caring for children still home from school.

For the past month, the construction site has also fallen prey to the traditional holiday slow-down. In doing this, it's reflecting the mood of the industry at large. Transport companies delivering material give drivers time off at Christmas. Truckers from the U.S. stay home to avoid holiday tie-ups at the border. Subcontractors scale down their work to give employees time off. The traditional biweekly site meeting of major trades and consultants is cancelled. Between Christmas Day and January 2, the project was closed for three statutory holidays. For another three of the days, just fifty of 250 construction workers were on-site, keeping up with only the most critical jobs.

But with only five months to go before the high-rise building must be finished, there is no time to relax. The construction site and the contractors' trailers hum. Phone calls with suppliers and impromptu meetings between managers, foremen and workers take on a hurried tone. All of Eastern's staff—save for field engineer D'Arcy Gorman, whose wife, Christine, has just given birth to a baby girl—are on the job. Every letter and set of meeting minutes includes a bold-typed reminder of the number of working days before the deadline for "substantial performance," when all but 1 per cent of the contract must be completed. The numbering system started when there were 207 days left. Now is the critical watershed, when more than half that time has elapsed. The message today reads emphatically: "Working days to substantial performance=103." The unwritten message is clear: there is not much leeway for time off, delays, surprises or excuses.

"We're not quite over the hump," Brian Gardner says, likening the process to a marathon race, where the determination to keep going has to overcome flagging stamina as the finish line approaches. "We have to get it in people's minds that there is some urgency." The construction manager's strategy relies a good deal on psychology, focusing minds on the task at hand while preventing people from becoming overwhelmed by the quantity of work to do. Schedules that were once broad, covering the entire two-and-a-half-year process of building the high-rise in just a couple of pages, are sharpened to the tiniest details. Where once the work on the ground floor occupied a fraction of the main plan, for instance, the lobby alone now has a huge schedule of its own. Even a specific process like the installation of granite panels on concrete columns at ground level has been broken down into ten different stages.

The work in this area is especially important. All of the activity around the base of the building must be finished by early spring so the builders can concentrate on sidewalks, light standards and landscaping. To this end, the three major subcontractors involved in the curtain wall, drywall and granite work on the first floor have been summoned to long meetings with Eastern, where they go over the precise order of installation. There are two important reasons for this process: Eastern can monitor the work frequently to make sure it is on time, and the subcontractors can be reminded that deadlines are no longer flexible. They must coordinate their activities, making sure, for example, that the scaffolding set up to adjust the curtain wall is not in the way of crews who come to prepare the ground for sidewalks.

Similar schedules are discussed and drawn up for the building's mechanical penthouses, as well as for the office floors, the elevators, the underground concourse and the tunnel that runs under the road behind the building. The next big job to come is the dismantling of the giant tower cranes, which will start once a few last tasks are finished and the derrick needed to take them down is installed on the building's roof, all under Gorman's direction. While his co-workers were excited to hear of the birth of his first child, they will be happy to have D'Arcy back, cracking the whip at the site. "The only thing we can't schedule for," Gardner says unhappily, "is babies."

As the field engineer, Gorman's role is particularly critical in coordinating the final lifting work of the tower cranes. Their last big task is to take away the raised trailers that have been home to him and the rest of the staff since the project began. It's time for the contractors, subcontractors and consultants to decamp from these temporary offices and head to new quarters in various parts of the unfinished building. From there, they will oversee the last months of the job.

In these days of corporate downsizing, outsourcing and re-engineering, most offices are going through a good deal of change, but not too many are picked up, loaded onto a truck and carted away. On construction sites, though, such upheaval is all in a day's work. People learn not to be terribly sentimental about their offices, sometimes moving three or four times over the life of a project as need be. Now it's time to get rid of the trailers altogether. The parking spaces below the scaffolding on which the trailers are perched must be dug up so drains can be installed and new asphalt laid down.

In the past two weeks, Eastern drew up moving plans and enlisted several of its labourers to carry desks, chairs, file cabinets and boxes to new offices scattered around the building. Most of the subcontractors have already set up operations in the building's underground concourse, in the space set aside for their workers to dress and store supplies. Visiting consulting engineers are now working in the control room, where Cadillac Fairview staff will eventually monitor alarms and oversee the building's operations. Eastern's crew has moved into the loading dock, a narrow, windowless, uninsulated space where desks are wedged between a bare concrete block wall and a series of bays covered with large metal garage doors.

Even the basic comforts of the trailer are missing here. The schedules, no-smoking posters, motivational sayings and family photos that once covered the homey walls and memo boards of the trailer have been tacked to bare plywood and exposed steel beams. Sheets of plastic and foam line the drafty doors, and electric heaters have been brought in to take the chill off. Far from being like the bridge of the ship, Gardner muses, the new office "is like being in the engine room." Space is tight, but the number of Eastern staff has recently dropped from ten to seven. Two of the engineers have gone to work for Eastern on the project to expand the Metro Toronto Convention Centre south of the site, where the contractor's large trailer office is being hauled. And secretary Rosy Pereira is taking time off from the stressful job before the birth of her own child, expected in two months. The due date in March is identified as "baby day" on the huge year-at-a-glance calendar stuck to the concrete block wall. Despite its aesthetic drawbacks, the new space in the loading dock has advantages for the practical and thrifty contractors. When it comes time for them to leave, moving vans can back right up to the temporary office to cart away their files, desks and computers.

Next, the load of steel poles, plates and towers, large spools of cable and assorted motors that the cranes are hauling to the top of the building and helping to assemble there will prove to be their undoing. More than a year and a half since they began work at the construction site, the red and white cranes have finally finished their last tasks and will be taken apart.

Slowly the pieces of equipment are fitted together over two days by Frank Baldassare and his crew of three men, who work 150 metres up at the edge of the roof in unseasonable winter fog. The finished product will be a derrick, a machine that looks much like the top of a crane, except it is anchored directly to the building on two giant legs rather than standing high on a mast. Considering it means the demise of the cranes, the machine has appropriately dark roots. Its name dates back to a seventeenth-century English hangman, known only as Derrick, who carried out public executions at Tyburn, in a corner of what is now London's Hyde Park. Such was Derrick's (or Mr. Derrick's) notoriety that his name became synonymous with the gallows itself. In the eighteenth century, when sailors rigged up lifting mechanisms to the masts of their ships, they named them derricks because their shape was much like the post-and-arm construction of the gibbet on top of the gallows.

In the nineteenth century, the derrick moved back to land, where it hoisted containers of goods in ports and blocks of granite in quarries. Finally, the derrick became the workhorse of construction, set up on taller and taller buildings to lift supplies and equipment. But the technology had its drawbacks. The squat device had a limited reach and was firmly fixed to the building, requiring contractors to use several derricks in different positions, dismantling and reassembling them on each new floor as construction progressed.

The versatile tower crane was introduced to help reconstruct large parts of Britain devastated by the bombing of the Second World War. While it couldn't carry as large a load as the sturdy and powerful derrick, it could lift faster and reach farther and, more important, climb within the structure as it grew. The new technology won. Today, derricks are used only to lift outsized loads and to dismantle their modern cousins when the time comes.

It can't come soon enough for the staff at Eastern, who plan several weeks of work for Baldassare's company. It must dismantle the red crane, install the heavy chillers, heat-exchangers and transformers in the upper penthouses, finish the roof and then dismantle the white crane. Installing the fifteen-tonne derrick itself requires foresight and precision timing. It will be stationed in three different places, two for working on the cranes and one for lifting the outsized equipment. Long before the roof of Simcoe Place was constructed, the consulting engineers drew up plans to reinforce the three positions. Steel shoring was erected between the floors immediately below to ensure the collective weight of the derrick and its load did not prove too heavy for concrete structure. And the floors have been tied together with steel cables so they don't tilt up if the load on the derrick suddenly shifts.

The crew of four from Baldassare's company, Euro Crane Erector, one of a small number of companies in the area that own derricks and can dismantle cranes, is mindful of the delicacy of the operation. There is only just enough room to manoeuvre. Cranes come apart the same way they are put together, piece by piece, but Baldassare says the process can be tricky thirty storeys up, especially if the weather is poor and space is tight. "If you pick something up on the ground and make a mistake, you have a chance to correct it," he says. "There's no second chance for us if we drop something from high up."

He had hoped mild weather would prevail and the red crane would take about two days to dismantle, but the weather gods have not looked favourably on this project and the last two years of inclement conditions have taken their toll. Even the most casual handyman knows the havoc that comes from exposing tools and materials to moisture, making metal rust and seize. It's even worse for crane deconstructionists. The job requires old-fashioned elbow grease, unfastening steel fittings that were firmly inserted much earlier and have since been exposed to a steady regimen of rain, drought, heat and cold.

With this in mind, Baldassare's team took nothing for granted. Two men switched on the power to the derrick while the others climbed to the top of the tower crane. With them they took several white pails, the sort used to hold vegetable oil for institutional kitchens but now filled with an array of tools. They selected large steel wrenches and sledgehammers and loosened the fastenings holding the crane's cable, hook and trolley assembly. Then came items known as bolt-ons, so called because they are incidental to the main structure. The derrick was hooked up and each piece in turn was lowered to the roof of the building.

The hard work was still ahead. A crane is a balancing act, the massive weight of the boom and its load offset by the slabs of concrete—its counterweight—in behind. Dismantling the device means subtracting a piece from each side of the equation at a time to maintain equilibrium. The process started with the removal of three of the seven concrete slabs, each weighing between two thousand and twenty-five hundred kilograms. Then the boom—the heaviest and most unwieldy component at nine tonnes and thirty-five metres long—was unbolted and lifted off. Finally, the four remaining concrete slabs, the crane's controls and the whole rear section were removed. So far so good. Next came the A-frame from which the boom and counterweight sections were suspended. The turntable that makes the crane spin, or slew, was unbolted and lowered to the top of the building. All of the heaviest pieces of equipment were dispensed with in a day.

When the dismantlers returned the next morning, the only part left was the twenty-seven-metre latticed-steel tower protruding from the top of the building, an impotent remnant of the once mighty machine. It was made up of seven sections, each of them weighing two tonnes. Baldassare had decided to take it apart in two pieces, and confidently predicted it would be gone in less than an hour. But then the trouble started. One of the massive bolts holding two sections together, just below the top of the building, refused to budge. It had become locked in place by exposure to rain and concrete, which gets into the threads of the bolt and dries the lubricating oil put there to aid its eventual removal.

It took all day for the men to work on the defiant bolt with every manner of tool. Finally, Baldassare borrowed an acetylene torch from the structural-steel crew and cut the ends off the bolt, making it easy to remove. It could have been worse. Once, when Baldassare was taking down a crane held together by pins—thick steel posts like those in hinges, which are knocked in and out with a mallet—the removal of a pin that should have taken minutes took three days. Baldassare shakes his head at the memory. "You never finish learning; you always have to be prepared for surprises."

The contractors at Simcoe Place are happy to see the red crane on its way. Now concrete crews can fill in the holes on the upper floors where the tower once stood. They can also remove the steel scaffolding that shored up the hole for twelve floors below the crane's massive weight, which inhibits work on the wires, pipes and ducts that surround the crane holes. The shoring for the white crane, which will be removed once the derrick moves some heavy equipment into the penthouses below, still extends down to the twentieth and twenty-first floors. This is some cause for concern. It is now several months past the original forecast for these final levels to be turned over to the tenants at the Workers' Compensation Board.

High above, on the thirtieth floor of the high-rise, everything is quiet. This is where you expect to find spacious suites filled with avant-garde furniture and wet bars, reserved for pampered executives who conduct business in hushed tones against a backdrop of the urban panorama. Standing on the unfinished floor with its impressive views of the city, it is easy to imagine the tinkling of ice in glasses of celebratory scotch at the end of hard-won business deals.

The sound of a thirteen-tonne chiller rolling across the bare concrete of the mechanical penthouse above interrupts the reverie. This is nothing compared with the cacophony that will follow. When the chillers begin cooling the air in the building, they will each emit bone-shaking vibrations and a constant one hundred decibels of high-pitched sound. The noise—equivalent to that of a jet plane at take-off—is so loud that technicians will wear heavy-duty ear protection in the space.

All of this noise and vibration could pose a problem for the tenants below, were it not for the intervention of Tom Paige and his crew of acoustical consultants and contractors at Vibron. The company was last on-site making sure underground vibrations from Simcoe Place and the machinery being used to build it did not trouble the delicate recording equipment at the Broadcast Centre next door. Having accomplished that task to his satisfaction, Paige, a senior project engineer, has turned to the problems that noise and vibration may present within Simcoe Place itself.

Some of the loudest features in a building are the pumps, air-handling units, boilers and other machines needed to keep temperature at a comfortable level. Most of this equipment—and the problem—is confined to the special mechanical floors. But other machines, such as the air-handling units on each level that make the ventilation system more efficient, spread the noise around.

Developers want to rent out as much space as possible, including areas near such heavy mechanical and electrical installations, but to maximize their profits, they first have to spend money muffling the noise. Tenants are not only bothered by unwanted sounds, they also worry about the effect on employees' health and productivity. Municipalities in turn impose their own constraints: codes require developers to consider how noise in a new building affects both its occupants and the neighbourhood.

All of this means business for Vibron. As awareness grows of the problems associated with noise, so do expectations. "Standards are getting higher and better," Paige says. The level of background noise in typical high-rise buildings, for example, before office equipment and workers move in, is roughly forty decibels, equivalent to the sound of light traffic. The Workers' Compensation Board, which wants a workplace that reflects its concerned corporate image, asked for a background level of just thirty-five decibels. Even more sensitive places, such as the radio drama studios in the Broadcast Centre, require background levels of just twelve to fifteen decibels, barely a whisper.

To meet the WCB's request, Vibron is installing buffers around the fans in the air-handling units and silencers for the galvanized-metal ducts that run from the units to the offices. Usually fibreglass is used to muffle the sound, but because of concern about microscopic glass fibres getting into the air supply, the silencers here are made of perforated metal. More extensive work must be undertaken to silence the larger equipment. On the floor of the penthouse where the chillers, pumps and transformers are stationed, Vibron is installing thick rubber pads, sheets of fibreglass and plywood. A layer of concrete will soon be poured onto this platform, thereby creating a second floor that is isolated from the main one directly below and can be used to install the machines. Known as a floating floor, it resembles the sprung floors in dance studios, but instead of cushioning dancers' joints, it will muffle sound from being transferred to the offices below.

The vibration generated by the huge rotating motors chugging away in the fans and pumps also poses a problem. When heavy equipment, be it an amplifier or a chiller, sits on the floor, Paige says, "It turns the whole structure into a loudspeaker." To isolate the shakes and rattles, such machines are mounted on large metal springs, some of them thirty centimetres high. These in turn sit on extra-thick concrete pads used to support the weight of the machine. In his time, Paige has installed the springs under a wide array of equipment, including washers and dryers that sit on floors above offices in health clubs and huge speakers in bars and night clubs.

The office workers below will rarely even see any of this heavy equipment, unlike the telephones and fax machines they will use every day. But even the commonplace can be overlooked. They'll switch on computers and make phone calls with hardly a thought for the work of Zdravko Crne. Four years of the electrical engineer's professional life have gone into mapping out the elaborate communications network spread over the WCB's nineteen floors. No telephones, fax machines, computers, modems or printers could come to life until Crne (pronounced Serny) plotted the best route for life-giving cable to take through the building.

Still, his accomplishments are not readily apparent to the casual observer visiting the offices taking shape on the third floor. Drywall crews erect partitions to make meeting and photocopy rooms, carpenters install cabinets in coffee stations and carpet-layers add colour to the reception area. Unnoticed, the most remarkable transformation of the office has already happened.

Hidden beneath the floor are kilometres of cables that will carry telephone and computer traffic from little boxes under the employees' desks to a central communications system that runs up the middle of the building. Crne, who works for electrical consultants Mulvey and Banani, was hired by the WCB to ready the company's technology for the twenty-first century. Cables can be a big worry for the tenant in an office building. Unlike apartment dwellers, whose services come with the rent, companies that lease office space set up their own wiring. They also have special needs that landlords can't anticipate, which is why Cadillac Fairview brings telephone service only as far as the telephone terminal room in the basement. The phone company takes over from there, threading a backbone of fibre-optic and copper cables through large ducts in empty communications rooms built on each of the floors. Then the tenant gets involved. To handle voice communications, the WCB has its own telephone system, known as a private-branch exchange, which allows for many more phone lines at a lower cost. The organization's computers are also on their own networks, linked internally as well as to a large mainframe in a data centre across the city.

Crne has been given the job of laying out the maze of wires, both vertical and horizontal, running from the central room through the organization's offices. Working with the information-systems experts at the WCB, he assessed the latest developments in technology while keeping in mind the future needs of the organization and the layout imposed by the project's interior designers, Rice Brydone. Without careful management, the cables in offices can get out of control. In most offices, redundant wires are rarely taken out. When no one knows what's what, it's easier to leave the tangle undisturbed than to risk disconnecting a wire that belongs to the president's telephone. Crne has seen ceilings collapse from the weight of the wires snaking above.

Some practices adopted in his industry in the last few years have simplified the process. Throughout the 1980s, personal-computer manufacturers provided cables specific to their own devices, so a company had to add or change wiring each time it bought new machines. Now manufacturers offer universal wires that suit any type of computer. Most offices were also reluctant to install more wiring for telephones and computers than they needed, which meant cable had to be tacked on every time the seating plan changed or equipment was added. Today, with what's called saturation-zone wiring, enough is provided at the outset for the maximum number of possible employees and equipment in an area.

At least one voice and one data line will be provided for each of the three thousand WCB employees. With an eye to the future, Crne has ensured even more than that—8,800 data lines and 6,400 voice lines—will be possible. In all, it will amount to 487 kilometres of data cable and 381 kilometres of voice cable. Anticipating the role new technology can play at the WCB, Crne recommended the board use high-capacity wiring. The data cable now being installed, for example, can carry one hundred megabits of information per second, much more than even some mainframe computers. The telephone cable includes four twisted pairs of copper wire, double that in homes. The added capacity will improve the speed and volume of data transmission, allowing WCB caseworkers, for instance, to transmit video images of broken limbs to assessors outside the building.

The better to organize all these wires, the floors are divided into sections, known in architectural terminology as bays. Each bay has a collection point for the wires called a bay box. Under Crne's plan, a wire flows from each worker's desk to the bay box, then on to a hub room built by the WCB's contractors in the core of the floor (there are two hub rooms on each podium level).

Each employee is likely to have different electronic requirements. These are now being reviewed by Rice Brydone and the WCB as they map out each new office and desk. A person with both a phone and a computer modem, for instance, may require two jacks for voice-communications, plus three data jacks if they also use a standard PC as well as one of the board's special imaging computers. This information is passed onto the subcontractor installing the cables on site, Lynx Cabling Systems. It's a complex process that Crne realizes will never be appreciated by the employees when they move in—"especially not if everything works."

Moored firmly on a city street, the building can't be mistaken for a sailing ship, but the language of modern construction is nevertheless anchored in the ancient ways of the sea. Now that the building is on its way to becoming finished, it's time for its commissioning, another term borrowed from the maritime lexicon. Just as a newly built ship must be proven seaworthy before it can be sent out on service, so a land-locked building about to take on thirty floors of office workers has to be shown to be shipshape.

At the helm as the building prepares to see active duty is Mel James, a quiet Welshman with a degree in electrical engineering and twenty years in the energy-management business. James has been hired by Cadillac Fairview as the commissioning agent to put the building through its paces and steer it through its first year of operation. His supervisory work begins with tests of all the mechanical equipment in the tower. As the months go by and tenants move in, he will ensure that everything from air-conditioners to fire sprinklers live up to the expectations of the architects and engineers who designed them.

When James and his team oversee tests, they rely on the volumes of technical specifications compiled by these consultants to accompany the building drawings. These not only detail every piece of equipment but also state how each should perform as part of the final mechanical system. For instance, precise levels are set for the pressure in the pumps and pipes bringing water from the building's boilers to radiators at the base of each window. The optimal temperature and humidity in the building are also stipulated.

As the project nears completion, it is necessary to make sure that the specifications have been correctly followed. The equipment is put through increasingly demanding tests and inspections that show how the building will function once it opens. In the past, such independent monitoring was rare. Contractors did their own tests, but they didn't always have time for the fine details, especially in the crunch before deadline. These days, quality-control experts such as James oversee the process, witnessing the tests, drawing up how-to manuals and making sure that the building's permanent operations staff is properly trained to run the equipment. Quality control, James says, has become more important as computers play a larger role in controlling everything from turning on lights in the morning to monitoring energy consumption throughout the building.

All of the water and air-circulation systems are filled and tested. For good measure, one and a half times the normal pressure is applied to make sure pipes and ducts won't leak: better to know about a drip now than later, after the painters have left and the broadloom has been installed. The next step will be to turn on the equipment, from starting each air-conditioning fan to firing up the three massive boilers. This ensures that a machine works as intended, is safely wired and doesn't produce more than the maximum amount of noise and vibration, showing that the acoustical people at Vibron have done their work.

Once the equipment is up and running, a balancing expert comes in to fine-tune it, adjusting valves and dampers to match the exact levels they're designed to produce or carry. The general contractor does a final check, and then it's the turn of the building's engineering consultants to examine the equipment, making sure it runs according to their original intentions. Meanwhile, officials from the fire department and government regulators visit the site, doing their own tests and inspections of the building's alarms, fire-fighting equipment, elevators and escape routes.

Once each group is satisfied, it gives its okay to Eastern, which is ultimately responsible for the building's performance. The most important approval will be the occupancy permit issued by the municipal building department, required before the contractor can officially hand over the building to Cadillac.

For the time being, Simcoe Place is still like a ship in dry dock. The sea trials will come after Cadillac takes the wheel, when James will conduct his final tests to make doubly sure the entire building works perfectly. At that stage, deficiencies can no longer be the fault of the contractor, who has shown the machinery was correctly installed and balanced. Responsibility will then rest with the designers. James's job won't end when Simcoe Place opens in the summer but will extend far beyond the next 103 days. He will return to the building in fall, winter and spring, to see how it stands up. Testing the heating system is more appropriate on a frosty winter morning than on a mild afternoon.

TWENTY

WOMEN'S WORK

Most gardeners cannot help rushing the season when the first signs of spring appear. Wading into muddy backyards or venturing onto windswept patios, they inspect the results of the winter's ravages, till long-neglected soil and plan the planting to come. The same impulse to make things grow has gripped Jack Campbell and Margaret Rankin. Supervising the landscaping of the park next to the building, Campbell hasn't wasted a minute of the sunny weather that has suddenly descended on the city. When his team from Bruce S. Evans suspended work on the frozen land in December, they did not expect to return to the site until the first day of spring. But now, in early March, with the project's June 2 deadline looming ever closer, the weather has suddenly turned unseasonably warm. Campbell gathers a crew of labourers, alerts Evans's six subcontractors and sets up shop on the site. It is time to get to work.

Because of his early start, the wiry, grey-haired Campbell has not even had time to bring in a trailer to serve as a temporary office. Instead of sitting behind a desk covered in plans like most construction managers, the landscape technologist and forester stands near a corner of the site at a simple table made of weathered wood, its legs studded by rusty nails and its top scarred by saw blades. Cellular phone in hand, he calls nurseries to find out if the ground has thawed enough to allow the trees that Rankin, the landscape architect, picked out last fall to be dug out and shipped to the site. The head start afforded by the warm weather should be good for the oaks, magnolias and hackberries, which are best transplanted in early spring while their tops are dormant. This allows the trees to sink roots before their leaves appear.

Leafy trees may be on their way, but the open space still looks more like a construction site. Concrete workers, electricians and plumbers are putting the finishing touches on underground installations, and a small team from Evans is layering fill, concrete and granite paving stones amid the debris. The work is all set out in a master plan that describes forty-nine tasks to be done in the next three months. Campbell honed the schedule last week with Rankin, Eastern and the companies that are laying the groundwork for the park.

A landscaper's lot is one of patience and dependency. In an ideal world, Campbell, thirty-nine, would have had the entire acre free to work on when he arrived on the site last summer. But the reality of building a park on a construction site is different. The work has been staggered much like that in the building, depending on Eastern's speed at clearing the area, the fluctuations in weather and the wait for materials such as the granite quarried in Finland, cut in Quebec and polished in Toronto. At the moment, the west end of the park, the section farthest away from the building, looks most complete, down to its large paving stones, granite seats, small patches of soil and a few honey-locust trees planted last fall. In the centre of the site, workers are making concrete footings for park fixtures like the huge sign that will bear its official name, still to be decided. At the east end, the bare concrete roof of the underground concourse, which has served as a driveway and loading dock for materials delivered to the two construction elevators, will soon be turned over to the land-scapers as the hoists are finally dismantled and the concrete below them is waterproofed.

Soon passers-by will be able to gaze on the different stages through orange plastic snow fences that will replace the wooden hoarding surrounding the site. This will allow the landscaping work to proceed around the edge of the site. Evans is responsible for the space right to the street, including the sidewalks. First Eastern prepares the area under the perimeter of the site, where steel-and-wooden shoring has held up the walls of the excavated hole. Crews will dig down about a metre, cut off the tops of the steel soldier piles and remove the top of the wooden lagging that stretched between them. Then they will waterproof the edges of the concrete structure now below.

Next, Campbell's team will take over, filling in the trench that remains with gravel and laying down the concrete sidewalk required by the city. To keep the Simcoe Place identity, it has been edged with granite paving stones, designed by Rankin to blend with those in the park beyond. One of the softening features Rankin suggested was a row of nine linden trees stretching along the Front Street sidewalk, but this pastoral touch had to be abandoned when Toronto Hydro reviewed the blueprints and realized the trees would sit on top of a high-voltage electrical duct that services the new building. It runs less than a metre underground, leaving no room for the linden roots, and also generates heat, which could dry them out. "In the city we want to have big beautiful trees," says Rankin with a certain regret, looking at the open space that would have held the trees. "But often we don't have great places to put them."

Meanwhile, in the building above, the efforts of another woman are under scrutiny. It's hard work, heaving panels of steel-and-concrete flooring into place and screwing them on top of pedestals. Jan De Cruz takes a break, straightens up and shakes a thick rope of raven-coloured hair down her back, wiping the beads of sweat from her forehead onto the arm of her lime-green T-shirt. Two labourers walking past stop and watch as she pulls out a pack of cigarettes, lights one and resumes work. She understands their curiosity. The sight of the first woman on the job at Simcoe Place, two years into the project, is enough to make anyone do a double take.

De Cruz, thirty-one, was hired six weeks ago by Building Systems Inc., the subcontractor responsible for the raised flooring under which the wiring will run. Most carpenters consider the job a chore, but De Cruz feels lucky to have it. She hopes the work will finally earn her enough time, after three years of sporadic employment, to complete the one-year stage of her apprenticeship as a carpenter. It will be a significant step in a rather unusual career path. De Cruz was born in England, one of four children, and came to Canada at the age of three. She found her interest in construction early, taking on the handiwork around the house because her father, a systems analyst, was all thumbs. As a teenager, she figured out how to put in a basement ceiling, build a shed and seal the family driveway.

After she graduated from high school in Toronto, she fell in love with a man who persuaded her to become a stripper, working for an agency that sent her to clubs around the city. The pay was good—"as long as you didn't have to drink too much to get yourself to do it," she says—but she found the work distasteful, leaving the job when the relationship with the man ended six months later. She moved on to more traditional jobs, working the phone at an answering service, peddling subscriptions as a telemarketer and selling sporting goods.

Frustrated with moving from job to job—and the low pay in these typically female lines of work—she took a vocational test at an employment centre. Her score in mechanical aptitude was the highest the centre had ever recorded for a woman. So, five years ago, she enrolled in a three-month course called Women in Trades and Technology at Toronto's George Brown College, where she learned basic construction skills with the goal of becoming a carpenter. Lacking the confidence to approach the union and enter the apprenticeship stream, she took a job instead as a labourer on a road crew. She finally gathered her courage and entered a twenty-week carpentry-training program for women, visible minorities and disabled people offered by Local 27 of the Carpenters and Allied Workers Union. The program unfortunately coincided with the depression in the building market, and the work has come slowly ever since for De Cruz. She had fourteen weeks of employment in the first year, fifteen weeks the next and twenty weeks last year. The work ranged from erecting displays at trade shows to installing cabinets in apartments.

Most jobs last no more than a week. The month and a half at Simcoe Place represents her longest stretch of work so far. Between jobs she collects money from welfare or unemployment insurance and works out with weights to stay in shape. It's a typical story for young women trying to get into construction. Only seventy of 5,500 active members at Local 27 are women and only thirteen have completed the four years (or 7,200 hours) of apprenticeship. A provincial committee is looking at ways of removing the barriers to women entering trades.

Legislation is not the best way to go, says Dawn Tattle, the vice-president of Anchor Shoring and Caissons. Tattle, a civil engineer, works with the Toronto chapter of the National Association of Women in Construction. To bring more women into the business, the organization holds power-tool workshops and seminars on electricity, offers scholarships to students and puts on monthly dinners. Teams of members talk to girls as early as Grade 1 about jobs in construction and engineering, and encourage older girls to stay in math and science courses. Tattle believes women who fight to overcome the barriers work harder than men to get ahead. Women made up only 8 per cent of her 1985 graduating class at the University of Toronto's engineering school, she says, but three of the top ten students were women.

The ratios throughout the construction industry are telling. In the U.S., goals and timetables were established in 1978 to encourage women to enter the trades, so that women would make up one quarter of the construction workforce by the start of the millennium. Instead, says Susan Eisenberg in her book, *We'll Call You If We Need You: Experiences of Women Working Construction*, just 2 per cent of construction workers are women. "Despite many examples of tradeswomen who were skilled, conscientious, and productive workers, despite many efforts by tradeswomen as individuals and through grassroots organizations to expand the participation and retention of women, the culture and the workforce composition of the traditionally male industry have remained fairly intact," she writes. Those who did make it in construction were considered exceptional. "For women, the pioneering phase of breaking into union construction was not followed by a critical mass of settlers. Instead, pioneering, contrary to its meaning, became a seemingly permanent condition."

De Cruz has not encountered much sexism on the job, beyond the "one-tenth of 1 per cent of guys who are insecure in some way." Granted, there is a nude centrefold tacked under the lid of the metal box that holds the carpenters' tools, but someone has gone to the trouble of covering up the model's private parts with a large magnet.

She herself wears no makeup and her now square figure is well covered by baggy work clothes. De Cruz uses the same washroom as the men, but checks first to make sure it's empty and calls out to anyone she hears approaching that she's inside. "It's their choice whether they come in—usually they're more embarrassed than me."

Once she's finished her 7,200 hours of apprenticeship and acquired her carpenter's licence, she hopes to start her own company specializing in home renovations, where the money is best. For now, she says, she's earning no more than she did as a stripper twelve years ago. "But I have my pride at the end of the day."

Mona Stephens is a woman happy with Simcoe Place for quite different reasons. As she walks through a large room, she is oblivious to the sound of hammers and saws reverberating through the long, bright space inside the base of the building, punctuated by the shouts of workmen installing radiators in rooms littered with scrap metal, sawdust and empty food and coffee containers. Instead she hears a chorus of playing children, sees a jumble of toys and games and imagines lunch being made for a hoard of hungry toddlers. Soon her dream will come true, when she and Elizabeth Ferguson, co-directors of DayCare Connection, will open their organization's newest child-care centre, which is being readied on the building's ground floor.

Cadillac Fairview has spent $1 million to build, decorate and furnish the centre with everything from cribs and couches to cutlery and computers. It will turn the facility over to the two non-profit operators for a fee of two dollars, the same nominal price it will get for the park. The story behind these bargains illuminates the unusual turns taken by the urban-planning process in the last decade. Simcoe Place's original design called for the 8,300-square-foot space in the northwest corner of the building to house an impressive restaurant looking out over the honey-locust trees, granite walls, splashing fountain and striking art in the new park next door. By the time city planners had their say, however, the food stations had turned into diaper-changing stations.

The issue dates back to when the CBC began developing the large parking lot, planning its own massive Broadcast Centre as well as several large commercial and residential buildings on the block. The city agreed to vary its zoning regulations to give the CBC extra density for its headquarters if the corporation anted up something extra for the community. An example of the let's-make-a-deal planning of the booming 1980s, such compromises transformed Toronto in the space of a decade. Developers built taller and denser buildings than set out in the city's official plan, much to the chagrin of critics and community activists. Guidelines dictating what kind of buildings, of which size and in which location were ignored.

In exchange for their generosity, however, the dealmakers extracted millions of dollars in benefits for the city: parks, low-cost housing, the preservation of historical buildings. In exchange for the deal at Simcoe Place, the CBC agreed to put in the park, spend $1.5 million on artwork, sell its old offices to the municipality for low-cost housing and provide a seventy-two-space day-care centre in the residential part of the development. When Cadillac won the contract to build the Broadcast Centre and lease the land from the CBC for the commercial project, it also took on responsibility for the park and artwork. Later, when the plans for the residential building were put on hold, Cadillac became obliged to build the day care at Simcoe Place, at least temporarily. Plans to put a restaurant in the prime northwest corner of the building were scrapped and the day care was put there instead.

The deal meant a trip back to the drawing-board for the architects, who designed the facility under strict government regulations dictating everything from the square footage of floors and windows to the amount of shade over the adjoining playground. As the day care neared completion, Cadillac invited applications from a handful of services—non-profit, as specified by the city—to run it. Stephens and Ferguson's progressive proposal to accommodate not only full-time workers but also job-sharing parents who need child care only part of the week and those on short-term contracts was successful.

The new and lavish facilities contrast sharply with the first centre the two early-childhood educators set up twenty years ago in a modest east-end house. Called DayCare Connection, it was typical of the times, closer to where clients lived than where they worked.

Back then, services were started with the help of government grants and operated on shoestring budgets—parents paid just thirty-five dollars a week. Day care, equated with baby-sitting, was almost unregulated, and mothers who took advantage of the service were often criticized for leaving their children with strangers rather than nurturing them at home.

Today there are few qualms about the place of day care in the working world. Children are enrolled in enriched programs that, day-care advocates say, make them more independent, confident and motivated than those looked after by their families. Many day cares also act as drop-in centres for children looked after by parents or nannies at home, both to relieve the adults and to provide stimulating activities with other children.

Day care today costs up to a thousand dollars a month for infants—"as much as a mortgage," Stephens says. And parents—fathers as well as mothers—take part in the running of the centre. This year the parents decided, for instance, that one of DayCare Connection's facilities, which is in a senior-citizens' home, should celebrate spring instead of Easter.

As Ferguson plans the finishing touches for the centre at Simcoe Place, parents are not her only guide; endless regulations govern almost every step of the operation. They stipulate how many building blocks, books and "cognitive toys and puzzles" must be made available for each child. "Drama centres" featuring mock-ups of hospitals, spaceships or train stations must be refreshed regularly. And the day care has a "pro-diversity" policy, extending to dolls outfitted with crutches and wheelchairs and play kitchens supplied with plastic matzo and chapattis as well as conventional bread. A political creation must be politically correct.

Carolyn Cooper is making her own list of necessities. Lists have been a lifelong obsession for her. Raised by parents who intricately mapped out every chore and activity they undertook, she learned to leave nothing to chance. Duffle bags were packed weeks in advance of family camping trips. Master shopping lists were run off on a Gestetner machine and filled in well before the weekly grocery run.

While neighbours looked forward to the weekend as a time to relax, the Cooper family worked their way through a detailed plan of operations that needed attention. "It wasn't a good Monday morning if everything on the list wasn't done," says Cooper, an administrative assistant who now resorts to the same practice when plotting her own weekend diversions.

On weekdays, she puts the family preoccupation to good use by plotting how to move thirteen hundred client-services staff of the Workers' Compensation Board into their new offices in Simcoe Place. With the first stage of the move coming soon, she's busy ordering new business cards for each employee, deciding who has authority to go where in the security-conscious building and booking staff seminars in meeting rooms that don't yet have lights, carpeting or walls. "There's a million details bouncing around in my head," says Cooper, thirty-eight, with typical rapid-fire enthusiasm.

To avoid lying awake at night, she spends her days making lists of what needs to be done. These are not the kind scribbled on the backs of envelopes or jotted on yellow Post-it notes but lengthy memoranda noted in her diary, plugged into computer spreadsheets and stuffed into huge binders with headings like Work-station Reviews and Unresolved Issues. The binders go with her as she makes her way from meeting to meeting with everyone from executives hiring movers to insecure employees who demand drawers on their new desks that lock.

The moving plans started taking shape four years ago, when the board needed more space than its midtown headquarters afforded. By the time construction was under way two years later, the interior designers at Rice Brydone had developed a second, more detailed plan for relocating the organization and its three thousand staff into the space. It was drawn up by a five-member committee made up of employees from the WCB and the interior designer.

A department's place in the building is determined by its function. Thus Cooper's client-services representatives, who deal with the hundreds of injured workers and employers visiting the WCB each day, are destined for the lower floors, closest to the entrance. The committee also established space standards for each category of worker, determining how much room and what kind of furniture they needed and whether they required walls for privacy or confidentiality. Until now, the WCB has had no such guidelines, so some employees will get more status in the new building, for instance, graduating to offices from workstations, while others, including Cooper herself, will lose it. Currently working in a sizeable office vacated by a doctor who evaluated WCB claims, Cooper will move to a much more spartan open desk in a back corner of the second floor.

After employees were allotted places at Simcoe Place, decisions had to be made on the kinds of computers, phones, desks and chairs each would get and how people would move to the new building. Cooper, who joined the board as an adjudicator in 1977 and currently works in a unit that deals with injured workers in the south part of Toronto, was named one of seven coordinators looking after this relocation. The actual move, to take place over the course of sixteen weeks, will be carried out on weekends. Cooper's division is the first to go, and she knows that for several months, her Monday mornings will be devoted to sorting out mix-ups.

Her work may be arduous, but she finds it endlessly interesting, figuring out, for example, how departments will continue to function in two buildings at the same time. Her day begins at 7:30 a.m. and she doesn't get home until eight or nine at night. Even then, she has to sort through as many as seventy-five messages that came in during her day of meetings. Oddly enough, in all the time she's been working on the plans, she's been to the new building only once, when she got to inspect the area where she'll work. That seat won't be hers for several months, though. In the meantime, her relocation team has to shepherd the last of the WCB employees into the new building. Then she will resume the more predictable job of preparing budgets and analyzing statistics for her old unit.

Meetings and details are a preoccupation for another woman involved in Simcoe Place. Mandy Scully's marketing presentation to the cluster of business executives begins not with the usual charts and graphs in an oak-lined boardroom but with the donning of steel-toed boots and hard hats. The group undergoing this transformation has come to Simcoe Place in search of five thousand square feet of office space—a fifth of one of the building's thirty floors. Their tour begins on the ground floor, where they run their hands along the smooth marble and granite of the lobby and size up the clothing stores and coffee kiosks beginning to take shape. They file into the alfresco construction elevator, which is about to be dismantled, for the trip to the twenty-second floor. There they take in panoramic views of the city, inspect a sample of specialty flooring and talk about the cost of turning the open concrete into impressive offices.

Within forty-five minutes the inspection is finished, but Scully knows there is much more to be done before the Now Leasing sign can be taken down. A director of office leasing for Cadillac Fairview, Scully uses brochures, gifts, slide-shows, lunches, follow-up calls and tours like this one to woo business for Simcoe Place. She needs to find tenants for the building's top nine floors, known as its "spec" space. During the development boom of the 1980s, whole office towers— a million square feet or more—were built almost entirely on specu-lation. Confident developers had an "If you build it, they will come" mentality; eager tenants would sign on once the construction was well under way. But with more than 16 per cent of the office space in the city core now sitting vacant, finding tenants for 225,000 square feet at Simcoe Place requires a huge effort from Scully and leasing director Stuart Wanlin.

The effort to sell the space is focused on two groups, the 250 commercial real-estate brokers whom Scully considers Toronto's most influential, and the businesses she terms prospects, the law firms, investment brokers and insurance companies who may be looking to move to new quarters. Some intelligence helps narrow the field: Cadillac has a computer database that lists all the major tenants in the downtown core and the dates their leases expire. The hottest prospects gleaned from the list get more attention, including what Scully calls a "significant direct-mail piece" that is hand-delivered each year. The most recent "piece" was a silver hardcover book enti-tled *Simcoe Place: Ready for Tomorrow* and a compact disc of the Toronto Symphony performing Beethoven's Eroica Symphony and

Romances No. 1 and 2 for Violin and Orchestra. The works were not composed or recorded with Simcoe Place in mind, of course. But they are deemed appropriate because they were performed at Roy Thomson Hall, next to the site, and are considered suitably "high-end" for the building's plush conservative image.

Simcoe Place is rated by real-estate brokers as an A-class project, which means that it is made with high-quality materials and equipped with the latest technology, such as the raised flooring to accommodate computer wiring. The only higher rating is Triple-A, given to similar buildings that are in the heart of Toronto's financial district a few blocks to the east. To make up for Simcoe Place's location, Scully tells her tour groups about the unobstructed views, hidden support columns and layouts that allow for 16 corner offices but also suit an open-concept plan. For brokers who needed a little extra prodding, Cadillac recently staged a barbecue in a large tent set up on the parking lot next to the project, featuring chicken, roast beef and tours of the floor.

This kind of marketing carries a bigger price tag, says Murray Dea, vice-president of office leasing and marketing for Cadillac. But it could save the developer from paying the realty taxes and operating costs for unleased floors once the building opens. Otherwise Cadillac will have to pay fixed costs of $18.50 per square foot a year while forgoing both base rents of about $5 a square foot a year and the money to be made by improving the space for a tenant. Patience is the most important virtue for someone trying to lease out an office. Scully knows from experience that most large tenants will take about two years to decide whether to move into a high-rise. So far, a number of interested parties are in the middle of this "sales-cycle," she says, but no deals have been made.

Meanwhile, amid the frenzy that surrounds the base of Simcoe Place, the appearance of a blue-and-white striped tent is giving seasoned construction-site observers pause. More marketing barbecues? A misguided carnival troupe? A head start on the building's opening ceremonies? A camp for workers burning the midnight oil? The curious who peek inside are not much more enlightened. Sitting within the tent is a large flat piece of concrete topped with a vast ring of aluminum. The explanation lies five thousand kilometres away, in the London, England, studio of sculptor Anish Kapoor. The ring, it turns out, is the first level of the mountain that he has been planning for fifteen years. The ten-metre-high aluminum structure being glued together ring by ring under the tent in the park is one of eight works of art taking shape around the high-rise development.

Kapoor's mountain should turn out to be one of the most ambitious sculptures Toronto has seen. Toronto, however, does not always like what it sees. So-called public art has long graced city boulevards and civic squares, but the public has often responded to such gifts with resentment and embarrassment. Criticism of a towering sculptural tribute to Canadian airmen—nicknamed "Gumby Goes to Heaven" because of its resemblance to the elongated green Plasticine character pointing to the sky—moved the city to action in the mid-eighties. It established a formal policy to regulate the monuments and memorials decorating sidewalks, parks and the plazas surrounding new buildings.

A public-art commission, made up of lawyers, developers, architects, artists and art dealers, oversees the process, and developers are directed to "enrich the public realm" by devoting 1 per cent of their gross construction costs to art. This philanthropy is not entirely self-less, because the developer is usually allowed to exceed normal building densities in return. Cadillac Fairview has agreed to spend $750,000 on art in the park and the same amount on the public areas inside both phases of its development. Cadillac asked consultant Karen Mills to come up with the art, and she organized competitions to choose the pieces. Approaching her task enthusiastically, the small blonde woman decided to spread the wealth among many works of art, rather than one or two large items—what she calls the "brooch approach."

As well as bringing to life Kapoor's imaginary mountain, which cost $425,000, she has earmarked $125,000 for the outdoor memorial to former Lieutenant-Governor John Graves Simcoe and his wife, Elizabeth, which takes the shape of a surveyor's tent and table and a pyramid-shaped fountain. Inside the building, the public art includes *Aurorae*, images of nebulae and galaxies sandblasted on the glass separating the day-care centre from the lobby. Downstairs in the food court, some countertops will be made of coloured concrete embedded with fossils, images of goblets, brightly coloured glass and petroglyphs.

Artist Karl Schantz of Toronto, who made the counters, says the thought of people eating burgers and pizza on his creation was unsettling at first, but, he says, "There's no reason why something that's essentially utilitarian can't be high art that people can relate to." Toronto artist Barbara Astman, who created *Aurorae* and another piece of glass artwork that will have all of the names of the people who created the building etched in it, says she prefers to be "part of the building rather than someone who came along later to decorate it." Like most artists who work in heavy materials, Astman, a self-proclaimed control freak, does not actually execute her designs. Instead, she gives the artwork she has drawn to a technician to be photographed and transferred onto the glass.

A continent away, Kapoor also took pains to make sure his design and intentions could be followed exactly, this time by the technicians at RCI Waterjet Cutting Services in Brampton. He made an eight-by-five-metre topographical drawing of the mountain's layers that would transfer readily to computer. The RCI staff are using a fine jet of water to cut rings from thirty-four tonnes of aluminum sheets. As the seventeen hundred pieces are made, they are trucked to the site, where metal fabricators do the assembly.

Kapoor, forty-one, who will first see his unusual sculpture in a month, when it's almost finished, says the idea for the mountain came from his work on artificial landscapes. It's intended to look man-made but appear more natural as it weathers and the aluminum darkens over time. "I hope it's going to be interesting enough," he says, "perhaps even beguiling enough, to be meaningful, in spite of the fact that no one has an explanation for it."

So far the only critical comments on the creative process have come from construction workers, who are not given to cutting-edge tastes in modern art. With predictable cynicism, they have christened the mysterious striped awning "the beer tent." One contractor said that he found it hard to believe that *Aurorae* could be considered art, but that he appreciated its intricate sandblasting work. Another refused to be included in the names project because he thinks it's a waste of money. Mills, whose tiny size belies her iron will, has responded to the reaction from her first audience with equanimity. This week she posted a prominent notice at the site explaining the art and pointing out that the execution and installation of it means jobs for technicians, fabricators and material suppliers. "It's a great way," she wrote, "to team art and industry."

TWENTY-ONE

IT'S A WRAP

I t is hard to be surprised by the sight of a new building. A cake can be iced at the last minute, decorated in delightful, eye-catching swirls and frills that hide its layers. A garden tended and turned is suddenly transformed by bright annual flowers. But the long process of cladding a building with a curtain wall, panel by panel, leaves little to the imagination. From most vantage points, the architects' vision and ironworkers' craft are laid bare.

In one place, however, the magic happens a little faster. For the last nine months, a rough patchwork of plywood and green sheets of insulation has covered the western flank of Simcoe Place. This is the building's working side, where the construction elevators hoisted materials and workers to each floor. A temporary wall fitted between the elevator cars and the building's concrete structure took the place of the curtain wall, keeping out rain and wind but also giving the building an unkempt appearance. Inside, the elevator bays were left without the fixtures and finishes—from radiators and drop ceilings to window shades—that the rest of the floor received.

Looks are not the only consideration in finishing off the wall on this warm April day. Contractors' reputations—and money—are also on the line. Within six weeks, all of the building's exterior must be completed and the area inside made habitable. In construction, this process is known as zipping up. All of the materials to do the work were left here long ago when the construction hoists and cranes were still operating. Starting at ground level and working floor by floor, the shabby temporary wall is removed. Then panels of the curtain wall are lifted into place with a winch operating on the floor above.

Each is secured with bolts and welding torches. Finally, the elevator bay is finished with the radiators, ducts, drop ceilings, raised flooring and window shades that were left out.

The sense of haste surrounding the procedure is palpable. The first labourers and carpenters start work at 1:30 in the morning, removing the temporary walls as well as the doors and ramps that led to the construction elevators. A crew of ironworkers arrives at 7:00 a.m. to begin an eleven-hour shift, fitting the six panels of mirrored glass missing from each level. Plumbers, sheet-metal workers, carpenters and drywallers quickly follow in turn, to transform each of the former elevator bays into completed floors.

With numerous construction trades vying over the same part of the building, the situation can easily get confusing, even dangerous. Maintaining order at this crucial stage is another job for field engineer Dean Sabean, who, since the project began, has been preoccupied with overseeing a number of different areas of the site. Now he gets a list of tasks ranging from scheduling the carpenters and labourers on staggered shifts and checking off every panel of curtain wall that is welded into place to making sure the day's weather forecast is available to the predawn arrivals. There is intense pressure. On the schedule that Eastern drew up when the project began, the zip-up was plotted to start in early January, but the endless delays, including the late opening of the service elevator, meant it could not begin until mid-April—almost the last point it could have started for the building to be "substantially complete" by June 2. That deadline looms heavily on the minds of those on the site. The current schedule calls for the last work on the zip-up to be finished just four days before.

The process starts slowly, as ironworkers take pains over the alignment of the mirrored glass panels installed on the lower floors. Their caution is prudent; if the first panels go on crookedly, those above will also be out of line. The pace eventually picks up to as much as a floor and a half a day, but the rate must reach two or more for the job to finish on time. "If the date is missed, everyone loses," Sabean says soberly. Indeed, each of the subcontractors he deals with has a vested interest in finishing on time, because 10 per cent of their payments have been withheld in case of claims from workers or suppliers. They will not recover their money until forty-five days after the completion date.

Despite the need for speed, the small-framed thirty-two-year-old engineer, who has worked for Eastern since graduating from university in Nova Scotia, is taking care to ensure that the job is done carefully. He knows the price that construction work can exact. He grew up in Halifax and Port Lorne, a small fishing village on the Bay of Fundy, the descendant of carpenters who had built many of the area's homes and shops. They suffered the consequences: Sabean's father twice fell from roofs on which he was working. The second fall, when he was in his early forties, left him with crushed spinal discs for which he spent six months strapped to a hospital bed. Now sixty-three, he wears a steel back brace.

Not wanting to meet the same fate doing hands-on work, Sabean decided to become an engineer. But while earning extra money working summers as a labourer, his right index finger was crushed by a board that fell on his hand from a tall platform he was moving. Doctors had to cut off his finger at the knuckle. The result is hard to look at, a thickened, scarred stub where the finger once was. There is traditionally a gulf between professional engineers and the workaday labourers and carpenters around a job site, but Sabean's experience has given him respect for the men on whom he depends to speed along the closing of the building. "It should be safety at all costs," he says. "I won't take chances myself, and I won't take them with anyone else."

One of the finishing touches on the site is, of course, cleaning up. In Kebba Manneh's village in the West African country of Gambia, nothing was thrown away. Clothing, wood, food containers, packing cases, machines and flour bags were used and reused in many different guises. Working as a labourer on the construction site, Manneh continues to practise a similar kind of conservation. While attention is focused on the finishing touches in the tower itself, he and two fellow labourers, also Gambians, spend their days on the ground around its perimeter, reducing the protective wooden hoarding to its component parts of plywood, beams, studs, bolts and steel plates. They work deliberately; handled carefully, these materials can be turned into sheds, floors, fence posts and garden borders, or remade into more hoarding for other construction projects.

"Nothing is garbage nowadays," says Manneh, thirty-seven, who came to Canada nine years ago. "You throw something out and someone else needs it." Responding to that need is the company he works for, Happy Harry's Used Building Materials, which specializes in reusing products once sent to landfill sites. The company is working at Simcoe Place courtesy of Eastern, which offered to give the hoarding to any takers as long as unionized workers were used in the process of taking it down and carting it away. The material is trucked to the Happy Harry's warehouse store in the north part of the city and sold for about half its original price.

This attempt to reclaim some of the waste generated on-site is unusual. "It's easier for construction companies to take all this stuff to the dump," says Marty Maier, the president of Happy Harry's, who figures the salvageable material from Simcoe Place's hoarding will fetch about twenty thousand dollars. The attitude towards all kinds of trash on construction sites has changed considerably. Builders once took care of it by holding infrequent clean-up blitzes, seconding a few workers from each of the trades to do the work, but while this approach seemed a model of cooperation, it wasn't efficient or safe. Waste would pile up around the site for as much as two weeks between clean-ups. Ontario's Occupational Health and Safety Act declared the garbage piles hazardous and labelled contractors responsible for them negligent. There was also another problem: most of the workers assigned to do the dirty work were young apprentices, hired to learn skilled trades. Instead, they were taught the finer points of loading dumpsters and sweeping. These were jobs better suited to general labourers, it was thought, and the labourers' unions successfully filed grievances to make the clean-up work theirs.

These days, salvagers such as Happy Harry's take some of the waste and contractors allocate labourers to look after the rest. Each of the subcontractors is still responsible for trade-specific waste, such as the crates, spools and skids that carry materials. In addition, they are charged a percentage of Eastern's clean-up cost for the leftover general debris, usually based on the number of workers they employ.

Sometimes the amount is adjusted if one company is noticeably tidier or messier than others.

Getting rid of garbage is becoming more necessary—and more difficult—as the building nears completion. Earlier in the project, waste could be sent rumbling through chutes, lowered in large wooden boxes by the cranes or transported by the two large construction hoists to dumpsters on the ground. These methods are out of the question now that the chutes, cranes and hoists are gone and the outside of the building is almost totally closed up. Instead, labourers transport the garbage on dollies or buggies down the building's already overtaxed service elevator to the second underground parking level. From there, it is loaded onto a small pick-up truck and driven up to dumpsters stationed two levels above at the cramped loading dock behind the building.

The dumpsters' owner, Dual Removal Systems, visits the site at least three times a week to pick up material and decide where it goes. Some of it, considered general debris, will be taken directly to a landfill site outside of the city, but if a good part of a load is considered salvageable, Dual must sort it so that just the garbage goes to the landfill and the rest goes to a recycler. A third category, pure recyclable material, is dealt with more directly. Clean fill, such as concrete, mortar and concrete blocks, is sent to build up the Leslie Street Spit or other construction projects. Decent wood can be sent to plants that chip it for fibreboard. Drywall will be chopped up and remade into more drywall. Mechanical contractors preserve the piles of metal shavings created by pipefitting and send them to steel mills, which melt them down for more pipes. Even sawdust left over from creating formwork and cabinetry is used by workers cleaning floors, who wet it and sprinkle it around to trap dust as they sweep. Eastern labourer Patrick Kelly, busy cleaning the rooms on each floor that house the building's mechanical, electrical and communications equipment, says the sawdust is free and works better than products on the market designed to control the dust.

It all sounds impressive, but the amount of waste recycled on the site is still dwarfed by what is thrown away. Builders pressed by schedules resist the time and effort required to sort material and ship it to the appropriate recycling companies, and manufacturers do not adhere to the first of the three Rs of conservation: reducing the packaging that comes from construction supplies. Everything from toilets to light fixtures comes in heavy cardboard containers or wooden skids, which eventually have to be disposed of. In Africa, such materials might make decent walls and roofs for houses or fuel for heating and cooking, but in North America, they mostly become landfill.

There may be more clean-up to do, but a sense of completion is in the air. The lobby ceiling is shining with its final coat of white paint, freshly formed sidewalks surround the building's perimeter and even the new magnolias in the park have produced a flash of pink petals for passers-by to admire on the early spring day. But hidden within a barricade of plywood hoarding behind the building, one part of the development is far from ready. What the architect's designs show as a neatly tiled and painted tunnel connecting Simcoe Place with Metro Hall to the north is still a hole in the ground.

Work on the tunnel has repeatedly stalled. First, there were the changes in design and price, and delays in approvals. Then came the complexities of dealing with in-ground gas, water, sewer and telephone lines. Now the excavation crew has been stopped short by an unexpected outcropping of bedrock. The hole is not even deep enough yet to put the tunnel's concrete footings in place. On a rainy morning, a place that should be bustling with activity is instead deserted; water pours into the hole and makes work in the cramped space impossible. Clay has turned into deep pools of mud that sticks to boots and pant legs in heavy clumps known in the excavation business as gumbo. Reinforcing steel bars destined for the concrete chambers that will channel sewage under the tunnel lie rusting in piles. The twenty-seven-metre-long passageway that will occupy the space is represented only by a line of orange dots spray-painted by surveyors on the wooden walls shoring up the sides of the hole.

"You have to have a good imagination down here," says D'Arcy Gorman, in a typically ascerbic tone, looking around the dark, empty worksite as cars and trucks rattle over the wooden planks of the temporary roadbed overhead. Gorman, who has taken on the job of supervising the tunnel work for Eastern, scrapes a boot along the ground to reveal the tough task still facing the excavators. His toe exposes a hard crust of boulders and bedrock that will take several more weeks to remove. It is an unhappy revelation to everyone involved. Tests conducted by soil technicians long before work on the building was under way indicated the excavators would hit bedrock 9.7 metres below ground level—exactly where they found it in the main building site just to the south. Since the lowest part of the tunnel is only ten metres down, the digging job looked easy. The excavators would have to work through only thirty centimetres of rock. Even better, the tests indicated the top layer of rock was an easy-to-dig variety known as weathered shale.

When Rumble Contracting got down to digging, though, they encountered the rock two metres higher than they had expected. And instead of soft, crumbling shale, they found a much harder variety mixed with limestone. This sort of aberration confounds soil technicians, who draw their conclusions about what's underground from core samples taken thirty metres apart. That the earth is full of surprises doesn't come as news to George Rumble, the president of the company that also excavated the hole for the main building. In forty years of digging under Toronto—he cleared the way for the city's first subway line and the foundations for the CN Tower—Rumble has learned that rock can change completely from one block to the next.

The variations can be traced back to the natural unevenness of the sea floor that once covered the area, along with later weathering of the rock or fluctuations in pressure over time that caused a section of rock to pop up. Excavators prefer softer clay and soil. Rock is more costly and time-consuming to remove, especially in a tight space like the tunnel, where the digging and hauling is done by a backhoe and a front-end loader that are a fraction of the size of those used in the building site.

The efficient approach used to construct the main building, where all kinds of different activities can overlap, will not work here. The narrowness of the tunnel prevents the different trades from working side by side. Besides, the excavators block the entrance, leaving little room for the pipe-fitters and concrete formers who could be getting down to their work. It's now clear the tunnel's construction will go on long after the deadline set for the completion of the project. This week, Eastern and Cadillac Fairview are still discussing whether to exclude the tunnel from the requirement because of the delays in getting started.

Underground in the main building, more unfinished business. Talk is curt and faces grim among the circle of men looking at two escalators that will shuttle people from the concourse food court to the lobby. What should be a busy work site is also idle. The escalator installers are waiting for panels of decorative stainless steel to cover the edges of the huge devices. The angry general contractors in the group complain that follow-on work on the floor and walls in the opening around the escalators has been delayed. A representative from subcontractor Schindler Elevator blames the plant that's making the panels, which did not fit properly and had to be redone. It's a typical dialogue that takes on more urgency this close to the building's completion date.

Meanwhile, the escalators are exposed, an unusual chance to look at the mechanisms underneath that transport people between floors of buildings the world over. Escalator stairs are connected to an endless chain that runs around a drive wheel. This is powered by a fifteen-horsepower electric motor called a bull gear. A similar chain and wheel keep the rubber handrail moving in sync with the steps. Like in the escalator's cousin, the traction elevator, a counterweight helps do the hoisting. In this case, the escalator's returning stairs are the counterweight to the ascending ones, so the motor has to lift the weight only of the passengers on board.

The technology has not changed much since the escalator was invented in 1891. The earliest model was a simple conveyor belt inclined at twenty-five degrees, which daring passengers rode by leaning forward or standing on cleats arranged along it. Soon the ride was made more comfortable by adding steps and a moving handrail, creating a travelling staircase. In 1900, Otis Elevator first coined the term escalator to describe the version it installed at the Paris Exposition. The invention was greeted with excitement as well as skepticism. A London critic predicted that "the sight of all those stairs gravely walking upward for ever and ever is calculated to seriously shock a man of nervous temperament."

Despite such reservations, the invention—and its new name— caught on, mostly because escalators are an efficient way of continually moving a large number of people between floors of a building. Banks of them can be found in transit stations, stadiums, airports, hotels, convention centres, public parks and even religious shrines. Today's escalators can ferry riders as much as eighteen metres and be inclined at a steep thirty degrees. They also include safety features that make them less risky to travel on than the early models. Interlocking grooves on the tops (known as treads) and the vertical risers of each stair ensure that they fit tightly together at each end of the ride, so nothing can get caught between the collapsing steps. As the stairs approach the landing, the grooves pass through what's called a comb, meant to deflect any objects. A computerized sensor cuts the power if anything becomes caught. The edges of the steps are painted yellow or lit from below to show riders where they separate. And a "finger-safety guard" prevents anything from getting trapped in the returning handrail.

Still, Don Reasin, the construction manager for Schindler, has seen a lot of accidents on a succession of escalator technologies in his thirty-eight years in the business. Usually, he says, it's because people are careless and do not supervise children when riding. The teenage grunge look can be especially hazardous. "Kids that go on escalators with their shoelaces undone—it's like committing suicide," he says. With long, drooping clothing in mind, the missing stainless-steel "skirts" on either side of the steps of Simcoe Place's escalators will be coated with the same Teflon used on baking pans to help stop objects from getting caught.

Keeping the two machines running smoothly will be critical. Operating at a speed of twenty-seven metres a minute, each escalator will carry as many as eight thousand people an hour during the lunch-time crunch. The sixteen-metre-long escalators, each of which weighs nine tonnes and costs $150,000, were made at Schindler's plant in Clinton, North Carolina, and shipped to the site on flatbed trucks early in the construction, while the underground concourse was still being made. They were not needed for some time but had to be lowered into place with a crane before the area was covered with the next level of construction.

Recently a crew of four used a large chain block to lift the escalators into place between the concourse and the ground floor. They now rest on thick rubber mats that will stop their vibrations from being transferred to the building. When the stainless-steel side panels are finally ready, two men from Schindler will return to the site to install them, as well as the narrow glass balustrades and handrails alongside the moving stairs. It will all be ready, Reasin reassures his audience of frowning contractors, long before the first office worker heads to the concourse for the morning break.

This is where Paul Harrs takes over. For the thousands of people who will use the escalators, some of the most critical details are to be found in his files at Cadillac Fairview: which of the food-court outlets will serve coffee and cappuccino, fruit drinks and frozen yogurt. The mall, spread over two floors under Simcoe Place, will include twenty-five shops, ten food-court stalls, four snack counters and a giant restaurant. Harrs, who leases stores and restaurants in the shopping malls that Cadillac owns, is the final arbiter of who sells what. His decisions are a matter of some importance to the chefs at Casa Manna, Sukiyaki, Chicken Quarters and eleven other food outlets that will be vying each lunch-time to attract workers from this and surrounding buildings.

A successful landlord makes sure a food court offers a good mix, both to bring back customers and to keep proprietors from undermining each other's business. This means leases that define what can and can't be sold. Carrotheads, for instance, a franchise serving health foods and juices, can offer only regular coffee on its menu—the cappuccino and flavoured varieties are left to the Second Cup upstairs. The health-food outlet also has had to excise frozen yogurt, the staple of Yogen Früz down the way.

"I guess as long as everyone's making money, everyone's going to be happy," says Carrotheads CEO Tim Mulcahy, a newcomer to both food courts and health foods. After seventeen years doing direct marketing, where he motivated agents to sell water filters, natural gas, long-distance service and home-security systems, Mulcahy was over-come by a sense of physical fatigue. When friends suggested he improve his diet, he became hooked on a chlorophyll-rich juice extracted from wheatgrass. Like a religious zealot, he searched for a supply of the concoction, and even found a source of the grass itself so he could squeeze his own. He began reading about health food and finally, with three friends, decided to start a line of fast-food outlets selling salads, fresh pasta, pita sandwiches, turkey chili, beans, grains and of course juices, including wheatgrass.

They chose the name Carrotheads, and developed a line of juices and power shakes made from fresh fruits, vegetables, yeast, lecithin and protein powder. For the squeamish, the drinks were given more enticing names—Fountain of Youth, Stress Buster, The Beautician, Green Rocket, Immune Builder, Love Potion #9, Skinny Minny—dreamed up during a summer weekend brainstorming session at Mulcahy's cottage. Infiltrating the grease-filled mall food court is tough for a health-food franchise, but he's confident converts are at hand. "When you eat a burger, fries and a pop, you're tired after-wards, because your body is digesting all of that garbage," he says, sitting at a small café table outside one of his franchise outlets quaffing a cup of juice called Mr. Clean. Made from parsley, spinach, carrots and celery, it is murky green and topped with a thick foam peppered with dark bits of vegetable. "We're offering something different."

The Simcoe Place outlet will be the fourth the Carrotheads company has opened since it started. The head-office management team designs and outfits each restaurant with a convection oven, stove and juicers, sets the menu and restaurant hours (opening at 6:30 a.m. for juice, carrot-nut loaf and vitamins sold individually), hires staff and supplies them with a small library of health-food books. Only then is the restaurant handed over to its owner. The one at Simcoe Place will be in the hands of Sarabjit Thind, who came to Canada last year from Chandigarh, in northern India, where his family owns a construction company that builds hydroelectric dams.

As an immigrant to the country from the entrepreneurial class, Thind, twenty-nine, was keen to invest in a Canadian business. For

$105,000, plus 5.5 per cent of daily sales, he bought the franchise and has studied the company's operation by working in the three other Carrotheads locations for the last two months. Once he starts up the 487-square-foot outlet in Simcoe Place, he'll also owe Cadillac about $4,500 a month for rent and to pay for his share of the common eating area's tables, chairs, trays and cleaning.

His closest competition along the food court is a fellow country-man, Ashley Vaz, an immigrant from Bombay who will serve more traditional Indian fare at his stall. Along with a chef friend, Vaz bought a restaurant called Indian Flavour in downtown Toronto in 1991. Recently they opened their first fast-food outlet of the same name in the basement of a nearby bank tower. Both there and at Simcoe Place, they have tailored their Indian menu to less daring Canadian tastes. They abandoned Bombay's pork, peppers and garlic-laced dishes for milder entrées typical of the Punjab region in the north and more commonly found in Indian restaurants around the world.

Because meals have to be cooked quickly in a small space that conforms to local fire and sanitation regulations, Vaz has had to further adapt his traditional recipes. A dish of biryani—layered rice, chicken and yogurt with spices and clarified butter—is typically steamed in a clay pot for five hours back home. Here it is mixed together and cooked in a matter of minutes. Vaz does not even attempt to serve naan, a chewy Indian flatbread. The charcoal-fired tandoori oven required to make it authentically is red-hot and smokes too much to use in the confined area. He would like to serve the spicy kabobs that are a part of his country's culinary tradition, but his contract forbids it. The landlord has reserved kabobs for a Greek restaurant that will serve souvlaki down the way. "The lease says we have to stick to Indian cuisine," Vaz says. "But here they don't know what Indian food is."

Sorting out matters in the food court is only part of Cadillac Fairview's responsibility as it prepares to take over the building. There are myriad details for the developer to work out, such as choosing a company to wash Simcoe Place's windows. Deskbound people sealed inside modern office buildings are affected by the sense of renewal that comes with the changing season as much as anyone else, but they are forced to watch the scene unfold through glass covered with a winter's worth of grime. Cleaners can be seen moving up and down buildings all over the city, sprinkling the streets below with tell-tale drops of soapy water.

Although window-washers are a fixture of urban life, most passers-by have little appreciation of how their job has evolved over time. Of course, windows in office buildings once opened, so cleaners could lean out to wash them, a manoeuvre that required tremendous balance. As windows became larger and harder to get at, builders anchored pins in sills where rope harnesses could be attached for added safety. Unfortunately, these fixtures corroded with age and exposure to weather, so they became unreliable over time. Exterior window-washing was the next logical step, becoming a larger, mechanized operation as sealed windows were introduced in ever-taller high-rises.

In the beginning, the business was largely unregulated, and accidents from overloaded washing platforms or working in high winds were common. Tough regulations introduced in the last decade have improved safety. Most modern window-washers work on platforms attached to the roof by sturdy wires. Known as suspended scaffolds or, even more commonly, as swing-stages because they resemble a child's swing, the platforms are similar to the temporary devices that construction workers use to move up and down the outside of buildings while they do their work. Indeed, there are currently three of them at Simcoe Place, carrying men sealing windows, finishing details on the external curtain wall and installing slabs of granite over the lobby entrance.

Owners of some buildings, looking for an economical way to keep their windows clean, can make use of these temporary construction devices, suspended from weighted beams on top of the building. Others opt for a system whereby a single window-washer hangs from a device called a bosun's chair, a seat slung from cables also anchored in the roof that resembles the board used by a ship's boatswain to do work over a vessel's side. Such techniques can be slow, because the position of the platforms and chairs constantly has to be changed, and their temporary nature makes them more risky to use, so regulations limit their use to lower buildings.

Permanent swing-stages are considered safer and more reliable, although they are also more expensive and complicated. The equipment being installed atop Simcoe Place looks like a miniature railway running around the three tiers of the roof and will cost $500,000. Already bolted to the concrete structure, the rails will easily transport the window-washing equipment around the building on carriages that are still to come. On the carriages are small cranes called davits. Another term borrowed from seafaring, the davit is the small hoist that lifts lifeboats and cargo over the side of a ship. Here, a wire cable runs from the top of each davit to electric motors at the ends of the window-washing platform, in order to raise and lower the cleaners on board.

The set-up was custom-designed by Swing Stage Ltd., a Toronto company that has worked out window-washing systems for buildings in Canada, the United States and the Far East. The need for such elaborate equipment highlights the dichotomy between practical-minded engineers and builders and fanciful designers. Straight-sided buildings would make window-washing easy. Architects, on the other hand, like to show their creativity in unusual configurations like overhangs, elaborate finishes and flourishes, with little thought for how the structure will be maintained and cleaned once it's built.

"There's always a way," says Swing Stage's vice-president, Hans Zander. He stands on Simcoe Place's roof and points to three neighbouring buildings where he has installed window-washing equipment on seemingly impossible roofs and walls. A rolling platform that runs around the outside of the main pod on the CN Tower, for instance, carries workers at two levels to clean the windows of the observation areas and revolving restaurant. For the lampshade-shaped Roy Thomson Hall, the company designed rails to go around the top and a small platform to hold cleaners that rolls down the sloping glass on cushioned rubber wheels. At the two towers of the Sun Life Insurance complex, with their V-shaped indentations and dramatic overhangs, the company devised window-washing platforms that can bend to fit unusual angles, as well as individual monorails that suspend platforms from the underside of the small cantilevered parts.

Swing Stage doesn't actually wash the windows, but turns over its equipment to a cleaning contractor hired by a building owner once its system is working. Cadillac will soon invite window-washing companies to bid on the job, worth about twenty thousand dollars a year. A contract will stipulate the windows be cleaned about four times a year, with each cleaning requiring two workers and taking about three days. Eastern is responsible for the first good cleaning, once the zip-up has been finished and before the building is fully turned over to the developer.

TWENTY-TWO

FINALE

Pacing around a part of the underground concourse that will soon house a row of shops, Dennis Ohlman surveys a vast white wall. Something's not right. He pulls a flashlight from his pocket, shining it high overhead to the point where the freshly painted drywall ends, exposing the crude concrete block directly behind. Eyes narrowed in concentration amid the whine of nearby carpenters' drills and the pealing of a fire alarm tripped by inspectors testing the emergency system in the tower above, he thinks back to the blueprints for the concourse that sit on his desk at NORR Partnership. Finally, he shakes his head. The drywall has been applied to narrow metal strips just two centimetres from the block wall, but he's sure the plans call for the material to stick out fifteen centimetres, on much wider studs.

The difference may seem slight, but it's no small matter to Ohlman, whose job it is to make sure the building is constructed according to each architectural drawing and specification prepared by the architects. His concern here is practical. A wider gap between the concrete and drywall would give store tenants a place to tuck away their electrical and telephone wires. He points this out to D'Arcy Gorman, who is responsible for the building's underground and accompanies him on each visit there. The tension is heavy as each man stands firm. Gorman's recollections of the plans are different, conforming with the wall the two men are standing in front of, but he finally shrugs. "Write her down," he says, and Ohlman takes out a steno pad and makes a note on a list headed Deficiencies, which will grow to ten items by the time his two-hour tour of the small area ends.

As part of his job overseeing the contract between Cadillac and Eastern, Ohlman looks for anything the building lacks. He works hand in hand with Jack Cusimano, who reviews each bill for the work and judges whether it is accurate and should be paid. It's a hectic time for the two men, with reason: today is the day when "substantial performance" is to be achieved. Eastern will give Cusimano a bill for almost $300,000, putting the total amount that Cadillac has paid or owes at the $99-million mark, within $1 million of the total contract price. That complies with the requirement that all but 1 per cent of the project be finished. Forty-five days after notice of the milestone is published in a local trade newspaper, Cadillac must release the $10 million in payments it has held back.

It's a strong incentive for builders to spend money quickly and finish on time. The construction site is a flurry of activity. Delivery trucks continually roll up with big-ticket items such as the park's granite walls, the massive light sconces for the walls around the base of the building and two chandeliers to grace the lobby entrance. But it's not just a matter of getting the job done fast—it has to be done right. That's where Ohlman comes in. He sniffs out anything that can be described as unacceptable and therefore requires improvements. The job can be trying, requiring an eye for detail, a ready familiarity with the building and a good measure of diplomacy—keeping calm when telling a contractor that he must redo or replace something for the second or third time.

Ohlman, an architectural technologist, has worked on this project for three years, first developing details on the building drawings to become familiar with it, then overseeing changes to the plans when construction was under way, before moving on to the deficiency inspections. His job will continue until the contractor reaches "total completion," when all but a thousand dollars has been spent, likely within about four months.

His inspections are requested by Eastern whenever a particular section of the building is considered complete. Ohlman tours the area two or three times with one of the field engineers. Over eight months, he has compiled an eight-centimetre stack of deficiency notices from the sessions, which are typed up from his steno-pad notes and sent to Eastern two days after each tour. During his rounds, he's often called aside to comment informally on an installation or technique that's not quite ready for inspection. He also doesn't hesitate to volunteer an opinion if he notices something he doesn't like, knowing that a word in advance could save time and paperwork later.

"There's a bit of give and take," he says. "I can't be unnecessarily demanding on areas that are not that important." Uneven brushstrokes on a freshly painted ceiling catch his critical eye, for instance, but he's willing to allow a certain artistic latitude. When it comes to the concourse wall, however, he's less flexible. Back in his office after the day's inspection, he sifts through stacks of plans. In one architectural overview, the wall appears as Eastern has indeed built it, the drywall almost flush with the concrete block. But a more detailed diagram shows larger, fifteen-centimetre studs separating the drywall from the concrete block. Ohlman feels vindicated, but it will take intense discussion to resolve the matter.

Those involved in the design and construction of the building are not the only ones scrutinizing it. For two years, Jeff Abrams has held his counsel. Looking out of his twenty-sixth-floor office in Metro Hall, he has watched Simcoe Place's disparate parts come together. At times he's had his doubts about features such as the building's façade, which he finds gloomy, with its predominance of grey-tinted glass and black granite. He has delighted over the grass and trees in the park, where he will eat his lunch. With dismay, he has seen the tower's thirty floors and three penthouses eclipse his own building and block some of his view of the city. But now that he can look at the finished product and not just its individual parts, he's willing to be positive. "Either it's an attractive building," he says, "or I've gotten used to it."

For the countless other sidewalk superintendents, as well as the professional architects, planners and urban designers who have watched the building go up, the time for judgement has arrived. Despite the last-minute tasks to ready it for occupancy inside and out, it appears pretty much complete. Now the building is being assessed both up close and from afar, to see whether it fits into its immediate neighbourhood as well as the city skyline, while at the same time serving those who will work inside. To the building's architects, a project lives up to its "design intent" if it fulfils these goals.

The reaction so far from the experts is largely positive. To Steven Fong, the associate chairman of architecture at the University of Toronto, it is a transition building, combining a "suave metal-and-glass stand-alone tower reminiscent of the 1980s prolific corporate architecture" with an arcade at its base, "built right to the street with amenities for pedestrians." However, he finds that the two separate parts, with their different types of curtain wall, clash. He says the tower is "elegant" but calls the podium floors below it "coarse," with their "heavy-handed cladding and thick aluminum bands running across the windows."

Marc Baraness, the director of architecture and planning for the city, disagrees. He feels the building's base is "handsome and tactile" and finds the overall structure sophisticated, although he's frustrated with buildings that have a single use, "piling one office worker on top of another." He'd rather that Simcoe Place included residential space as well.

John Sewell, the mayor of Toronto in the reform-minded 1970s and one of the most vocal opponents of the deal that would have spread high-rise development across these railway lands at the bottom of the city, likes the shape of this building. He says pedestrians can appreciate its base through the sidewalk colonnade and thinks the top actually looks like a roof, although it still has the angular shape of a modern high-rise. Sewell, author of *The Shape of the City: Toronto Struggles with Modern Planning*, says the architecture is an improvement over the austere monoliths he once rebelled against, which rose out of vast downtown plazas in the 1960s and 1970s, but he would have added trees and more retail shops to Simcoe Place and dumped the building's "anonymous" mirrored glass exterior for something warmer.

From his perspective in the Broadcast Centre next door, radio reporter Michael McIvor has come to share this feeling. "There's a lot of glass in the city," he says. Like many of the building's neighbours who have watched the day-to-day progress and have to live with the result, McIvor's early fears that Simcoe Place would be as "humdrum" as the Bay Street towers behind it have lifted as the façade has been embellished. "I quite like it—I'm surprised that I do."

The ability of a mere office building to give pleasure should not be underestimated. It has done that for Barrie Ralph and Paul McGrory, the low-income-housing coordinators who work in the gothic bell tower of St. Andrew's Church, kitty-corner to the site. They say the building's angled ends give it a Manhattan-like quality but also help Simcoe Place blend in with its surroundings. "It has a visual feel to it, if you can say that," says Ralph excitedly. "It's different, it's really different."

Not only outsiders feel compelled to offer a critique of the new creation; the creators themselves have a special interest in how their plans have turned out. The architect's ability to shape the space around him, to master and organize a new environment, is unique. Nietzsche referred to the designer's craft as "a sort of oratory of power" in which "the pride of man, his triumph over gravitation, his will to power, assume a visible form." Six years after he and fellow architect Carlos Ott first scribbled the building design on a piece of graph paper, Bill Neish continues to feel like an apprehensive guardian. He's still involved in the project, brought in by the contractors from time to time to consult on finishing issues such as lobby lighting, while worrying about the larger question of how the building will be received. When he has business in various parts of the city, he seizes the opportunity to examine Simcoe Place from different angles and distances. He is pleased with what he sees. "I feel it adds something to the total composition of the downtown."

Walking through the building—usually with an on-site guide from his firm to help him negotiate the labyrinth of corridors and stairwells that he once mapped out—Neish finds even more to like: the relaxed atmosphere created by indirect lighting in public areas, the grand entrance columns and chandeliers, and the design themes carried through the structure such as the vertical fins of stainless steel that grace the top of the building and appear in a number of other places. Such flourishes are what make most observers take notice, although the reaction to them is mixed. To Steven Fong's academic mind, the fins look as if they were "dreamed up by an Oldsmobile stylist," while Barrie Ralph thinks they give the building a sleek, "art-deco-ish" look.

The final test, of course, comes when the contractors start to move out and the first tenants move in. Then Jeff Abrams, who has only observed the building from afar, will get an insider's perspective: his wife, Brenda, will be setting up shop on Simcoe Place's nineteenth floor as the director of human resources for the Workers' Compensation Board. But there are already signs that this elevated sidewalk superintendent's interest is waning. With little more construction activity to observe across the street, he's starting to train his high-powered binoculars on a new obsession: work on the Metro Toronto Convention Centre expansion that has just got under way to the south.

If he looked down, though, he'd see the final act at Simcoe Place. A trailer truck pulls up, piled high with rolled strips of Kentucky bluegrass sod that have been stacked and covered with heavy green netting to keep them moist and steady during their ninety-kilometre trip. Harvested at 5:00 a.m. from a dewy field in the fertile farmland north of the city called the Holland Marsh, the crop headed cityward within hours to beat the sweltering summer heat. By 10:00 a.m. a team of landscapers stands ready with forklifts, shovels, steel rakes, rollers and streaming hoses. Within minutes they turn a mound of soil at the centre of the park into a lush carpet of green.

Fringed with rows of shrubs and perennials—the previous day's arrival—the grass brings a final touch of soft landscaping to what had been a sterile concrete and granite plaza. "Now it looks like a real park," says Margaret Rankin with a satisfied nod, as she surveys the transformation of the acre of land that has kept her occupied for many months. Divided among a crew of six, the sod work goes quickly. Two men level the soil and spread granular fertilizer. Three others following behind lay out the strips of grass, and another coaxes the roots into the soil with a heavy roller and a generous soaking of water. Time is of the essence in the intense heat, which could quickly dry out the delicate roots before the grass is planted, but there's another reason for hurrying. In less than twenty-four hours, the park must be declared complete. For Rankin and landscaping project manager Jack Campbell, the push to finish the $1.7-million project quickly has meant pressing suppliers, overseeing already harried work crews, pitching in to help with the planting and nervously following officials from the City of Toronto and Cadillac Fairview as they make inspection tours.

There's good reason for the fervour. In one week, the park is to be part of the Taste of Toronto food festival, an event spread out over two downtown blocks that promises to attract tens of thousands of people. For the public to use the space, however, it must first be handed over by Cadillac to the city's Parks and Recreation department. For this to happen, Rankin must formally declare it finished, and the developer's lawyers have to file documents conveying the title for the land to the city from its owner, the CBC. If the paperwork is not complete, the park will still be deemed a construction site, like the building itself. This would require anyone using it to wear safety hats and boots—hardly attire at a picnic. For the parties involved in creating the park, this means packing activities into a few days that would normally take at least a month to complete.

Oddly enough, the haste that's in evidence everywhere surrounding the high-rise is lacking inside it. Since the first tenants do not arrive for a couple of weeks, work is proceeding at a more measured pace. The contractor must still do a lot of work and undergo more inspection before it gets an occupancy permit from the city's building department. Luckily for Taste of Toronto organizers, the park does not require the permit, but there is still much to be done. A list of defects made up by Rankin after each of her inspections, which is to accompany her letter of certification, currently includes thirteen items. The landscapers, for example, must install grates at the base of the fountain to keep debris or tiny feet from falling into the works. At the direction of a city forestry official, the lower branches of several trees will be trimmed to protect the eyes of passers-by (and avoid costly lawsuits). Two of the trees in the plaza, large red oaks planted in April, appear sickly and must be removed—and replaced next spring—if their shrivelled leaves and drooping branches do not revive within a couple of days. Park benches, café tables, chairs and garbage bins are still missing, and lighting around the grass mound awaits installation.

The final touch will be a three-metre-high sign made of six tonnes of Finnish granite, which was engraved by a monument company this week and is to be dropped into place by a mobile crane on the south side of the park. With the arrival of the sign, the space gets its formal name, Simcoe Park, which was recently approved by Toronto's city council. There will also be a small logo identifying it as a newly acquired property of the city's Parks and Recreation department.

After spending two years creating the park, Campbell and his landscaping crew will quickly disappear, staying just one more week to beautify the edge of the parking lot behind the building before leaving to create a golf course. But he'll still feel an attachment to his work. The strips of sod usually take at least a month to knit together and sink roots, and Campbell worries about the damage that thousands of feet at the festival may inflict so early in the grass's growth. He's suggested to the city that the mound be roped off during the food festival, but he realizes that come next week, his sod and the whole project will be part of the public domain.

The building itself is not open to the public—yet. But still the construction workers are sporting a new look: badges that give them permission to enter the building they created and have called home for the last two years. Cadillac Fairview has taken over the building, and the ID cards are just one sign of the change. There is a guard stationed at the polished reception rosewood desk in the empty lobby, watching for unauthorized visitors and keeping in radio contact with colleagues on patrol. Cadillac has brought in elevator operators to oversee the many movers who are beginning to invade the building. Fire doors once propped open for easy access to various work sites are closed and connected to the alarm system. And after having the run of the place, the men in hard hats and safety boots suddenly find themselves asking permission to enter electrical rooms or adjust mechanical equipment.

Some of them resent being treated as strangers, but the prevailing feeling for what they've accomplished is still satisfaction. "It's a big relief to get to this stage," says Renato Tacconelli, the site construction manager at Eastern known as Tac. "We did it and that's all that people remember, what happened at the end, not all the headaches along the way."

The last headache disappeared when Eastern obtained an occupancy permit and handed over the keys for the building to Cadillac. It's time for Eastern to cede control. The number of people working in the building has dropped to eighty. From this point on, Cadillac is responsible for maintaining equipment and paying the bills for electricity and other services. Tac can't leave quite yet. Over the next few months, as the tenants move in, his team will continue to apply finishing touches and repair a long list of deficiencies spotted by consultants. Of more immediate concern is the contract close-out, a requirement in the building specifications that Eastern explain the workings of all equipment, hand over equipment manuals and guarantees and make sure the building is clean inside and out.

For the group of ten Cadillac managers and technicians now running the building, this means a crash course in operating forty-three different systems, from the massive air-conditioning chillers in the penthouse to the machine that will crush and bale cardboard boxes on the loading dock. There's so much for the newcomers to absorb that the training sessions are videotaped for later reference. Taking over a newly completed high-rise isn't easy. Already, in the first week of Cadillac's regime, the service elevator has broken down repeatedly, the keys issued by Eastern didn't open the revolving doors in the lobby and worried eyes still point skyward as Eastern and Cadillac await the equipment that will let them use the window-washing rails on the roof. In the meantime, window-washers hanging in individual bosun's chairs have been hired to clean the grime on the building's four-storey podium.

They'll have to work hard to catch up to Taylor Cleaning, the firm dusting and polishing the interior in preparation for the opening. Company owner Lawrence Taylor understands the demands of construction, and begins soliciting final clean-up jobs when the projects are first excavated. A tall, burly man with a rapid-fire delivery that makes an auctioneer sound like a remedial reader, he came to Canada fourteen years ago from the Bahamas, where he worked as a limbo dancer, fire-eater and nightclub owner. Having little luck with the entertainment business in Canada, he drew on his childhood experience washing hotel windows and took a six-week janitorial course that brought him work as a school custodian. Soon he started his own business cleaning offices and restaurants, before moving on to construction sites.

Taylor is galvanized by the kind of dirt left in the wake of a construction crew. His people moved into Simcoe Place to tidy each floor as Eastern finished with it, before handing it over to the interior contractors for the WCB, Jackson-Lewis Co. He has also been hired by Jackson-Lewis to do the final clean-up of the completed offices before people move in. This weekend, his cleaners will work on the day care as well, before moving on to the lobby and other spaces on the ground floor, which must be sparkling when the building opens.

The transformation from work site to public space will be rapid. Over the next week, the sheets of plywood protecting the granite lobby floor from trolleys and forklifts will be removed and tasteful hoarding erected around any stores that remain unrented and unfinished. Decorators will outfit the area with benches, potted plants and signs. Artists will oversee the installation of the sculptures and paintings commissioned by Cadillac. Once the area has been given its makeover and the building opens, the construction workers will feel even more like second-class citizens: not only must they wear ID badges when they enter public areas but they will be allowed here only after business hours.

The dawn sky grows steadily brighter, bathing the new mirrored walls of Simcoe Place in a pink glow. The shimmering skyscraper stands out from the rest of Toronto's skyline, but Corrado Patullo barely glances at what he has just helped build. Other things on his mind keep him from admiring his handiwork. A few blocks short of the finished entrance to Simcoe Place, he pulls his pick-up truck into a rough gravel parking lot, dons a hard hat and walks to a trailer perched on the edge of a giant hole in the ground. Even though it's only 5:30 a.m., the area below is bustling with backhoes and trucks that are clearing the way for a new development, the underground expansion of the Metro Toronto Convention Centre.

Corrado and the other Patullo brothers will make this site their new workday home for the next two years; Avenue is building the huge facility's concrete skeleton. Although a group of Avenue's concrete workers will return to Simcoe Place next week to finish making the adjoining tunnel, the company has turned its attention to several other projects it recently took on, including a concert amphitheatre and the Toronto headquarters of the Bank of China. Corrado will long remember Simcoe Place for the raw winter day when he plunged head-first from the top of a scaffold, which stands as the site's worst accident. On this mild summer morning, though, he feels little effect of the fall, beyond some difficulty reading and a tendency to tire easily. "Old age, maybe," he says, and shrugs.

Now sixty-one, he is not ready to slow down. He works from before sunrise until late afternoon, overseeing the construction of the centre's massive ballrooms and display halls starting deep in the ground. There's so much to be done that he'll likely forgo his annual pilgrimage to his home town of Boiano. At its peak in the next few weeks, the job at the convention centre will require 150 Avenue carpenters, labourers and concrete finishers, almost twice as many as the company employed at Simcoe Place. Many of the faces are familiar. There's Corrado's best friend, foreman Amadeo Pozzobon, as well as crane operator Bob Hughes and swamper Abel deCarvalho, already at work on the bustling site.

For these men, the completion of Simcoe Place has meant a new beginning somewhere else. For others less fortunate, there's worry about finding work and anxiety over the future of construction in North America. It's been a summer of golf and fishing for Glen Pestrin of Gem Campbell. Since supplying the marble, granite and tile flooring to the project, his company has found little work in the city beyond a three-month renovation project in a downtown building. Companies such as structural consultants Quinn Dressel Associates are exclusively working on projects in faraway cities such as Shanghai, which are experiencing the sort of building booms that are a distant memory here.

Architect Bill Neish has moved on to designing a courthouse and a government office building. Such public projects have been critical to the industry with the collapse of commercial real-estate development. NORR Associates isn't currently working on any private office blocks, which once accounted for at least 60 per cent of its business, and the change has hit the firm hard. While Simcoe Place was under construction, NORR restructured, at the request of its creditors, cutting its staff almost in half to 120 employees and losing four of its nine partners. Two years ago, the company occupied four floors of a building that bore its name in lighted letters. In 1995 it has moved to the building's ground floor and basement, and the roof lights spell out the name of a prominent hotel chain that has taken up residence in the prime quarters.

Cadillac Fairview, which has endured its own tumultuous period of adjustment to redistribute its billion-dollar debt, has rented out half the retail space in Simcoe Place and found tenants for just one and a half of the nine floors not occupied by the WCB. Cadillac has shelved the second phase of Simcoe Place and has no more buildings in the works.

That means fewer large-scale projects of the sort favoured by Eastern Construction. Already some of Eastern's Simcoe Place staff have scattered to other sites, three to build the convention centre, one to construct a Chinese gallery at the Royal Ontario Museum and another to oversee the renovation of a student residence at the University of Toronto. The team of six still at the site will likely dwindle in a couple of weeks to two or three.

There is little sentimentality associated with Simcoe Place, just a sense of pride and new enthusiasm for what comes next. "You go to a new site, a new employer, a whole new set of challenges," says Brian Gardner, Eastern's project manager. "It's like getting a new sheet of paper to work on when you're a kid. You can scribble away until it's full again." After working on buildings in the immediate area for fifteen years, including the Broadcast Centre and Roy Thomson Hall, Gardner has little on his plate beyond heading back to work at Eastern's head office. In his mid-fifties and set in his ways, he does not favour making the move to Windsor, Ontario, where the company has its only big job, constructing a casino. Maybe it is time for a break. He has his eyes on a boat at a rowing club he visited during a recent regatta, the first since his days in the rowing club in London. He plans to take a Christmas trip to England, which he has not visited since he left more than two decades ago.

For those who have built Simcoe Place, there will be no ribbon-cutting ceremony or opening celebration, but they do have an unusual opportunity to sign their creation—the glass sculpture in the underground concourse. The artwork, to be installed between the still-unfinished escalators, bears the names of 1,411 people who had a hand in the building, from Jaye Skeoch-Brewer, a secretary at Quinn Dressel, to Peter McAlister, a vice-president of Cadillac Fairview. "Years from now," says McAlister, who had the original idea for the sculpture, "someone can come in and see that their brother or father or grandfather was involved in this. I think it's important for people who built this building to say, 'Hey, here's what I did.'"

AFTERWORD

The buzz of conversation and clicking of computer keys are all that can be heard from behind the partitions adorned with memos, Post-It notes and family photographs in the bank offices on the twenty-seventh floor of Simcoe Place. Paperbacks and portable cassette players, diversions on the subway ride to the office, have been neatly tucked away in overhead cabinets, replaced with thick files, executive desk toys and telephone headsets. Floors sheathed in corporate grey carpet smell of fresh adhesive and walls are adorned with paintings from the bank's art collection. Gusts of wind whistle in the huge windows and scatter plumes of steam rising from the roofs of surrounding buildings. A commuter train rumbles back and forth below, shunting into position for the afternoon rush hour. There is an announcement over the public address system that the room where securities are kept will close in ten minutes.

Two years after its opening, Simcoe Place works. All but one tiny part of the building—ironically the very office on the northwest corner of the twenty-second floor that was shown to potential tenants while the tower was still under construction—is occupied, although, the nine empty floors were leased at bargain-basement prices of just $1 to $5 a square foot above the developer's yearly tax and operating costs. The leasing deal even altered the building's identity. Although it is still referred to as Simcoe Place, the roof is now adorned with two huge neon Bank of America signs, a condition of the bank's agreement to lease the twenty-fifth, twenty-sixth and twenty-seventh floors. Reflecting the new economy, two floors are occupied by Walt Disney Animation, others by software and communications companies. The

Workers' Compensation Board continues to inhabit the lion's share, but seems unable to escape controversy connected with Simcoe Place. A year after moving in, it was criticized for spending $70,000 to install an executive washroom in the new offices of its chairman, considered an extravagence while its unfunded liability remains above $10 billion. Now renamed the Workplace Safety and Insurance Board, the agency is also bursting at the seams, testing Simcoe Place's ability to accommodate change by moving many of its employees around in a massive reorganization. It is already looking at taking over unrented shops in the underground concourse for extra offices, storage and a library.

The board is not the only one growing. Commercial real estate development in North America is recovering. At one time it seemed Simcoe Place would be among the last big commercial developments in Toronto, with a depression in the office market and a trend away from downtown development in favour of telecommuting and "virtual" offices. But the economy has improved, and vacancy rates in the core, once 20 per cent or more, have dropped to less than 5 per cent. There are few buildings with large blocks of empty space for tenants, such as a number of banks that recently merged, and rents have climbed to $25 to $30 a square foot. It also turns out that the death of the downtown high-rise building as a place to work was greatly exaggerated, with the realization that companies are communities where workers need to see and speak to each other.

A number of developers appear ready to build massive projects, as long as major tenants can be found. The first and most symbolic is the dormant fifty-one-storey Bay-Adelaide Centre, a monument to the collapse of the commercial real estate market when it was shut down in 1993. The next could very well be the second phase of Simcoe Place, the twin tower that would stand forty storeys tall at right angles to the first. There are no guarantees that the same people would design and build it, although there would be some efficiencies if they did. For them, Simcoe Place was a life-raft during the worst of the recession. Since it was built, many have kept busy by renovating or simply cosmetically updating buildings to make them more desirable to existing tenants in the slow market. Sleek stainless steel, dark granite and rich rosewood replace weathered tiles, stained carpet and 1970s pine. The only true growth has been in the shopping centres, entertainment complexes and sports stadiums expected to draw baby boomers with money and leisure time to burn.

Cadillac Fairview, after almost disappearing under a mountain of debt in the early 1990s, is considered strong after its restructuring, albeit more in the business of managing its real estate assets (among them Simcoe Place) than development. Peter McAlister, the vice-president of Cadillac Fairview who was in charge of Simcoe Place, wanted "to build things, not sit on them" and left the company to join a large architectural and engineering firm.

The urge to build—and the tendency to relocate—is shared by contracting crews, who reconstitute themselves with each new project. Most of those who worked for Eastern Construction at Simcoe Place have scattered to various other Eastern jobs or left the company altogether, part of the continued retrenchment of the industry. Brian Gardner's new "sheet of paper" to work on is a massive project in North York that will include condominiums, movie theatres, restaurants and electronic game parlours. The only member of his staff who made the move with him is Rosy Pereira, the project secretary, who has worked with Gardner for seven years.

Corrado Patullo, whose Avenue Structures has the contract with a partner company to form the concrete structure for the twenty-seven- and twenty-nine-storey condominium towers, will rejoin Gardner. Since Simcoe Place, Avenue has built the expansion on the Metro Toronto Convention Centre, the casino in Windsor and a stadium to house the Toronto Raptors basketball team. But now the company is showing signs of winding down, returning to its roots in building apartment buildings and selling its $2-million inventory of cranes and flying forms, especially to hungry builders in China.

There is little likelihood that the company will be passed along to the next generation, says Corrado, whose own son Jimmy has joined Grant Milligan and the structural engineers at Quinn Dressel as a designer. "This is heavy work and I don't think our kids will do it; they'd like to do some nice desk job. . . . Who knows? Maybe they're going to make it better than we did," Corrado says. "And if there is nobody to pick up after us, we may as well get rid of the equipment now." Tony says that the problem with the family business is that the brothers are poor at delegating work and grooming others to take over. "We keep on getting involved ourselves, we're very hands on, and it's very difficult to bring someone in if you don't let them get fully involved." The division of labour among the five means that no one is able to relax. Nearing sixty-five, Corrado is as active as ever. "I still like to come and get my hands dirty on the site, because otherwise what am I going to do?" he shrugs. "Up to the time that I can get up in the morning and go to work, I'll go to work." Observers say the ethic among the brothers and their ability to get along despite their different personalities are in no small measure due to the influence of their mother, Concetta, who has just celebrated her ninetieth birthday. She still lives in her house behind the cul-de-sac where the five brothers and their sister live. Because she has circulation problems a nurse looks after her during the day and one of the brothers stays each night. "The nurse, she calls us the nursing boys," Corrado adds.

Like Avenue, other companies have managed to survive by scaling back. Grant Milligan says that Quinn Dressel has taken on jobs as small as fixing parking garages with cracks in them. It's like working on an assembly line compared with huge, customized projects like Simcoe Place, but the work is steady. Architect Bill Neish will retire from NORR Partnership at the end of the year, leaving the company with just four partners, down from a high of nine during the boom. He expects NORR and others to rebuild with the improvement in the market, but does not think the industry will ever grow to what it was when he and designer Carlos Ott conceived Simcoe Place. "I don't know if we're ever going to see the likes of that. I don't think I will in my lifetime."

John Cartwright of the Construction Trades Council says many of the unions are getting to the point where they will begin to accept new apprentices again, having severely cut back on training for the last eight years. Already unemployment among structural workers such as carpenters and ironworkers has dropped from 50 per cent or more to just 10 per cent, and the finishing trades are expected to pick up. Much of the new blood in construction will come from the newest immigrant groups to the country, Latin Americans and

Eastern Europeans, although older Portuguese workers continue to dominate the industry.

One notable hold-out is labour foreman Leo De Jesus, who at sixty-seven still happily places and finishes concrete and has no plans to retire. "Leo, he'll die and they'll probably put him in a column and pour the concrete in," says crane operator Bob Hughes. "They'll just put a plaque on the edge saying 'Here lies Leo.'" Hughes, for his part, has no desire to remain in construction much longer. He intends to retire at fifty-five, in two years, assuming the stock market where he has invested his substantial earnings remains strong. It is a good feeling to have added thirty buildings to the landscape, but having built Simcoe Place, his tallest project, and mastered "every crane that was ever built," there are no more challenges, the stress level is high and the job can be dull. "One floor after another, it's exactly the same," he says. "I don't like the pressure, I don't like the push, working fourteen, fifteen hours a day with no lunch, no coffee breaks. It's just not worth it." He plans to travel south, especially in the winter to escape the wind and cold that have been such a feature of his job, and is not attracted by the prospect of another construction boom. "I don't care if there's a crane every square mile, there's a lot of young guys out there who can take my place."

His job is also diminished without his swamper, Abel deCarvalho, who a year ago suffered a fall while carrying an armload of steel formwork jacks, spraining his left knee. Now fifty-one, he had little relief from an operation on the ligament and has tried twice—unsuccessfully—to return to swamping. "I'm not young any more, the work is catching up to me," says Carvalho, who still rises before 6:00 a.m. each day but can do little beyond light housekeeping in the family duplex and visiting doctors and physical therapists. There is fear that the ligament damage in his knee could be permanent. Carvalho misses the construction site but is considering opening a bakery, his dream since leaving Portugal.

There is little connection between the workers who created Simcoe Place and those who have moved in, apart from the irony that the organization that occupies three-quarters of it deals heavily with members of the construction industry. When Carvalho arrived for a meeting with his compensation case-worker on the second floor of the building, he got terribly lost, much like the doctor who does not recognize a patient with clothes on. "I couldn't believe this was the place I had built," he says with a laugh. Carolyn Cooper, who helped with the board's move into the building, has settled back to work as an administrative assistant, although with the WCB reorganization, she has moved from the second floor to a new perch in a sunny corner of the fifth floor. She makes use of her intimate knowledge of the offices by showing new employees around, something she never tires of doing in the building she loves. "I think they really got it."

The feeling is shared. Architecture critic John Bentley Mays, in a review of Simcoe Place in the *Globe and Mail*, called the building suave and sophisticated, praising its "secular, business-like cosmopolitanism" and calling it "modern rather than modish." Simcoe Place received an award from the World Wildlife Fund as a "bird-friendly building" for turning off its lights at night and was given a plaque by Metro Toronto for its aggressive waste recycling program.

There are still small follow-up items for the major contractors and consultants who worked on the building, like the cracks and nagging maintenance problems that arise in a new home—only, of course, much bigger. "It's not like this building was four walls and a door and a roof," Gardner says. "It doesn't all work exactly like it's supposed to work the first time you try it." Many problems at Simcoe Place are related to the building's complex mechanical systems, largely controlled by computer. The entire building is run by a team of only six operators and four office staff. There are six videotapes that show how to run the mechanical and electrical equipment and a thick file of warranties that stretch until as late as 2005 for major components such as the curtain wall and the waterproofing under the park. The art-deco light fixtures mounted around the ground level of the building are rusting due to pollutants in the atmosphere that were not anticipated when the lower grade of the metal was chosen. The list of such items is getting shorter but never seems to end. "You'd like some closure on these things so you can stop spending money," says Bill Neish.

As an architect, Neish hopes to see the rest of the block around

Simcoe Place finished with the second office tower and residential building. "It wasn't a stand-alone project, it was designed as part of a larger complex adding up to some significant urban design. That's an opportunity that very few architects really have, seeing the broader context of the area and enhancing a whole neighbourhood. Eventually it will all happen." With those buildings, the eventual development of the railway lands and the relaxation of the industrial zoning to the west, the area will truly return to its earlier incarnation as a place for homes and offices.

Gardner, now fifty-seven and approaching the end of his building career, is pleased to have left his mark there. "An accountant can work all his life doing great things and he ends up with a filing cabinet of all his work," he says. "We end up leaving something on the land-scape that indicates our accomplishments. It feels pretty good." He does not worry about whether the people now working in the build-ing appreciate his involvement and the full scope of Simcoe Place around them. "The person going to his desk on the twenty-seventh floor in the southeast corner may have the feeling that it is a nice building, as opposed to not a nice building. But they're concerned about whether it is hot or cold and whether the shade should be lowered, not whether they're standing on marble, granite or some space-age concrete tile."

For me, walking around the twenty-seventh floor brings an end to my scrutiny of Simcoe Place, stirring memories of the day I stood at about the same level, in the cab of the crane. Long on good terms with the contractor, I was still interested in going up to talk to the crane operator. Such visits are seldom allowed because guests can sometimes freeze in terror while climbing the narrow steel ladders. Unfortunately, the long delay in granting my wish meant that instead of being a few metres off the ground, the white crane was now close to its full height. The appointed day dawned calm and sunny, but on top it was cold and gusts of wind howled through the rigging. Slowly I climbed the crane's ladder, one rung at a time, staring ahead at the sunlight dancing on the lake in the distance rather than at the ground far below the swaying column of steel.

When I got to the cab at the top of the ladder, a hatch was opened by Bob Hughes, listening to blaring rock music while he confidently manipulated the two levers that controlled the intricate movements of the crane and its hook. Once inside, I sat on the floor behind his chair and talked to him about his job, which is known for having the highest level of stress and danger on the site. Throughout the day, clouds gathered and the wind grew stronger, buffeting the cab and whistling through the radio microphones that the two crane operators depended upon, making them useless. The biggest challenge for Hughes was to watch out for the red crane; the booms of the two were at different levels so they wouldn't touch, but their cables could become entangled if one crane swung around while the other was hoisting a load. When the shorter crane's massive counterweight section came precariously close to the bundles of steel that ours was lifting, Hughes switched channels on his radio and shouted, "Back off!" The other operator appeared not to hear but eventually swung away.

There were more pressing matters to deal with. A worker on the deck below gestured to Hughes that something was amiss with our crane. He swung out of his chair to look out the hatch and cursed softly. Contracting companies, like some homeowners, often leave Christmas lights strung up on the frame above the crane's cab. Those on ours had been knocked loose by the wind and were close to getting caught in the mechanism that makes the crane turn. He left the cab to secure the lights and I was left inside, hovering over his chair, listening to his name being called over the radio. I picked up the receiver and explained weakly that Bob was outside. When he returned, windblown and red-faced from the effort to retie the lights, there was more trouble. With our crane's hook fully extended out along the boom and holding a full bucket of concrete, the back of the red crane again threatened. This time it didn't stop but sharply yanked our cable, the other operator oblivious to the fact that he was dragging a length of steel weighted with several tons of concrete behind him. The men below scattered, fearing the bucket would fall or the crane would topple altogether. For a few seconds we both watched, horrified, to see what it would do. Finally the second crane retreated. Without much more than a sigh, Hughes returned to the job of delivering concrete, after playing out the cable like a fishing line to check that it was not frayed.

The interview was long over but leaving the comfort of the cab was not attractive. However, black thunderheads were approaching from the north and Hughes had already worked two hours of overtime. I edged out and down the narrow ladder, surprised at how much the wind had increased with the coming storm. When I reached the building my legs were still wobbly; the ground felt much better. Finally approaching the raised wooden scaffolding, the so-called "bridge" that supported the construction trailers at the edge of the site, I noticed a knot of contractors, looking like generals on a reviewing stand. At first I thought in my detached way that they were studying the threatening weather as I had seen them do so many times before. Suddenly, I realized they were watching for my safe arrival, and for a moment, I feared they would applaud. But coming nearer, I saw only crossed arms and knowing grins, tacit acknowledgement of my rite of passage. By the time I climbed the wooden steps to where they had been standing, they were gone.

ACKNOWLEDGEMENTS

This book would not have been written without the imagination of William Thorsell, the editor-in-chief of the *Globe and Mail*, who asked me to chronicle the construction of a high-rise building as a weekly series for the newspaper. Work in Progress eventually ran to 110 installments and provided the foundation and scaffolding of *A Building Goes Up*. My editors, Jerry Johnson, Phil Jackman and especially the erudite and exacting John Allemang, cheerfully shaped unwieldy prose and only rarely complained about handling untold stories on concrete. The *Globe's* excellent librarians, including Rick Cash, Celia Donnelly and Amanda Valpy, were enormously helpful. Bernie Bennell and his team of artists provided illustration where words failed. The *Globe's* photographers scaled Simcoe Place and surrounding buildings to produce stunning pictures, the best of which are displayed here with the assistance of photo librarian Sonja Lindegger. Associate Editor Sarah Murdoch kindly cleared the way for me to pursue the book.

On the construction site, I am deeply grateful to the workers I interviewed and observed for sharing their stories and views with me. Despite their doubts I had no trouble finding enough to write about; in fact, I regret the mountain of material I had to leave out or simplify here. The team at Eastern Construction was a precious and patient resource. Brian Gardner—project manager, ship's captain, poet, tutor and friend—put up with constant queries and visits over the course of more than two years and has continued to be a tremendous help on the book. I hope it puts the lie to his fear that the more I knew, the more I would get wrong. Hundreds of people generously provided information, often with nothing to gain. I also must thank readers from across the country and even abroad who offered help and advice and suggested that I turn the work into a book.

Bringing *A Building Goes Up* to fruition was a long process. Peter Goddard and Sean Luxton first suggested that I write a book on the tenth week that the series ran and helped me in the early stages of its development. Literary agent Jan Whitford took up the project and helped tame the material into a manageable manuscript. I thank Iris Tupholme of HarperCollins for her faith, eagerness and ideas. Karen Hanson was a gentle but firm warden, and Jocelyn Laurence carefully and precisely edited the text.

Many people helped by reading sections or suggesting ways to broaden the scope of my investigation. Christine Bourolias of the Ontario Archives and the staff at the Multicultural History Society of Ontario helped with background material. Historians Stephen Otto and George Rust-D'Eye provided time and insight into the evolution of Simcoe Place. Roger Hall, the author of a superb book on the Ontario Legislature, guided my research, suggested contacts and read and commented on the final work. Sidewalk superintendents Barrie Ralph and Paul McGrory lent an ear and an important perspective. The remarkable Patullo family opened their hearts and homes.

Finally, I must express my gratitude to Andrew Cohen, an award-winning journalist and author as well as my husband, mentor, critic, editor and unfailing supporter. Also to my two children, Alexander and Rachel, who have endured a distracted, disruptive mother for all of their young lives, I can only wish for them the same awe and fascination of watching a building go up.

Mary Gooderham
June, 1998

SOURCES

Books on the Simcoe Place site and surrounding area:

Arthur, Eric. *From Front Street to Queen's Park: The Story of Ontario's Parliament Buildings* (Toronto: McClelland and Stewart, 1979)

Arthur, Eric. *Toronto: No Mean City* (Toronto: University of Toronto Press, 1964)

Careless, J.M.S. *Toronto to 1918: An Illustrated History* (Toronto: James Lorimer & Company, 1984)

Dendy, William, *Lost Toronto* (Toronto: Oxford University Press, 1978)

Fulford, Robert. *Accidental City: The Transformation of Toronto* (Toronto: Macfarlane Walter & Ross, 1995)

Hall, Roger. *A Century to Celebrate 1893-1993* (Toronto: Dundurn Press, 1993)

Kilbourn, William. *Toronto Remembered: A Celebration of the City* (Toronto: Stoddart, 1984)

McHugh, Patricia. *Toronto Architecture: A City Guide* (Toronto: McClelland and Stewart, 1985)

Rust-D'Eye, George. "A Walk in Downtown Toronto," a paper prepared for a walking seminar, 1994.

Scadding, Henry. *Toronto of Old* (Toronto: Oxford University Press, 1966)

Threndyle, Gene and Martins-Manteiga, John. *Clearcut* (Toronto, 1997)

Van Steen, Marcus. *Governor Simcoe and his Lady* (Toronto: Hodder and Stoughton, 1968)

Books on construction materials and methods:

Boorstin, Daniel. *The Creators* (New York: Random House, 1992)

MacKay, Donald A. *The Building of Manhattan* (New York: Harper & Row, 1987)

Mumford, Lewis. *From the Ground Up: Observations on Contemporary Architecture, Housing, Highway Building and Civic Design* (New York: Harcourt Brace Jovanovich, 1947)

Rybczybski, Witold. *City Life* (Toronto: HarperCollins, 1995)

Sandstrom, Gosta E. *Man the Builder* (New York: McGraw Hill, 1970)

Trefil, James. *A Scientist in the City* (New York: Anchor Books, 1994)

Yarwood, Doreen. *Encyclopaedia of Architecture* (London: B.T. Batsford Ltd., 1985)

Social and historical books:

Bagnell, Kenneth. *Canadese: A Portrait of the Italian Canadians* (Toronto: Kenbar Productions Ltd., 1989)

Eisenberg, Susan. *We'll Call You If We Need You: Experiences of Women Working Construction* (Ithaca: Cornell University Press, 1998)

Harney, Robert F. *Gathering Place: Peoples and Neighbourhoods of Toronto, 1834-1945* (Toronto: Multicultural History Society of Ontario, 1985)

Harney, Robert F. *Italians in Ontario* (Toronto: Bulletin of the Multicultural History Society of Ontario, 1985)

Iacovetta, Franca. *Such Hardworking People: Italian Immigrants in Postwar Toronto* (Toronto: McGill-Queen's University Press, 1992)

Marques, Domingos. *With Hardened Hands: A Pictorial History of Portuguese Immigration to Canada in the 1950s* (Toronto: New Leaf Publications, 1993)

Marques, Domingos. *Portuguese Immigrants: 25 Years in Canada* (Toronto: Marques Printers and Publishers, 1980)

Perin, Roberto. *Arrangiarsi: The Italian Immigration Experience in Canada* (Montreal: Guernica, 1992)

Spada, A.V. *The Italians in Canada* (Montreal: Riviera Printers and Publishers, 1969)

INDEX

A

AFG Industries, 137-139

Abrams, Jeff, 71,280, 283

Access floors, 11,178-180

Air distribution, 131,161-162, 241-242, 246

Alonzi, Dominic, 230-231

Alonzi, Ersilia, 230-233

Alsi Contracting, 194

Aluminum, 130-131,155

Amber Tile and Terrazzo Inc., 228

Anchor Shoring and Caissons, 40, 194, 252

Angove, Linda, 78

Antamex, 81,130-131,155

Appio, Robert, 148

Apprentices, 206-207, 251, 253, 266, 294

Art, 259-262, 287

Architects, 16, 60-63, 72, 76; curtain wall, 132, 136; drafters, 63; environmental studies, 214-215

Architectural Dimensions, 67-68, 81-82

Astman, Barbara, 261-262

Aube, Jean-Guy, 176-178

Avenue Structures, 13,15, 34-35, 44, 46, 49, 81, 27, 154-156, 197, 206, 217-218, 220, 288

Azores, 197-199, 205, 207-208

B

B.W. Haggart Crane Service, 107,162

Backhoe, 9, 40, 96-97, 103-106, 259

Bailey Bridge, 47

Bains, Bahadur, 224-226

Baldassare, Frank, 237-240

Banani, Husayn, 90-91

Bank of America, 291

Baraness, Marc, 281

Bassken, Ted, 67-68, 70, 82

Bay-Adelaide Centre, 78, 292

Bedrock, 41-42, 98, 163, 268-269

Belanger, Richard, 176-178

Bessemer, Sir Henry, 222

Billing, 113-115, 170-171

Birnie, John, 79-80

Boiano, Italy, 46-49, 127, 217, 288

Boilers, 91

Boire, Dominic, 117

Boire, Guy, 117-119, 220, 228-230

Boire, Sebastien, 117

Boorstin, Daniel, 51,135, 223

Boundary layer wind tunnel, 213

Briolo, John, 94-95

Bristow, Eugene, 33, 147

Bruce S. Evans Ltd., 187, 191, 248-250

Building Systems Inc., 250

Bull float, 74, 129

C

C.A. Tedesco Waterproofing, 187-189

CBC Broadcast Centre, 6, 27, 33, 34, 44, 55, 56, 71, 88, 96-97, 242, 281, 284; meetings, 110; neighbours action, 107-108; planning, 253-254; wall, 105-106;

CN Tower, 17, 26, 71, 144, 154, 259, 276

CGC Inc., 175,178

C-TEC Inc., 180

Cadeau, Gil, 163-164

Cadillac Fairview Corp., 6, 30, 32, 35, 289, 293; billing, 114; building design, 60-62, 215-216; CBC 106, 110-111; consultants, 65; early garage opening, 165,195-196; marketing 67-70, 257-259; planning, 254-255, 260

Camino Systems, 179-180

Campbell, Jack, 248-250, 284-285

Canadian General Electric Co., 24

Canadian National Railway, 26

Canadian Standards Association, 152

Carpenters, 29, 31, 37, 49, 108, 206, 250-251

Carpenters and Allied Workers Union, 205, 251

Carrotheads, 272-274

Carter, Ross, 86-87

Cartwright, John, 79, 294

Catering truck, 93-95, 210

Ceilings, 176-178

Cement finishers, 53-54

Cesaroni Contracting, 174-182

Chillers, 91, 241, 286

Christmas, 112, 219, 230-233, 298

Chomski, Ab, 93

City Wide Catering, 93

Clarke and Adamson Construction, 29

Clean-up, 125, 265-268

Coleiro, Eusebio, 206-207

Columns, 53, 91, 96-97, 115, 125, 136, 173

Commissioning, 245-247

Computers: access floors, 178-180; building controls, 91, 296; elevators, 159-160; shades, 181; wiring, 243-245

Concourse: 193-195, 231, 278, 292; billing, 115; elevators, 158; escalators, 270-272; finishes, 136; services, 90,166

Concrete: block, 139-141, 173, 237; bucket, 54, 98, 211, 299; chemical reaction, 50-51,110, 149; cost, 7; crews, 101; fly-forming, 120-121, 128, 143, 162; forming, 44-46, 49, 81, 99, 200, 217; high-strength, 52-53, 75, 147, 151, 153; history, 50-52; immigration, 26,200; park, 190; pump, 97-99; tolerance, 133; tests, 149; trucks, 5, 98, 126, 150; weather conditions, 75-76; winter techniques, 13,109-110,

Conduits, 72, 101,168

Consultants, 34, 57, 62-63, 65, 112-115, 132, 236, 245-247; concrete tests, 149-153; electrical, 90-91, 168-171; elevators, 148; environmental, 212-216; mechanical, 88-90, 161-162; soil, 38, 259; structural, 53, 103, 106, 109, 149;

Construction Lien Act, 76, 114

Consumers Gas Co., 92, 109

Contract, 114, 143, 149, 189, 193, 279, 286

Contract drawings, 64-66,170-171

Contract specifications, 65-66, 169-171, 245-247

Control room, 236

Cooper, Carolyn, 255-257, 296
Core, 53, 76
Counterweights: construction hoist, 118; elevator, 160; escalator, 270; mobile crane, 107
Crane: see tower crane
Crane, mobile, 106-108, 162
Crne, Zdravko, 243-245
Crowne Plaza Hotel, 33, 107
Crusades, 129
Curtain wall, 112, 130-139, 142, 161, 221, 281; assembly, 133-134; history, 130; installation, 134; "storefront" 174; windows, 137; zip-up, 263-265, 277
Cusimano, Jack, 113-115, 279

D

Daoust, Mike, 133-134, 155-156
Davenport, Alan, 212-213
Davis, Norma, 93-95
Davit, 276
DayCare Connection, 253-255
Dea, Murray, 259
de Carvalho, Abel, 4, 15, 203-205, 209, 216, 288, 295-296
De Cruz, Jan, 250-253
De Jesus, Leo, 53-55, 295
Derrick, 237-238
Dobson, Kim, 167
Dover Corp. 157-161
Doyle, John, 117, 123
Drywall, 174-177, 226, 267, 278
Dual Removal Systems, 267
Dufferin Custom Concrete, 75, 149-150
Dunlop, Gary, 10-11, 33, 80, 117
Dupuis, Maurice, 123-127

E

East-West Elevator and Crane Ltd., 117
Eastern Construction Co. 31, 289; base building responsibilities, 160, 183; billing, 113; CBC 106; changes in plans, 171; Christmas party, 230-233; commissioning, 247; construction hoist, 118; crane movements, 58; floor turnover, 186; meetings, 111-112, 143; park 249; -77, 116, 143; safety, 124, 127; schedule, 76; toilets, 86-87; trailers, 35; visitors, 73-74; winter heating, 92
Egyptians, 139, 174
Eisenberg, Susan, 252
Electricity, 34, 89-91, 195-196
Electromagnetic radiation, 154-156
Elevators, 25, 117, 157-161, 183; assembly, 160-161; construction hoists, 117-119, 134, 161, 121, 228-230, 249, 258, 263, 267; hydraulic, 159; service, 161, 229, 267, 286; shaft, 144; traction, 159;
Engineers, 33, 36, 52, 63, 121, 205, 276
Escalators, 270-272
Esplanade, The, 20, 23
Euro Crane Erector, 238
Evans, Bruce, 191-192
Excavation, 37-42, 76, 96, 103-108, 194, 268-269

F

Factories, 24, 41, 136, 152
Ferguson, Elizabeth, 253-255
Fire-fighters, 89, 91, 121, 166-167
Fly-forming, 44-45, 49-55
Foden, Glen, 179-180
Fong, Steven, 281, 282

Food, 93-95,110, 198, 225, 230-233
Food court, 187,193, 270, 272-274
Foundation, 96, 105, 268
Fountain, 190, 284
Front Street, 88, 100, 107-108, 166, 195, 250
Fulford, Robert, 201-202

G

Gardner, Brian, 7, 11, 35-36, 73, 220, 237, 289, 293, 296-297; accident, 122-123; anniversary, 142; concrete pump, 99, meetings, 111; metric vs. Imperial 102; parking garage, 100; schedule, 12, 77, 235, 236; superstitutions 7,154
Gas, 91-92
Gem Campbell Terrazzo and Tile, 135-137, 173-174
Generators, 91,168
George Brown College, 73-74, 251
Gerhardt, John, 103-104
Gilbert Steel, 102
Glass, 137-139; heat-treated, 138; low-emissivity, 138-139
Goldstein, Frank, 144-146
Gorman, D'Arcy, 33, 120-121, 146-149, 234, 268-269, 278-279
Gouveia, Joe, 205-207
Grand Trunk Railway, 22-25, 224
Granite, 135-137, 190, 238
Gravel, 99
Greeks, 62, 113, 174
Grey, Al, 228
Gypsum, 174-175

H

Happy Harry's Used Building Materials, 266

Hard Hats, 45, 53, 84, 125, 148, 211, 225
Hare, Don, 94
Harnesses, 104, 128-129,134
Harrs, Paul, 272
Health and safety 37, 197, 265, 271; accidents, 120-128, 204; equipment, 11, 53-54, 104, 126; organizations, 126; toilets, 86; weather, 74, 119:
Heaters, 92, 110-111, 231
Hoarding: 15, 29-31, 196; dismantling, 31,249,265-266; peepholes, 8-9, 29, 31, 71; standards, 121
Hoeram, 106
Hughes, Bob, 209-211, 213, 288, 295, 298-299
Hung, Henton, 65-66
Hyde, David, 177-178
Hydraulics: climbing crane, 146; concrete pump, 98; elevators, 159

I

I-beam, 222-223
Iacovetta, Franca, 46, 49, 200-201, 204-205
Immigration, 199-202, 205; British, 24; Italian, 48, 199-202; Portugal, 197-202;
Southern Europe, 26; India, 224
Imperial units, 101-103
Indian Flavour, 274
Industrial Revolution, 172, 222
Inspections, 195-196
Interior design, 182-186
International style, 25, 177
Ironworkers, 49,133-134, 224-226, 263-264
Italian language, 15, 148, 198

J

Jackson-Lewis Co., 186, 230, 226-227, 287
James, Mel, 245-247
Jamieson, Bill, 165-166
Johnson, Phillip, 27
Journeymen, 206

K

Kapoor, Anish, 260-261
Kelly, Patrick, 267
Kharrazmi, Kianoosh, 73
King Street, 21, 28
Kotanidis, George, 73, 112, 170

L

Labourers, 37, 49, 53, 108, 173, 197-198, 205, 230, 266
Labourers International Union, 78,197, 207
Lake Ontario, 207
Landscaping, 187-192,248-250, 283-285
Laser level, 155-156, 178
Lavoie, Claire, 182-186, 226
Leonardelli, Robert, 111,170-171, 231
Leslie Street Spit, 41, 267
Life Safety Systems, 163
Lighting, 113, 130, 167-171, 178
Lightning, 91
Little Italy, 48, 201
Little Portugal, 200
Loading dock, 140, 162, 187, 236-237, 249
Lobby, 135, 172-174, 183
London, England, 35-36, 237, 260, 290
Lovely, Len, 130
Lyle, John M., 23

M

Maier, Marty, 266
Malloy, Michael, 68-70
Manneh, Kebba, 265-266
Mannella, Cosmo, 205
Marble, 112, 173-174
Mariani Metal Fabricators, 222
Mariani, Vince, 223-224
Marketing: scale models, 66-68; graphic design, 68-70; tours, 257-259
Marley, Pat, 158
Martin, Ted, 212
Masons, 139-141
Masonry, 48, 111, 130, 135, 139-141
McAlister, Peter, 290, 293
McClellan, Bob, 127
McGrory, Paul, 72, 82, 282
McIvor, Michael, 281
MacKenzie, Alistair, 73
Maxted, Doug, 117
Meetings, 110-112, 143
Metric units, 101-103
Metro Hall, 27, 71, 193-194, 280
Metro Toronto Convention Centre, 26, 30, 33, 44, 72, 237, 283, 287, 293
Mies van der Rohe, Ludwig, 27,61,130
Milligan, Grant, 30,53, 63-64, 81-82, 96-97, 153, 293
Mills, Karen, 260-262
Mirvish,Edwin, 25, 28
Mock-ups, 131-132, 180-182
Moorhead Associates, 187, 189-190
Moorhead, Steven, 189
Mulcahy, Tim, 272-273
Mulvey, Gerry, 169-170
Mulvey and Banani International, 90-91; 168-171, 243

N

National Association of Women in
Construction, 252
Nature's Call, 86
Neish, Bill, 60-62, 64, 70, 81, 282,
288-289, 294, 297
New Town, 19,25
Nietzche, 282
NORR Partnership Ltd., 60-66, 81,
227, 294; billing, 113; changes,
170-171,183; curtain wall, 130-131;
inspections, 278-280

O

Ohlman, Dennis, 278-280
Old Town, 25
Ontario Building Code, 102, 162,
165-166, 185
Ontario Ministry of Consumer and
Commercial Relations: construction
hoist, 119; elevators, 161
Ontario Ministry of Labour, 85, 123,
126-128
Ontario Occupational Health and
Safety Act, 86, 124, 128, 266
Otis, Elisha Graves, 158
Ott, Carlos, 60-61, 70, 282, 294

P

Paige, Tom, 97, 241-242
Palace, The, 20, 23, 28, 33
Parliament Buildings, First and
Second, 18-19; Queens Park, 78-
79;Simcoe
Place, 21-22, 72, 78
Park, 187-192,248-250, 283-285
Parking Garage: 150, 187, design, 99-
101; early opening, 165, 195-196;
elevators, 111, fire safety, 165-166;
floor 97-99; wall, 105-106
Parmalee, Henry, 163
Parsons, Constable Stuart, 108
Patry, Donald, 181-182
Patullo brothers, 14, 45, 47, 122, 288
Patullo, Carmine, 14, 48-49, 128
Patullo, Corrado, 13,15, 44-49, 48-49,
58-59, 201, 217-219, 287-288, 293;
accident, 120-124, 126-128
Patullo, Emilio, 14, 48, 154
Patullo, Tony, 14, 46, 49, 81, 127-
128, 154-155, 199-200, 294
Patullo, Victor, 14
Pavic, Nick, 174-175
Pavic, Tony, 174-175
Pavic, Vlado, 174-175
Penthouses, 89, 91, 158, 161-162,
167-168, 219, 235-237
Pereira, Rosy, 37, 87, 120-121, 171,
237, 293
Pestrin, Glen, 134-137, 288
Pestrin, Mario, 135
Petrilli, Domenico, 167-170
Plan Electric, 168-171
Plaster, 173-175
Plobner, Anton, 103
Plumbing, 34
Plywood, 50, 125-126
Podium, 11, 62, 116, 121, 136, 142,
214, 281, 286; mechanical floor,
161-162
Police, 107-108
Porciello, Joe, 187-189
Portland cement, 51
Portugal, 5, 15, 198-199, 203-204,
295
Portuguese language, 15, 148
Pozzobon, Amadeo, 217-218, 288
Provincial Sign Service, 196

Q

Quinn Dressel Associates, 30, 63, 81, 106, 224, 288, 294

R

RCI Waterjet Cutting Services, 261
Rabideau Czerwinski Ontario Land Surveyors, 32
Railways, 157, 297; yards, 41-42, 26
Rain, 89
Ralph, Barrie, 72, 282-283
Ramires, Cesar, 102
Rankin, Margaret, 189-192, 248-250, 283-284
Reasin, Don, 271
Recycling, 41,153, 217-218, 296
Rice Brydone, 183-186, 226-227, 244-245, 256
Robbins, Vince, 162-163
Romans, 50-51, 62, 88, 135, 139, 158-159
Roof, 70, 224, 239
Rowan Williams Davies and Irwin, 212-215
Roy Thomson Hall, 26, 33, 259, 276
Royal Alexandra Theatre, 23-26, 64, 148
Rumble Contracting, 40-41, 103, 194, 259
Rumble, George, 259
Russell, Peter, 19, 32
Russell's Creek, 19, 21
Ryell, John, 152
Ryerson Polytechnic University, 73

S

Sabean, Dean, 33, 147, 264-265
Safety glasses, 53

St. Andrew's Church, 21, 72, 282
Salamanders, 110, 129
Salmon, John, 149-151
Sayers and Associates, 162-167
Scaffolding, 235; concrete forming, 50; formwork, 149; re-shoring, 145, 238, 240; trailers, 35,236
Scale models, 66-68
Schantz, Karl, 261
Schedule, 12-13, 76-77, 111-112, 115, 122, 129, 142-143, 227, 235-236, 264-265, 270
Schindler Elevator, 270
Sciortino, Tony, 206
Scotia Plaza, 154-155
Scully, Mandy, 257-259
Second World War, 45-47, 130
Security, 110, 169, 236, 285-287
Sewell, John, 281
Sewer, 11-13, 88
Shades, 180-182
Sheet Metal Workers International Union, 79
Sheridan, Steve, 207
Shoring, 9, 37-43, 104, 194
Sidewalk superintendants, 9, 21, 28, 71-73,144, 280-283
Simcoe Place phase two 193, 292
Simcoe Place square, 19
Simcoe, John Graves, 18-19, 190, 260
Simcoe Street, 19, 32, 89
SkyDome, 27, 71, 86
Smith and Andersen Consulting Engineers, 88, 161, 165-166
Solarfective products, 181
Soldier piles, 39-40, 42, 129
Soligo, Mike, 212-215
Spark Steel Erectors, 222
Sprinklers, 163-165
Standpipe (fire hose), 165-167

Steel: access floor, 179-180; galvanized, 131, 175; reinforcing (rebar), 50, 97, 99, 101, 102-103, 110, 115, 125, 223; rods, 140; structural, 23, 25, 45-46, 209, 221-225;

Stephens, Mona, 253-255

Stonemasons, 172-174

Strachan, Reverand John, 20, 23

Students, 73-74

Substantial performance, 12, 143, 234-237, 265, 279

Subway, 193, 259

Summer construction, 74-76

Superstitions, 7, 153

Surveyors, 31-33, 148

Swamper, 4, 57, 203

Swing-stages, 275-277

Swing Stage Ltd., 276-277

T

TCG Materials, 140

Tacconelli, Renato, 36, 111, 285-286

Tattle, Dawn, 40, 43, 252

Tarps, 109-110

Taste of Toronto, 284-285

Taylor and Browning Design Associates, 68-70

Taylor Cleaning, 286-287

Taylor, Lawrence, 286-287

Teixeira, Artur, 197-199, 207-208

Teixeira, John, 78

Telephones, 34, 149, 243-245

Thind, Sarabjit, 273-274

Thirteenth floor, 153-154

Toilets, 61, 84-88, 112, 136, 165, 210, 253

Torkos, Jim, 229

Toronto: building department, 102-103, 284; building standards, 30; by-laws, 195; city council, 26, 28, 65; entertainment district, 17; financial district, 17,25; geology, 38-39, 72; immigration, 48, 199-203; inspections, 284; name, 20; parks and recreation, 189; public works, 30, 88; street occupancy permit, 195, 247, 284-285; urban planning, 61, 100, 212-215, 253-254; Vacancy rate, 80; zoning, 102.

Toronto Building Trades Council, 79

Toronto Dominion Centre, 41, 61, 66

Toronto Dominion Bank, 114

Toronto Fire Department, 167

Toronto Hydro, 90,250

Toronto Islands, 34,71

Toronto Symphony Orchestra, 63, 258-259

Tower crane, 14, 55-59, 118, 162, 297; assembly, 56; cable, 148; capacity, 57-58; climbing, 58-59, 143-146; dismantling, 187, 219, 236-240; electrical needs, 90; failures, 58; holes, 240; malfunctions, 154-156, 220-221; operator, 57-58, 209-211, 216; parts, 55-56; position, 56-67; safety, 72; schedule, 143; types, 55

Trailers, 15, 34, 87, 115, 126, 133, 147, 168, 170, 236-238

Trees, 190,192, 248-249, 250, 268, 281

Trow Consulting Engineers, 149-153

Trulite Industries, 137-139

Tunnels, 171, 192-194, 268-270

U

Unemployment, 8, 79, 251, 294

Union Station, 22, 26, 71, 162

Unions 77-80, 230, 231, 251, 294

University of Toronto, 22, 155, 252, 281

Upper Canada 17-18
Upper Canada College, 21, 23-24

V

Vaz, Ashley, 274
van Deventer, Emilie, 155
Vibron, Ltd., 97-98, 241-242, 247
Vitruvius, 51, 62,158
Vulcan Asphalt and Supply, 195

W

Walt Disney Animation, 291
Wakie-talkie radios, 147-149, 168,
    211, 216, 298-299
Wanlin, Stuart, 258
Waterproofing, 188-189,192
Weather: crane conditions, 144; fore-
    cast, 264; rain, 76-77; spring, 142,
    248; storms, 115, 211, 216;
    summer, 74-76, 133; wind, 76, 119,
    131, 211-216, 219-221; winter, 13,
    109-110, 115, 221, 298
Weick, Alex, 173-174
Wellington Street, 194
Wheatley, Jim, 227
Whitehead, Bruce, 72
Williams, Colin, 212-215
Winches, 134, 221, 263-264
Windows, 130-134, 137-139; shades,
    180-182; washing, 274-277, 286
Winter construction, 13, 109-110;
    115-119
Women, 74, 207, 250-253
Wordtmann, John 158
Work abroad, 80-83, 103
Work boots, 54, 84
Workers' Compensation Board, 8, 27,
    242, 283, 292, 296; accident notifi-
    cation, 125; billing, 114-115; build-

to-suit, 10, 65-66, 172-173, 179,
    183; controversy 78-80, 180, 292;
    elevators, 158; floor turnover, 161,
    240; interior design, 182-186, 243-
    245, 226; move, 255-257; on-site
    safety, 37, 124
World Trade Centre, 167

Y

York, 18, 38
Yorktown Catering, 93-95

Z

Zander, Hans, 276